Social Analytics

Network and Text Methods with NodeXL and R

Shaila Miranda
Price College of Business at the University of Oklahoma

NodeXL igraph
LIWC

R LDA
topic models S&R 1,2,4

Founded in 2014, Prospect Press serves the academic discipline of Information Systems by publishing innovative textbooks across the curriculum including introductory, emerging, and upper level courses. Prospect Press offers reasonable prices by selling directly to students. Prospect Press provides tight relationships between authors, publisher, and adopters that many larger publishers are unable to offer. Based in Burlington, Vermont, Prospect Press distributes titles worldwide. We welcome new authors to send proposals or inquiries to Beth.Golub@ProspectPressVT.com.

Editor: Beth Lang Golub
Assistant Editor: Tom Anderson-Monterosso
Production Management: Rachel Paul
Cover Design: Annie Clark

eTextbook
- Edition 1.0
- ISBN 978-1-943153-58-9
- Available from RedShelf.com and VitalSource.com

Printed Paperback
- Edition 1.0
- ISBN 978-1-943153-59-6
- Available from RedShelf.com

For more information, visit
http://prospectpressvt.com/titles/miranda-social-analytics/

Contents

Preface

Social Analytics deals with the collection, management, and analysis of social data. Social media offer a rich source of social data, but are not the only source of social data. Other sources include company reports and press releases, news media coverage, analyst reports, and conventional websites. Social data typically assume three forms: (1) data about who connects with whom; (2) data about the content of a conversation, typically textual information; (3) the nontextual cues transmitted during conversations (e.g., nonverbals), typically in photographs and videos. All these forms of data typically are unstructured (not in a database or formatted in a database-ready fashion) prior to being subjected to social analytics. The scope of this book is limited to the first two types of data, focusing on concepts, methods, and tools related to social network analysis and text analysis and mining, and the preprocessing of social data to ready it for these analyses.

This book will introduce readers to concepts and methods relevant to social analytics. The objective of the book is twofold. First, it will develop the reader's understanding of what they can do with social analytics and of the concepts underlying social analytics. The reader will have the vocabulary necessary to engage with social analytics tools and teams. Second, readers will attain at least a rudimentary familiarity with tools and techniques for social analytics. We will alternate between learning social analytics methods with the help of easy-to-use software and learning to implement those methods using R. Readers therefore will get the most out of this book if they engage with it in a hands-on fashion.

Key Features of This Book

- Covers social network analysis, text analysis, and text mining. Presenting these methods together helps readers understand both the structure and content of social media conversations.
- Readers practice using NodeXL, LIWC, and Weka, and progress to implementing in R using RStudio.
- Includes software tutorials and exercises
- Relevant, engaging examples throughout

Organization of the Book

In Part I, the book introduces the reader to the domain of social analytics and the opportunities it provides. Part II deals with the area of social network analysis. It introduces the reader to underlying concepts and the fundamentals of visualization and measurement of social networks. It then addresses SNA packages available for R. Part III introduces the reader to concepts and practices involved in text analysis and text mining, and the text analysis and mining packages available for R. Part IV concludes with some of the challenges posed by social analytics. Part V includes appendices.

Intended Audiences

This book has three intended audiences. The first is MBA or graduate management information systems (MIS) students in courses related to social analytics. These courses often are taught by MIS departments, but also may be offered by marketing departments, where social media use for advertising and customer relationship management is a growing concern.

The second audience is PhD students in disciplines ranging from MIS and marketing to sociology and political science, for whom social media provide research data. If not already being offered, methods classes with a significant component on gathering, storing, and analyzing the unstructured data that is the basis of social analytics will be a valuable addition to such PhD programs.

The third audience for this book is analysts and researchers conducting business analysis or scholarly research with social media data. The concepts, methods, and tools covered also will be useful in helping these constituents update their analytics and research skills for the era of big, unstructured data.

Prior Knowledge Assumed

Ideally the reader will have at least a rudimentary knowledge of statistics. They should have a fair amount of skill with MS Excel, as we will use that to parse and clean text data, visualize networks, and combine relational and conversational data into more complex visuals. Finally, the book presumes readers' familiarity with R. Readers without prior knowledge of R can get up to speed with R quickly by working through Appendices A and B or by taking one of the myriad online courses on R.

Required Resources

Prior to beginning this book, please obtain a copy of NodeXL, LIWC, Weka, R (version 3.3.2 or later), and RStudio. If reading this book as part of a course, please consult your instructor on which versions to obtain and discounts that may be applicable. If using this book on your own, I provide the websites from which the software currently can be obtained. Be aware though that the websites change over time, but the software will remain accessible easily through a Google search. Once you have located the sites for the software, be sure to pick the downloads compatible with your Windows or Mac environments.

The data files referenced in the examples, tutorials, and exercises in the book are available from the Prospect Press student companion site: http://prospectpressvt.com/titles/miranda-social-analytics/student-resources/.

Regarding Social Analytics Services

The objective of this book is to get the reader up to speed on a range of techniques used to analyze social data. The book does not cover social analytics services such as the ones listed below. Even if you use such services in the future, the skills acquired through this book will help you "look under the hood" and make more informed service choices.

A Sampling of Social Analytics Services

Free	Paid
Web Analytics	
4Q Suite Facebook Insights Google Analytics Google Website Optimizer Klout	ClickTale Kissinsights Crazy Egg Compete Optimizely
Social Media Analytics	
Facebook Grader Sentiment140 Social Don TweetStats Twitalyzer	TwitSprout Kissmetrics PageLever Radian6 Socialbakers Wildfire

Book Notation Conventions for R

The first occurrence of syntax describing a particular R function is boldfaced and italicized. Required function arguments are depicted, but optional arguments are not.

In most cases, capital letters indicate a value for a function argument that needs to be replaced. When this is not the case, I note that in the text.

Examples of syntax are italicized. These may be copied into your RStudio script, but be sure to change the quotes appearing in RStudio from smart quotes, which are special characters that R cannot interpret, to simple quotes.

Syntax and code do not contain hyphens. When these occur at the end of a line, they represent automatic hyphenation inserted at the time of publication and should be deleted from code you copy into RStudio.

For Instructors

Pedagogical Notes

The objective of the exercises in this book is twofold. First, the exercises are oriented toward developing individual students' understanding of social analytics concepts and facility with the tools to conduct social analytics. Second, they attempt to develop and sharpen students' problem-finding skills (i.e., their ability to notice patterns in the data and develop insights that can inform strategic initiatives and/or policy for organizations). Consequently, most exercises have individual components that are competence-oriented and team components that are insight-oriented.

An ambitious instructor may cover the material provided in its entirety within a three-credit course. However, the material is better suited to a four-credit course or to two two-credit courses. Instructors able to assume higher levels of student comfort with programming, in general, and with Excel and R specifically, will be able to cover more of the material. Instructors unable to assume such student preparation may wish to choose a subset of topics to cover. Possible subsets may be (1) social network analysis; (2) text analysis; (3) social analytics with NodeXL, LIWC, and Weka; (4) social analytics with R.

Resources

Supplementary resources for instructors can be accessed at the Prospect Press instructor companion site: http://prospectpressvt.com/titles/miranda-social-analytics. These resources include the following:

- Sample syllabus. See how one might develop a course with this text.
- Teaching notes
- PowerPoint presentations. Instructors may use these as is or customize them.
- Data files. All data files referenced in the examples, tutorials, and exercises. These files are also available to students at the Student Resources page.
- Solutions to end-of-chapter questions
- Test questions. The test bank includes multiple-choice, short-answer, and problem questions and solutions.

Acknowledgments

I owe many a debt of thanks for this book coming to fruition: to the Digital Societies and Social Technologies (DSST) 2013 Summer Institute organizers—Brian Butler, Susan Winter, and Diane Travis—for getting me hooked on social analytics; to former TAs extraordinaire, Inchan Kim, Luke Reese, and Tiffani Allison, and four batches of social analytics students at the University of Oklahoma, from whom I have learned so much; to reviewers Akshay Bhagwatwar (Northern Illinois University), Dazhi Chong (California Lutheran University), Mike Hine (Carleton University), Lester Allan Lasrado (Copenhagen Business School), Feng Mai (Stevens Institute of Technology), and Paul Witman (California Lutheran University), for their feedback on the book; to early adopter Satish Krishnan (Indian Institute of Management, Kozhikode), who provided detailed critiques of the materials he used; to Craig Russell for being a sounding board and for painstaking copyedits of a few chapters; and to Tristan Miranda-Sohrabji for his diligent testing of examples, tutorials, and exercises. Thank you for your support and efforts to bring this project to life.

—Dr. Shaila Miranda

About the Author

Shaila Miranda is John E. Mertes Professor of MIS at the University of Oklahoma's Price College of Business. She obtained her doctorate from the University of Georgia, with a major in management information systems and a minor in computer science. She also has an MA in sociology from Columbia University, along with a master of management studies and a BA in psychology from the University of Bombay.

Professor Miranda's research, which has been published in *MIS Quarterly* and *Information Systems Research*, most recently applies the core methods of social analytics to investigate topics such as how Fortune 50 companies describe their use of social media in press releases and how traditional news media versus social media cover public policy issues. Professor Miranda has served as Senior Editor and Associate Editor for *Information Systems Research* and as Associate Editor for *MIS Quarterly*.

PART I

Introduction

CHAPTER 1

What Is Social Analytics?

> **Learning Objectives**
>
> The purpose of this chapter is to acquaint you with
> 1. the scope of what analytics professionals and academic researchers can do with social analytics,
> 2. the types of data social analysts work with, and
> 3. the range of skills required of and tools used by social analysts.

#WhereIsRey? The central figure of Disney's much-anticipated 2015 release *Star Wars: The Force Awakens* was missing from holiday merchandise. On September 1, 2015, the Disney Star Wars site had announced, "This Friday, there will indeed be an awakening . . . for Star Wars collectors everywhere" [1]. As early as October 2015, though, shoppers were noting the absence of female characters in the Star Wars merchandise lineup. One tweeted, "@Target exclusively released a @starwars toy set with ZERO female characters. #wheresRey . . ." While stock-outs partly explained Rey's absence, in many cases products featuring the movie's central character simply were not released [4-6]. One shopper sarcastically noted, "Oh look they even included some women IN THE BACKGROUND of this #StarWars bed cover, gee thanks #Disney #wheresRey?" The Star Wars Monopoly game featured only male characters—Finn, Luke Skywalker, Kylo Ren, and Darth Vader. In response to claims by Star Wars merchandiser Hasbro that their failure to merchandise Rey was to avoid a spoiler, fans pointed out that the central character already appeared on movie posters. Through November and December, holiday shoppers used the *#WheresRey* or *#WhereIsRey* hashtags to chastise stores, Hasbro, and Disney for this merchandising gaffe: "@Hasbro Why do you always leave the girl characters out of your toy packs? Seriously #Epicfail #wheresRey"; "Disney sexist marketing alive and well . . . #wheresRey?" Even kids weighed in—for example, calling out the companies concerned, eight-year-old Annie Rose noted, "boys and girls need to see women can be as strong as men."

Well past the holiday gift cycle and many thousands of social media posts later, Hasbro responded on January 5, 2016: "We love your passion for Rey, and are happy to share that we will be including her in the Monopoly: Star Wars game, available later this year" [4]. Figure 1.1 (created using R and Excel) depicts the social media conversation that unfolded over the ten-week period preceding Hasbro's ultimate announcement. The size of the word clouds for each of the ten weeks is proportional to the number of tweets posted. The size of the word within each word cloud (produced in R) is proportional to the frequency with which that word occurred within the week. The amount of red in a word cloud is proportional to the amount of negative emotion (computed in R) expressed in the week's tweets and the amount of blue is proportional to the amount of positive emotion expressed. So, in the fourth week—the week of November 16—there were the fewest tweets after the conversation began in late October, and the tone of the posts was exclusively positive. With the exception of this week, Figure 1.1 depicts fans' mounting negative sentiment toward the missing merchandise overwhelming their positive sentiment toward the movie. Notice especially the frustration expressed in key shopping weeks—at the beginning of November and the two weeks prior to Christmas. Social analytics, coupled with other organizational ***listening posts*** (see the "What Is a Listening Post?" insert), could have forestalled this debacle.

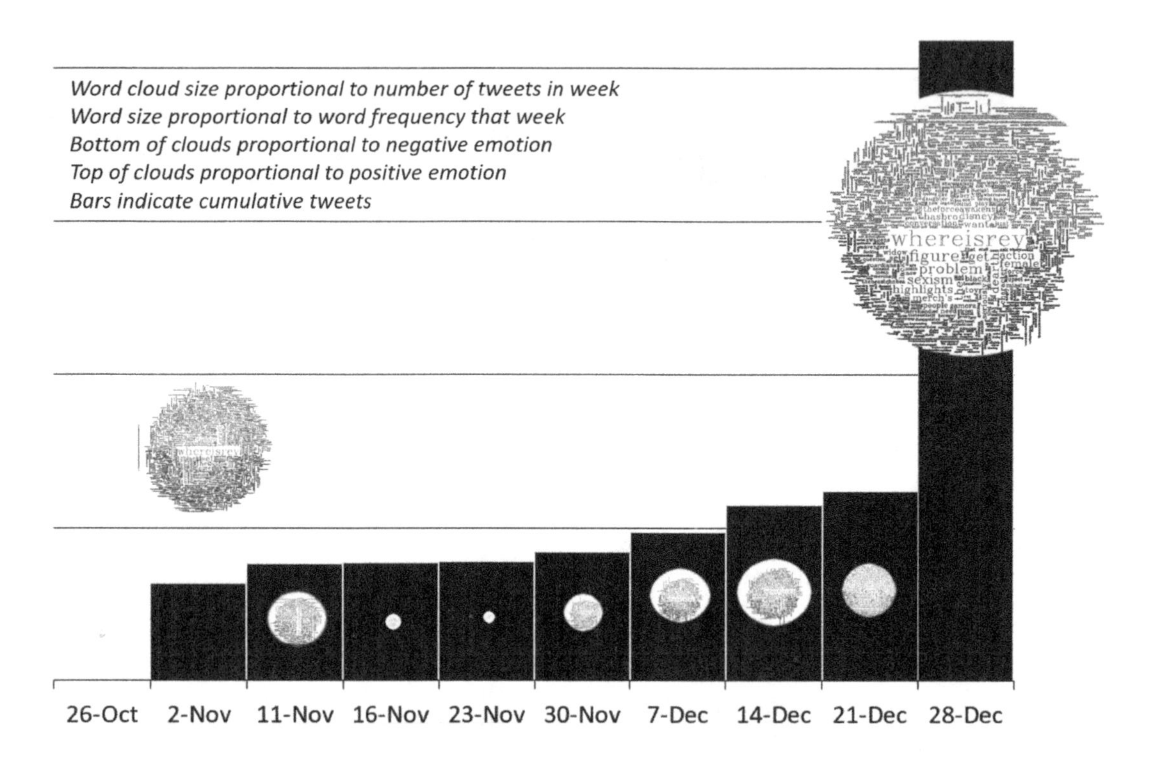

Figure 1.1 Ten Weeks of *#WhereIsRey* (Interaction Data) on Twitter

The proliferation of social media platforms and their use have opened up a multitude of opportunities for organizations, including knowledge sharing, social marketing and brand promotion [8], enacting and representing corporate social responsibility (CSR) initiatives [10], social customer service [12], and social recruiting [13]. Without analytics, though, organizations cannot optimize their returns from these initiatives. Analytics of social knowledge sharing can apprise organizations of the success of such initiatives and help organizations make decisions on knowledge retention, prioritization, and pruning. Analytics of social media posts permit firms to anticipate customer receptiveness to products and to their brand. Analytics of public participation in CSR campaigns can apprise organizations of social causes that garner public support rather than indifference or even ire.

By increasing the flow of information and the public's opportunities to network and communicate about organizational activities, social media also is making organizations' use of social analytics a competitive necessity. The social media era has increased activists' and regulators' reactiveness to organizational activities [14]. It also has increased organizations' vulnerability to privacy [15] and security violations [16]. Without analytics to glean insights from the data collected at social media listening posts,

What Is a Listening Post?

A listening post is a virtual or physical locale for intelligence collection. Historically, listening posts were communication stations positioned near enemy lines to intercept enemy communications. Disney defines listening posts as "customer-centric tools companies use to assess the customer experience and identify areas where customer needs are not being met" and enumerate the following listening posts that they use:

1. Face-to-face research of customers by employees;
2. Guest communications in the form of emails and letters;
3. Website and social media monitoring;
4. Conversations with front-line employees. [2]

Of course, listening posts can—and should—attend to audiences other than customers too. We can learn much by monitoring employees, fans, investors, activists, rivals, governments, and also criminals.

organizations can be blindsided by reactions from employees, customers, fans, investors, activists, rivals, governments, and even criminals.

As we will see, social analytics is not only limited to social media data. For example, Disney's listening posts aim to harness also information emanating from front-line employees, face-to-face customer interactions, e-mail, and letters. Social analytics can help us gain insights into a range of phenomena such as political affiliations, public policy reactions, the connectedness of boards of directors, fans' reactions to music and movies, or the content of firms' news releases. We begin by examining the meaning of social analytics. To do so, we take apart ***social*** and ***analytics***. We then consider what we can do with social analytics and the skills required for undertaking social analytics.

The Meaning of "Social"

The Merriam-Webster dictionary defines *social*, in its adjective form, as "relating to or involving activities in which *people* spend time *talking* to each other *or doing* enjoyable things *with each other*." The three aspects of this definition—people, talking or doing, with each other—map to the three key types of social data: profiles, interactions, and relationships [17].

Profiles describe people, organizations, and other social entities. For example, Figure 1.2 depicts the Facebook profiles for the Star Wars movies and for Daisy Ridley, who plays Rey in *The Force Awakens*. Profiles include structured data such as the page category, which appears directly under the screen name—"Movie" for Star Wars and "Actor/Director" for Daisy Ridley—as well as details such as the series' and movie's release date, and Ridley's gender. Outside of the social media arena, too, we see profile data such as a customer's age and hometown—captured through an order entry form—or an organization's buying behavior, reputation, and financial viability, collated by financial analysts over time. As is evident in Figure 1.2, profiles also include unstructured data such as a person's description of him/herself, career objectives, or qualities desired in a mate. Social analytics is at least as concerned with such unstructured data.

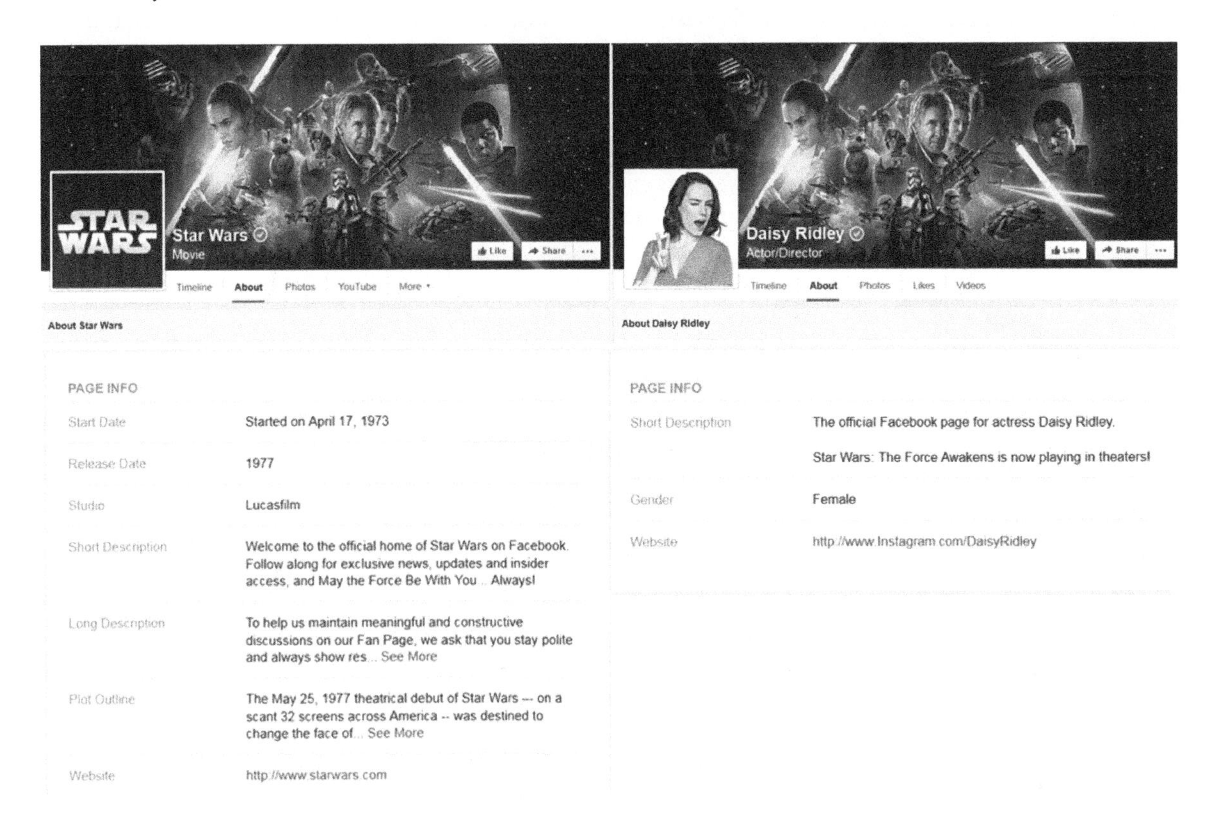

Figure 1.2 Profile Data

Interactions refer to the nature and content of people's communications or actions. Figure 1.1 represents an analysis of interactions (i.e., conversations) about the focal Star Wars character, Rey. Within an organization, this could be transactions such as customer orders processed. It also could be press releases issued by a company, articles written about a company, or social media posts by an individual or an organization. Behaviors caught on film or video also provide data about people's interactions.

People have two types of ***relationships***. The first type is standing or long-term relationships that exist by virtue of membership in a family or other social group. On social media, this manifests in users connecting with other people (as on LinkedIn), following them (as on Twitter), or friending them (as on Facebook). The second type is the ad hoc relationships people enact around conversations by responding to, reposting, or liking/favoriting posts. For example, in Figure 1.3 (created using NodeXL), we see relationships enacted around the *#WhereIsRey* conversation as fans responded to and retweeted each other's posts. Each node (a dot or a thumbnail picture) in Figure 1.3 represents a person; each line connecting nodes represents one person replying to or retweeting another. Figure 1.3A depicts fans' activity levels relative to the entire network. Here, larger nodes indicate more active actors; the five most active fans are represented with thumbnails of their profile pictures. Relationships give rise to social orderings such as groups, status, and hierarchy. Figure 1.3B depicts emergent groupings among fans, based on patterns of retweeting and responding, as well as the most influential fans across the network. (*Influence* here roughly translates to those whose posts are retweeted or responded to more frequently, but more on this later.) Analysis of such relationships provides actionable insights. Figure 1.3, for example, highlights the most active (those posting frequently) and the most influential (those whose messages diffused farthest) fans in the *#WhereIsRey* conversation. In the event that Disney, Hasbro, or the various retail organizations implicated should wish to change the conversation, the relationship graphs quickly identify optimal targets for information and persuasion.

Organizations also have long-standing relationships such as partnerships, vendor/customer links, and enact ad hoc relationships such as consultations and one-off vendor-customer engagements. Relationships also may exist between people and other social artifacts such as locations, events, and technologies. Social data thus are data that describe social actors (i.e., profiles about people and organizations, about interactions among social actors, and about actors' relationships among themselves and with other social artifacts).

Social data epitomizes the four qualities of "big data": high volume, variety, velocity, and problems with veracity [18, 19]. Social data is ***voluminous***. Twitter users post an average more than 537 million tweets per day; Facebook's more than two billion active users generate almost four billion total Facebook posts daily [20, 21]. One hundred pages of text require approximately 1MB of storage space; 1GB can hold 7 minutes of

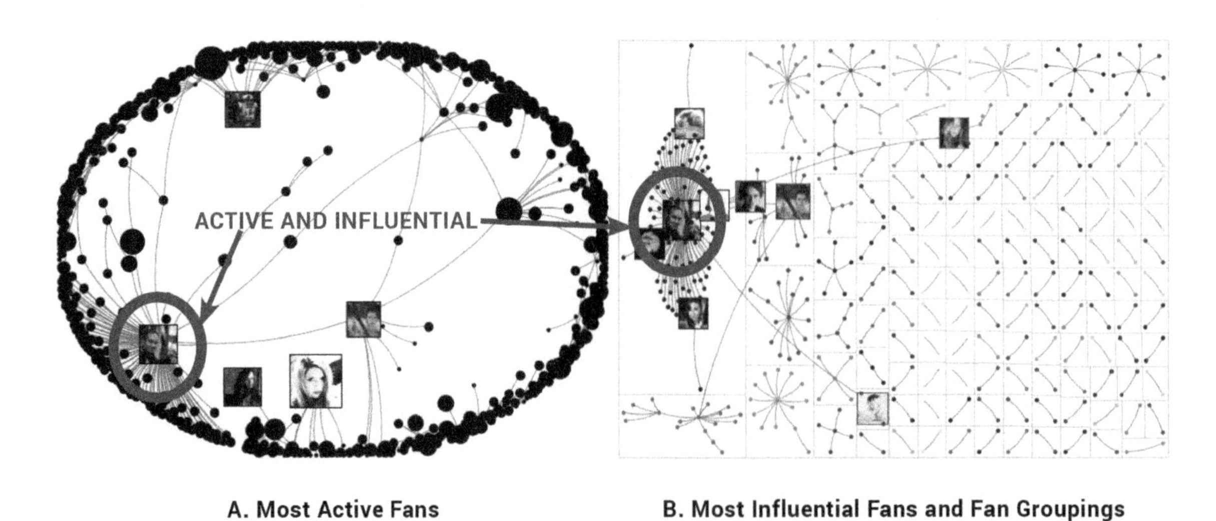

Figure 1.3 Relationship Data—The Most Prominent Fans in the *#WhereIsRey* Conversation

HD-TV video [22]. The 10 weeks of *#WhereIsRey* tweets use more than 70MB of storage space (see the "Measuring Big Data Volume" insert). Thus social data get big quickly! Voluminous social data increases the computing (storage and processing) resources required, and necessitates unconventional and creative data management.

Social data come in a wide ***variety*** of data types—social media feeds, video, audio, photographs, documents, and genomic data. Emerging technologies in the areas of the Internet of Things and the Quantified Self also provide real-time sensor data. For example, a Smart Home can analyze data collected about your arrival and departure times, use of lights, and when you open and close blinds to determine the optimal time to turn your lights off and on and draw the blinds, so as to mimic your presence when you are traveling [23]. And of course, there is all your workout, diet, sleep, biometric, and mood data! To effectively analyze the social world, we have to be vigilant to the data possibilities around us.

Measuring Big Data Volume

1 kilobyte (KB) =1024 bytes
1 megabyte (MB) =1024 KB
1 gigabyte (GB) = 1024 MB
1 terabyte (TB) = 1024 GB
1 petabyte (PB) = 1024 TB
1 exabyte (EB) = 1024 PB
1 zettabyte (ZB) = 1024 EB
1 yottabyte (YB) = 1024 ZB
1 brontobyte (BB) = 1024 YB

Social data is dynamic—that is, it has high ***velocity***. More so than most types of data, social data is generated and diffuses rapidly—which is why "going viral" is an epithet applied so often to social data. Consequently, analysts often employ in-memory analytics (i.e., real-time analysis of data that bypasses data storage) with social data [24].

Finally, social data are subject to problems of ***veracity*** (i.e., accuracy and verifiability). In the virtual world, a teenager may present himself as a mature woman, a graduate student as a truck-driver. Social data therefore either must be verified (see the "Should You Have a Verified Twitter Account?" insert). Failing this, the analyst must find ways to account for noise, deception, and irrelevance in their analyses.

Additionally, unlike traditional data, which resided in corporate databases, social data is everywhere. On the one hand, this provides organizations with unprecedented opportunities for intelligence gathering. Firms now can make decisions not only based on analyses of data about their own activities and customer reactions, but also based on data about rival firm activities and customer reactions. On the other hand, such data often defy traditional structuring. Imposing a structure on a series of social media posts about movie memorabilia is not something taught in a traditional database course.

The Meaning of "Analytics"

Googling "What is analytics?" reveals the following meanings:

- The ***systematic*** computational analysis of data or statistics
- ***Information resulting*** from the systematic analysis of data or statistics.

Analytics therefore speaks to a process that is systematic and a resulting product that is informative and insightful.

As a ***systematic process***, social analytics entails the following tasks: gathering, cleansing/prep, and analysis of data. Social data may be gathered manually, obtained from archives, or harvested using Application Programming Interfaces (APIs). In addition to using planned data gathering, those undertaking social analytics frequently undertake ad hoc data gathering tasks. This is because of the velocity of social data. The social world changes on a dime. Today's fad is tomorrow's faux pas. Using only planned-for data fails to take into consideration the dynamic nature of the social

Should You Have a Verified Twitter Account?

If you embed a "Follow" button on your website, Twitter *may* verify your account. Is it worth the effort? You decide! Below are the average numbers of likes and retweets obtained by participants with and without verified accounts in the *#WhereIsRey* conversation.

Account Type	Likes	Retweets
Unverified	14	16
Verified	48	36

world. For example, if Disney, Hasbro, and other organizations tracking fan sentiment related to Star Wars were following and gathering only social media posts referencing "Star Wars," they would have captured only about 16% of the posts. Careful attention to the "Star Wars" posts, though, would have drawn analysts' attention to the *#WhereIsRey* hashtag, which then would have flagged the problem in time to impact holiday sales and before it became an image problem for the organizations concerned.

Social data need to be cleansed and prepared prior to its use. During this process, where possible, the analyst addresses data validation issues. For example, validation of the *#WhereIsRey* data set revealed many tweets matching the search criteria actually were from a @WhereisRey account and did not contain the hashtag; these tweets had to be dropped prior to analyses. Additionally, the analyst pares down the data so as to focus on data elements that are relevant to the insights (s)he wishes to glean. This is particularly true for textual data emanating from sources such as articles, conversations, and social media posts.

Finally, the analyst commences the process of data analysis. This likely will be an iterative process, where insights gleaned at one stage raise further questions that prompt the analyst to gather additional data, prepare the data differently, and/or conduct different analyses.

The goal of the analytics process is an ***informative and insightful*** product—that is, one that ultimately provides value to the organization or to society. This product should tell a coherent story about an organization, its employees, customers, fans, investors, activists, rivals, governments, or even criminal threats, or foster participative democracy. It should help the audience visualize the problem or opportunity space through graphics such as those provided in Figure 1.1 and Figure 1.3. It should provide appropriate metrics that describe salient characteristics of the problem or opportunity, and—where appropriate—couple those metrics with inferential statistics that speak to how those characteristics do or do not go together. Ultimately, to add value, the story should accomplish one of two things: (1) it should legitimize a strategic direction or tactical maneuver, or (2) it should point the organization or group in a new strategic direction or help it craft new tactics. For example, recognizing the unfolding story about sexism in Star Wars memorabilia sooner could have pointed Hasbro toward an early solution, potentially boosting Hasbro's holiday sales and preserving customer goodwill toward Hasbro, Disney, and associated retail organizations.

Skills Required for Conducting Social Analytics

Social analytics begins with strong ***domain knowledge*** (i.e., knowledge about the problem area being studied). This is necessary so the analyst can determine which data are meaningful and be able to recognize valuable insights. A social analytics team also should comprise individuals with cognitive, quantitative, technical, and visualization skills. Essential cognitive skills are problem identification and pattern recognition. ***Problem identification*** refers to the ability to notice problems. For example, a good analyst monitoring social media feeds about Star Wars would have noticed the repetitive *#WhereIsRey* hashtag, and would have identified the absence of female figures from their merchandise as a problem. Surfacing insights such as the pacing of fan frustration with the absence of Rey merchandise around the holiday shopping cycle requires ***pattern recognition*** skills.

Yes, ***quantitative skills*** are essential. Social analytics uses some conventional statistical analysis approaches. Because time and space are relevant to much social data, statistical techniques that account for time and geography tend to be used frequently in social analytics. There also are metrics and nonstatistical quantitative procedures specific to analyzing social data that we will need to learn. Finally, because relational data violate assumptions of conventional statistical models, we need to get acquainted with advanced statistical techniques. These are currently beyond the purview of this book.

The ***technical skills*** one can bring to bear on social analytics are numerous. Further, the more skills one possesses, the greater one's facility with data management and analysis. To begin with, basic data management and analysis skills using commonplace Microsoft products such as MS Access and Excel are invaluable for data preparation and porting. Special-purpose PC-based network and text analytics packages abound. And of course, understanding nonrelational databases like MongoDB is important. These provide good entrée into social analytics concepts and frequently will suffice for analyzing smaller data sets. While one certainly can begin social analytics without strong programming skills, programming skills in R, Python, Java, and even VBA will prove invaluable.

We have all heard the dictum, "a picture is worth a thousand words." Data ***visualization*** skills therefore are of paramount importance to good storytelling. While this book will cover visualization techniques specific to social data, generic data visualization skills with products such as Excel and Tableau can help craft a more interesting or coherent story.

Finally, ***curiosity*** and a facility for ***creative problem solving*** are imperative. Curiosity keeps analysts digging for insights; for the curious analyst, insights prompt further questions. Creative problem solving enables a social analytics team to (1) identify social analytics opportunities, including prospective data sets that supply independent and dependent variables that can tell an interesting story; (2) find workarounds to solving a problem when they lack a specific skill or resource; and (3) craft a story based on their analytics that provides value to their organization.

What Can We Do with Social Analytics?

While corporate uses of social analytics are yet emerging, over the last decade, academic researchers have been developing and applying social analytics techniques to understand a variety of economic, sociopolitical, and organizational phenomena. Business can learn much from these endeavors. For example, researchers at Indiana University and the University of Manchester wondered whether social media data could predict economic outcomes [25]. Foregoing the conventional efficient market hypothesis, which holds that stock market prices are driven by current information, the researchers adopted a collective mood hypothesis, wherein stock prices are believed to be a function of the investors' mood. Using OpinionFinder and Google's Profile of Mood States, they found that the public's mood, as expressed in Twitter posts, predicted changes in the Dow-Jones Industrial Average with an accuracy of 87.6%. (This defies the efficient market hypothesis, which anticipates that stock prices—because they are driven by new information—cannot be predicted with better than 50% accuracy.)

Researchers at Temple University, the University of Texas at Arlington, and George Washington University found that social media data, positive and negative blog posts (subjectively, and labor-intensively, assessed by human raters), and rating level and volume are leading indicators of the equity value of hardware and software firms [26]. The researchers also found these social media indicators to be better predictors of share value than web traffic and Google search indicators. Such information can guide investors' and venture capitalists' decisions about their investment portfolio.

Researchers at the University of Munich investigated the extent to which Twitter coverage of German political parties predicted

How Are Businesses Leveraging Social Data?

Cutting-edge businesses are capitalizing on social analytics to garner value from social media initiatives and social media data. Below are some examples of how social analytics can be used to deliver business value.

1. Retail demand forecasting:
A manufacturer of replica sports jerseys tracks players' popularity over the season. Demand for replica jerseys of players whose social media popularity surges is expected to increase, and the company manufactures more jerseys [3].

2. Improving product safety:
By mining social data, scientists and manufacturers are able to identify drug interactions that prior drug trials failed to reveal [3, 6].

3. Improving HR processes:
Human resource departments are using social media data to screen applicants [3] and identify prospective recruits. In fact, by leveraging social data, a pharmaceutical company was able to add 350 scientists to its team on short notice, while also ensuring their cultural fit [7].

4. Precision marketing:
When you click a "Facebook Connect" button on an eCommerce site, you give the merchant access to your Facebook posts. The merchant then is able to mine your posts to glean information on your product preferences, which then are used to customize your view of that site [9].

5. Insurance claims adjusting and underwriting:
Some insurance companies scour social media data to combat insurance fraud. In addition to triangulating incident reports filed along with claims, social media posts are used to determine customer premiums [11].

election outcomes [27]. Using LIWC to analyze the content of tweets, the researchers first noted that a third of tweets posted were conversational—deliberating on, not just disseminating, political opinions. They observed that tweets reflected the variations in political parties' campaigns; they then found the volume of posts about a political party anticipated subsequent election results.

Social analytics is more than simply mining social media feeds. Social analytics can be applied to data other than that emanating from social media. For example, researchers at the University of Texas, Austin, and Fetch Technologies examined the effect of negative words—measured using the General Inquirer software with the Harvard-IV-4 psychosocial dictionary—in traditional news media articles about firms and firms' earnings and stock value. They found that higher proportions of negative words herald firms' low earnings and stock value, and that the negative effect of negative words on stock value was highest for stories focusing on firms' fundamentals [28].

Researchers at the University of Illinois, Urbana-Champaign, and the University Arizona used LIWC to analyze effects of the favorability of media coverage on firms' strategic change [29]. They found that negative media coverage prompted firms' changes in resource allocations, especially among under-performing firms and those with more independent boards of directors.

In recent research, my colleagues and I compared traditional news media versus social media coverage of a legislative proposal—the Stop Online Piracy Act (SOPA) [30]. Figure 1.4 (created with NodeXL) depicts actors participating in the coverage and the relationships they forged in citing or referencing other actors they deemed newsworthy.

What can we learn from the figure? First, from the sheer number of nodes and lines, we see that coverage of the legislation was greatest on Twitter and sparsest on television. In fact, participation on social media was so dense that not all participants could be depicted. Second, we see the influential participants were mainly

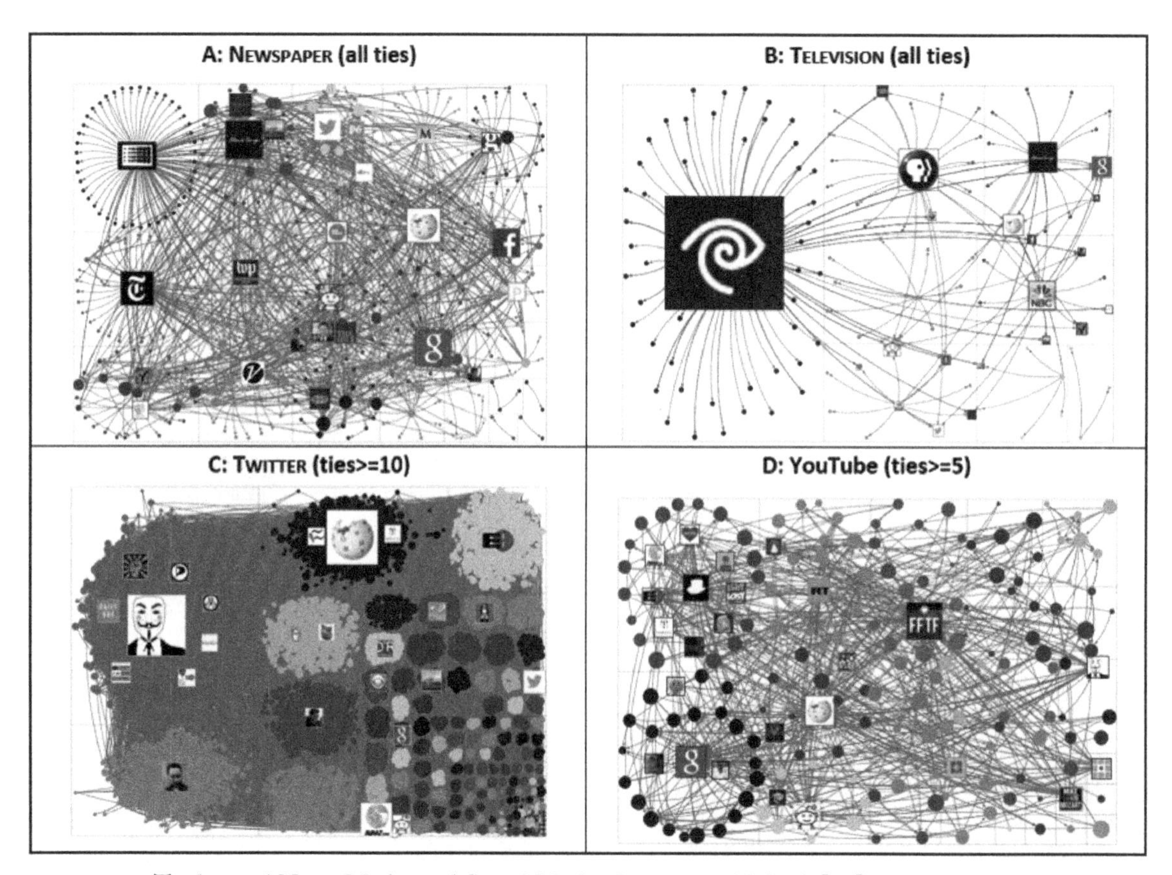

Figure 1.4 Traditional News Media and Social Media Coverage of SOPA [30]

recognizable traditional media brands (e.g., NewsCorp, the *New York Times*, Time Warner, and PBS), emerging as influential on traditional news media platforms. In contrast, while recognizable social media brands such as Google and Wikipedia featured in social media coverage, the diversity of influential actors was higher, including also the hacktivist organization Anonymous, lesser-known activists organizations such as Avaaz and Fight for the Future, Hollywood actor Wil Wheaton (of *Star Trek* and *The Big Bang Theory*), and private citizens. Follow-up statistical analyses confirmed that participation and influence was much more constrained on traditional news media than on social media. Using LIWC to compare the emotional tenor of the conversations across media, we found that while Twitter conversations manifested more positive and negative affect than did newspapers, the emotional tenor otherwise was comparable across media. Such data provide actionable insights into multiple constituencies. Identifying who is influential on social media and what posts are trending provides traditional news media with sources and copy for their own news coverage. Lobbyists or congressional staffers can identify and lobby actors influential in the news coverage of the legislation and manage the emotional tone of their posts in a manner that is consistent with their targeted media.

In the next chapter, we will take a closer look at some applications of social analytics. Through the rest of this book, we will revisit some of these applications as tutorials. Through these, we will raise and answer many different questions of potential concern to data analysts working with social data.

The Focus of This Book

The focus of this book will be on gathering, cleansing and preparing, and analyzing social data—that is, data about profiles of social actors (individuals, organizations, or other collectives), their interactions, and their relationships. Data about interactions assume two primary forms: (1) data about who connects with whom, in the form of ***social network analysis (SNA)***; and (2) data about the content of a conversation, typically textual information, in the form of ***text analysis*** [31]. These forms of data typically are relatively unstructured prior to being subjected to social analytics. Much is also being done with audio/video data. For example, scientists are working on detecting human emotion [32] and deception [33] from mouse cursor movements. For now, such data are beyond the scope of this book.

This book will develop your familiarity with concepts underlying SNA and text analysis, and your technical skills in gathering, managing, and analyzing such data. To do so, we will alternate between relatively simple-to-use PC and SaaS products such as ***NodeXL***, ***Tagul***, ***LIWC***, and ***Weka*** to absorb the concepts, and ***R***, which will enable us to analyze large data sets and perform repetitive analytics tasks more effectively.

In our analysis of social networks and texts, this book will focus mainly on developing the metrics to describe the properties of individuals with networks, of the networks themselves, and of the conversations the individuals have. As Gartner [34] notes, social analytics also entails "predictive modeling and recommendations"—that is, using those metrics to predict customer loyalty, revenue growth, voter turnout, or some outcome of interest to the organization. Such modeling currently is beyond the scope of this book.

Works Cited

1. "Force Friday Event Guide," StarWars.com, 2015, http://www.starwars.com/articles/ffeg.
2. Jones, B., "Harness Your Listening Posts to Enhance the Customer Service Experience," Talking Point: The Disney Institute Blog, 2014, https://www.disneyinstitute.com/blog/harness-your-listening-posts-to-enhance-the-customer/.
3. Morgan, L., "7 Smart Ways to Leverage Social Data," InformationWeek, 2015, https://www.informationweek.com/7-smart-ways-to-leverage-social-data/d/d-id/1321453.
4. Domonoske, C., "#WhereIsRey? She's on Her Way, Says Hasbro," The Two-Way: Breaking News from NPR, https://www.npr.org/sections/thetwo-way/2016/01/06/462144156/-whereisrey-shes-on-her-way-says-hasbro.
5. Hanks, H., "'Star Wars' Monopoly Adds Main Character after #WheresRey Movement," CNN.com, 2016, https://www.cnn.com/2016/01/06/entertainment/star-wars-monopoly-wheres-rey-feat/index.html.

6. Lardon, J., et al., "Adverse Drug Reaction Identification and Extraction in Social Media: A Scoping Review." Journal of Medical Internet Research 17(7; 2015): e171.
7. Ferrar, J., "The War on Talent: How Social, Analytics Are Reinventing the Art of HR," Wired Analytics, 2013, https://www.wired.com/insights/2013/04/the-war-on-talent-how-social-and-analytics-are-reinventing-the-art-of-hr/.
8. Saas, E., "CMOs Plan to Invest More in Social," Social Media and Marketing Daily, 2015, https://www.mediapost.com/publications/article/242626/cmos-plan-to-invest-more-in-social.html.
9. Hill, K., "How a Company Takes Full Advantage of Access to Your Facebook Information," *Forbes: Tech,* 2012, http://www.forbes.com/sites/kashmirhill/2012/10/25/how-a-company-takes-full-advantage-of-your-facebook-information/
10. Miranda, S., I. Kim, and J. Summers, "Jamming with Social Media: How Cognitive Structuring of Organizing Vision Facets Affects IT Innovation Diffusion." *MIS Quarterly*, 39(3; 2015): 591–614.
11. Osakwe, M., "Do Insurance Companies Look at Your Social Media Profiles?," *Huff Post Tech*, 2015, https://www.huffingtonpost.com/nextadvisorcom/do-insurance-companies-lo_b_7844070.html.
12. Samson, E., "5 Social-Media Opportunities Businesses Mostly Overlook," Social Media, Entrepreneur, 2015, https://www.entrepreneur.com/article/254046.
13. Morgan, H., "6 Things You Should Know about Social Recruiting," On Careers, U.N. Money, 2014, https://money.usnews.com/money/blogs/outside-voices-careers/2014/10/22/6-things-you-should-know-about-social-recruiting.
14. Kim, I., and S. Miranda, "Buffeting the Technical Core: Entraining Contention to Innovation in the Social Media Era." Paper presented at the Academy of Management Conference, Orlando, Florida, 2013.
15. Sánchez Abril, P., A. Levin, and A. Del Riego. "Blurred Boundaries: Social Media Privacy and the Twenty-First-Century Employee." *American Business Law Journal*, 49(1; 2012): 63–124.
16. Rose, C., "The Security Implications of Ubiquitous Social Media." *International Journal of Management & Information Systems*, 15(1; 2011): 35–40.
17. Boyd, D., and N.B. Ellison, "Social Network Sites: Definition, History, and Scholarship." *Journal of Computer-Mediated Communication*, 13(1; 2007): 210–30.
18. Goes, P., "Editor's Comments: Big Data and IS Research." *MIS Quarterly*, 38(3; 2014): iii–viii.
19. Dumbill, E., "What Is Big Data?," On Our Radar, O'Reilly Media, 2012, https://www.oreilly.com/ideas/what-is-big-data.
20. Osman, M., "28 Powerful Facebook Stats Your Brand Can't Ignore in 2018," SproutSocial, 2018, https://sproutsocial.com/insights/facebook-stats-for-marketers/.
21. "What Happens Online in 60 Seconds?" SmartInsights, 2018, https://www.smartinsights.com/internet-marketing-statistics/happens-online-60-seconds/.
22. Phillips, G., "Memory Sizes Explained—Gigabytes, Terabytes & Petabytes in Layman's Terms," Make Use Of, 2017, https://www.makeuseof.com/tag/memory-sizes-gigabytes-terabytes-petabytes/.
23. Tuohy, J., "What Is Home Automation and How Do I Get Started?" NetworkWorld, 2015, https://www.networkworld.com/article/2874914/internet-of-things/what-is-home-automation-and-how-do-i-get-started.html.
24. Marr, B., *Big Data: Using SMART Big Data. Analytics and Metrics to Make Better Decisions and Improve Performance*. Hoboken, NJ: Wiley, 2015.
25. Bollen, J., H. Mao, and X. Zeng, "Twitter Mood Predicts the Stock Market." *Journal of Computational Science*, 2(1; 2011): 1–8.
26. Luo, X., J. Zhang, and W. Duan, "Social Media and Firm Equity Value." *Information Systems Research*, 24(1; 2013): 146–63.

27. Tumasjan, A., et al., "Predicting Elections with Twitter: What 140 Characters Reveal about Political Sentiment." *ICWSM*, 10 (2010): 178–85.

28. Tetlock, P.C., M. Saar-Tsechansky, and S. Macskassy, "More than Words: Quantifying Language to Measure Firms' Fundamentals." *The Journal of Finance*, 63(3; 2008): 1437–67.

29. Bednar, M.K., S. Boivie, and N.R. Prince, "Burr under the Saddle: How Media Coverage Influences Strategic Change." *Organization Science*, 24(3; 2013): 910–25.

30. Miranda, S., A. Young, and E. Yetgin, "Are Social Media Emancipatory or Hegemonic? Societal Effects of Mass Media Digitization in the Case of the SOPA Discourse." *MIS Quarterly*, 40(2: Special Issue on ICT and Societal Challenges; 2016): 303–29.

31. Beyer, M.A., et al., "Big Data Drives Rapid Changes in Infrastructure and $232 Billion in IT Spending Through 2016 in Gartner Research," 2012, https://www.gartner.com/doc/2195915/big-data-drives-rapid-changes.

32. Hibbeln, M.T., et al., "Inferring Negative Emotion from Mouse Cursor Movements." *MIS Quarterly*, forthcoming.

33. Valacich, J.S., et al., "Identifying Insider Threats through Monitoring Mouse Movements in Concealed Information Tests," presented at the Hawaii International Conference on Computer and Systems Sciences, Symposium on Rapid Screening Technologies, Deception Detection, and Credibility Assessment, Maui, Hawaii, January 2013.

34. "Social Analytics," Gartner IT Glossary, 2018, https://www.gartner.com/it-glossary/social-analytics.

CHAPTER 2

Some Uses of Social Analytics

Learning Objectives

The purpose of this chapter is to understand the range of ways in which social analytics can be used, including:

1. as a listening post;
2. for understanding social groups;
3. for benchmarking organizational strategies; and
4. for managing conflict.

There are numerous applications of social analytics. The last chapter briefly introduced some. In this chapter, we consider four key ways in which organizations—including corporations and nonprofits—do and can use social analytics. This chapter also will introduce you to data sets used in the tutorials in later chapters. Through this chapter, we revisit the central purpose of social analytics—or any form of analytics, for that matter—which is to produce ***actionable insights***. Actionable insights refer to new knowledge that can inform organizations' strategies or tactics. While many techniques and analyses offer diagnostic value—shedding light on problems and opportunities—without actionable insights, our analytics efforts contribute little to the organizations for which we are conducting the analytics.

Social Analytics as a Listening Post

One key way in which social analytics is useful is as a tool for monitoring key stakeholders. In the last chapter, we considered one way in which organizations can use social analytics as a listening post (i.e., to ***detect problems***). In the *#WhereIsRey* example described in Chapter 1, we saw that by monitoring their customers, organizations like Disney and Hasbro could have detected and addressed customer dissatisfaction with their merchandising strategy early. Awareness of prospective customers' dismay about the absence of Rey merchandise could have prompted manufacturing and distribution of merchandise in time for the Christmas season. In Tutorial 7.1, by inspecting word clouds of tweets about Donald Trump captured before the 2016 presidential primaries and after the 2017 presidential inauguration, we see that the focus of the public and of President Trump shifted from election-related issues such as the debates and party politics to immigration policy and international politics. In answering the first question (Have public sentiment and motives changed between the primaries and the 2017 presidential inauguration?), in Tutorial 7.3, social analytics helps us determine how public sentiments and motivations changed between the two periods. Answering these questions yields actionable insights. For the presidential candidates before the election, insights inform them of key public concerns and ways in which the public could be motivated to vote for them. For the government after the election, insights gleaned from public discourse on social media can inform them of their constituents' key concerns. These concerns then can shape public policy, enabling a participative democracy.

A second example is to ***understand sentiment*** around events and issues. In answering the second question in Tutorial 7.2, we consider the sentiment customers express in their posts on Delta Airline's Facebook page when discussing or not discussing delays and when discussing five major Delta hub cities. As with any organization in the service industry, customer satisfaction is important to Delta Airlines [14]. While it ranks second on JD Power's customer satisfaction survey—after Alaska Airlines—relative to traditional North America carriers, it falls substantially behind low-cost carriers Southwest Airlines and Jet Blue [17]. Our comparative analysis of sentiment across posts complaining about delays across different locations provides actionable insight that is useful in training airline gate agents operating at different locations. (See the insert on "Sentiment Analysis and Emotional Labor" for more information about the significance of sentiment analysis for employees' performance of emotional labor.)

A third example of using social analytics as a listening post is to ***identify emotional hotspots***. Emotional hotspots refer to the coincidence of strong sentiment and centrality (influence) within a social network. In tracking a brand, event, or issue, it is useful not only to understand the public's sentiment; if we wish to harness or turnaround that sentiment, we may wish to leverage the phenomenon of emotional contagion. To do so, we need to identify and take advantage of individuals at the center of emotional hotspots, since it is logistically impossible to interact with every member of the public. Qualifying or addressing grievances of those central to discussion of the brand, event, or issue permits efficient intervention and is critical to maintenance of brand image.

Individuals who express strong sentiment toward a brand but are not particularly central to their network lack the ability to diffuse their sentiment through the network. In contrast, individuals who are strongly disposed—or opposed—to the brand and influential within their network can diffuse their sentiments widely, affecting the community's perceptions of the brand. In addressing the third question in Tutorial 7.3, we find a negative correlation between the use of emotional language—both positive and negative—and individuals' centrality or influence on social media before the primaries. In other words, people highly influential in the Donald Trump tweets before the primaries tended not to use emotional language. However, following the inauguration, we find a positive correlation between use of positive emotional language and influence on social media. We conclude from this that there were no emotional hotspots before the primaries, but there were positive emotion hotspots after the inauguration. Our actionable insight here is the identification of the central individuals in discourse about Donald Trump. We can co-opt these individuals to shape public opinion.

Sentiment Analysis and Emotional Labor

Sentiment analysis can provide useful input into organizational employees' emotional labor. Emotional labor refers to "the act of expressing organizationally desired emotions during service transactions" [2]. Customer-facing occupations especially necessitate high amounts of emotional labor, wherein employees are expected to feel a particular way and manifest certain types of feelings in their interactions with customers. For example, flight attendants are expected to be cheerful, nurses empathetic, and funeral directors somber [2]. In service relationships, employees' authentic displays of positive affect induce positive customer affect and increase customers' sense of rapport with the service agent, which in turn increases customers' satisfaction with the transaction and customers' loyalty [9].

Understanding customers' state, however, is important for effective performance of emotional labor. This is where sentiment analysis provides invaluable input for service personnel. First, it is useful to know that negative sentiment expressed online tends to be perceived as more negative than it was intended to be, and positive sentiment expressed tends to be perceived as neutral [13]. Second, emotions are contagious (i.e., tend to be communicated from one person to another). A large-scale study that manipulated posts appearing on users' Facebook feeds found that decreasing the incidence of posts with negative content decreased users' posts with negative words, and decreasing the incidence of posts with positive content decreased users' posts with positive words [16]. This tells us that negative sentiment should be squelched quickly or it runs amok. Effective emotional labor therefore requires that service personnel have a good understanding of customers' negative emotional states.

Finally, social analytics can help us determine ***where to listen***. For example, addressing the first question in Tutorial 7.2, we consider whether Delta Airlines customers experiencing travel delays post to the airline's Facebook page or post to other Facebook pages, including their own. J.D. Power and associates reported that 21% of business travelers and 8% of leisure travelers reported on their airline experiences on social media, with Facebook being the dominant medium used [17]. It therefore behooves an airline company interested in customer feedback to monitor Facebook. But Facebook's myriad local communities raises the question of whether the airline should monitor all Facebook posts or just posts to its own Facebook page. Using a custom dictionary to identify posts in which people report problems with flight delays from two samples of Facebook posts, we find that while 22% of the public's posts to Delta's page concern flight delays, only 3% of posts about Delta on other Facebook pages mention flight delays. This provides us with the actionable insight that we can focus our monitoring on Delta's Facebook page without losing much information about customers' reactions to flight delays.

Social Analytics for Understanding Social Groups

Applications of social analytics of groups range from the whimsical to the momentous. One example is a pop culture application mapping the relationships among *Game of Thrones* characters (based on them being mentioned within fifteen words of each other in *A Storm of Swords*) "to make sense of the intricate character relationships and their bearing on the future plot" [20]. In a health care application, using the premise that the friends of randomly selected individuals tend to be more centrally located in their social milieu, researchers studying the outbreak of the H1N1 virus on the Harvard University campus in 2009 found the sample of friends on average contracted the virus approximately fourteen days sooner than the randomly-selected students [21]. Using this finding, the researchers suggested immunizing individuals central to social networks to control the diffusion of contagious diseases. In a national security application following the 9/11 terrorist attacks, scholars have applied social analytics techniques to uncovering covert terrorist networks [22]. Such networks are particularly problematic to construct, because members are motivated to mask and fudge relationships underlying a criminal conspiracy.

When analyzing groups, social analytics enables us to ***visualize configurations of social ties*** within groups. For example, in addressing the question of whether an instructor's pedagogical approach (i.e., team-oriented learning) can change a class's network structure in Tutorial 3.1, we look at the configuration of acquaintance and friendship relationships of a graduate knowledge management class. This class was composed of students pursuing different specialties (e.g., MBA, master of accountancy, and master of MIS) and of full-time and part-time students. Figure 2.1, which depicts the evolution of the class's friendship network over a four-week span, shows us that the class became much more integrated within that time. The actionable insight gleaned here is that pedagogy can be leveraged to foster a more integrated student experience.

A second way in which social analytics helps us understand groups is to ***identify influential actors***. In Tutorial 3.2, using social network metrics, we identify MH as the most influential student in the class. How is this an actionable insight? If I need a sounding board about classroom issues, or if I want to get the word out on a schedule change, MH is my go-to guy! Similarly, through Tutorials 4.1 and 4.2, we identify two legislative "linchpins"—congressmen Randy Neugebauer and Steven Palazzo. Such linchpins are able to transfer knowledge across different bills that they co-sponsored.

A third way in which social analytics helps us understand groups is to ***ascertain group fault lines*** and the basis for these fault lines. (See the "What Are 'Fault Lines'?" insert for more

What Are "Fault Lines"?

A "fault line" originally referred to a geological break in the bedrock. These geological fault lines—such as the San Andreas fault in the United States and the Kunlun fault in Tibet—create stress zones beneath the surface of the earth, which manifest as seismic events.

The concept of fault lines has been appropriated by social scientists to refer to fractures in a social space. In this social context, fault lines "divide a group's members on the basis of one or more attributes," such as race, gender, job tenure, status, and functional area [4]. Rather than demographic characteristics, fault lines also may stem from factors such as shared ideology or shared history that are more difficult to uncover.

As with geological fault lines, social fault lines also manifest as social disruptions. Fault lines influence the information and other resources to which individuals in a group or other social context have access, how they process those resources, how the individuals interact (or don't) with each other, and the group's political processes. As you might imagine, fault lines also influence group outcomes such as work product quality and cohesiveness. When fault lines are formed by multiple attributes (e.g., we have a subgroup of men from IT, aged 25–40), the impact of fault lines on group dynamics and outcomes is exacerbated.

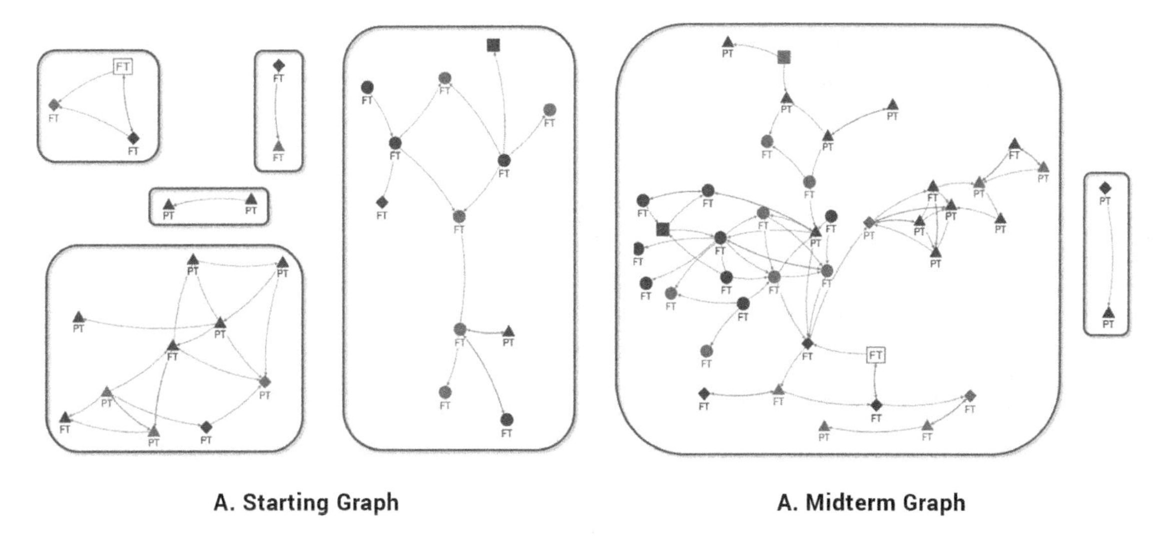

Figure 2.1 Evolution of the Knowledge Management Class Friendship Network

information on the concept.) Through Tutorial 5.1, we see that gender, often believed to be a significant factor determining business affiliations [23], has very little to do with how the class was fragmented; rather, the class initially was fragmented based on students' majors (MBA, MAcc, and MS-MIS) and their full-time versus part-time status. As will be seen in Tutorial 5.2, we also can use social analytics to surface cliques that are not related to an identifiable demographic characteristic. This is actionable for faculty, as it suggests that instructors should create teams that cross majors and status and break up cliques if they wish to foster a more integrated student experience. In Tutorial 6.1, we find party membership and commensurate levels of member influence provide the best explanation for the likelihood that representatives will coauthor a bill. From a public policy perspective, this is more diagnostic than actionable, confirming current perspectives that partisanship is a growing problem in U.S. politics [24].

Social Analytics for Benchmarking Organizational Strategies

Social media users must make several critical decisions. As they get started, benchmarking the social media strategies of referent others can provide invaluable input. One decision users must make is ***whom to friend***. Friending has two major consequences. First, friending exposes the user to information shared by their friends within their own news feeds. Sure, we can search for any information we want. But that's the difference between information push versus pull. Having information show up in our feeds (i.e., pushed to us) can make us aware of information we otherwise would miss. In social network terms, our social media friends supply the weak ties that apprise us of business and other opportunities [25]. But too much information in our feeds means we don't read any of it, right? Second, friending has symbolic consequences. People who do not know us make inferences about our identity based on who our friends are [26]. If many of our friends tend to post politically-conservative messages, people who don't know us will assume that we are also politically conservative. So we need to choose our friends judiciously.

In a corporate environment, one approach to choosing friends on social media is to see who the top social media brands friend. In Tutorial 3.3, we address the question of whose friending strategy a brand or person new to social media can imitate. To do so, we benchmark a sample of twenty-seven high profile social media brands that have appeared on two social media funds—the Wired-Kapitall fund [27] and the Buzz Social Media Insights Index [28]. After identifying these brands' friends, we can determine the Twitter accounts most frequently friended by these brands. As of July 2017, the five most-frequently friended accounts are Forbes (by thirteen brands), Mashable (sixteen brands), the New York Times (fifteen brands), the Red Cross (eleven brands), and the Wall Street Journal (sixteen brands). Under conditions of uncertainty, such competitive intelligence provides actionable insight, as it enables imitation [29].

A second decision related to ties is ***whether to reciprocate*** when someone friends or follows us. Not reciprocating a tie online can weaken the underlying social relationship. But indiscriminate friending can clog up our feeds and muddy our identity. In Tutorial 5.3, we address the question of how much the University of Oklahoma's Price College should reciprocate ties and which ties it should reciprocate. To do so, we benchmark the ten business schools (BSchools) in the Big XII conference. The schools' Twitter profiles are summarized in Table 2.1. This table suggests that OUPriceCollege is in the middle of the pack (ranks fifth) in terms of its reciprocity rate, but differs considerably from its sister Oklahoma institution, SpearsSchoolOSU, which ranks second on reciprocity rates in the Big XII.

Figures 2.2 and 2.3 depict the business schools' followers and friends, highlighting reciprocated accounts as spheres (and in the schools' colors). Across the two figures, we see the reciprocation pattern by OUPriceCollege actually is similar to that by SpearsSchoolOSU, in that both tend to follow their prominent followers (i.e., those accounts with a large number of followers). All other schools tend *not* to reciprocate follower ties from accounts with many followers. These accounts typically are traditional mass media accounts such as the Wall Street Journal (WSJ), the New York Times (NYTimes), and CNN; emergent mass media accounts such as Mashable and TechCrunch, accounts of social media organizations such as Instagram and Twitter, and accounts of noteworthy corporate and political figures such as Bill Gates and Barack Obama.

What about the relationship between reciprocity and the number of likes the schools' tweets get? For the ten Big XII schools, the correlation between reciprocity and the number of likes the schools' tweets get is a mere –0.02, suggesting that reciprocity is unimportant. So far, benchmarking against the Big XII has produced little actionable information. But are we benchmarking correctly?

From Table 2.1, we notice that the ten business schools have diverse activity levels. The total number of tweets to date for KStateBusiness, NeeleySchoolTCU, OUPriceCollege, and SpearsSchoolOSU fall below five thousand (as of July 2017). Activity rates, computed as the number of tweets per day, also are the lowest of the ten schools at one or fewer tweets per day. In contrast, the remaining six schools, depicted in Figure 2.3, have more than five thousand tweets to date and an activity rate exceeding three tweets every two days. When benchmarking against schools with a comparable activity level, we find a modest negative correlation between reciprocity and likes for the highly active schools (i.e., –0.34). In contrast, for schools that are less active on Twitter, the correlation between reciprocity and likes earned is 0.97. Clearly, for these schools, reciprocating ties is important.

Our actionable insight is that schools can attract attention by pursuing a strategy of using Twitter to disseminate information or to forge

Benchmarking and Strategic Groups

A prerequisite for effective benchmarking is understanding strategic groups. A strategic group is a collection of organizations that share characteristics beyond industry membership, including size, structure, strategy, business models, and reputation [3]. Strategic group members are the reference group that organizations then seek to emulate (i.e., to strive to be equal to or to exceed) [3].

Sometimes determining strategic groups can be straightforward. The restaurant industry, for example, may be broken down into fast-food and fine-dining groups. At other times, it may be unclear which organizations constitute our strategic group. In fact, researchers have suggested that organizations may belong clearly to a strategic group, may be inconsistent in some ways with members of their group, or may even transition from one strategic group to another [8].

Additionally, an organization simultaneously may be a member of multiple discrete or overlapping strategic groups [12]. For example, the University of Oklahoma simultaneously is a member of public/state institutions (versus private institutions) and a member of the Big XII conference (versus the Big 10, PacTen, or other athletic conferences). As we shall see, these are not the only groups meaningful for the university to consider when benchmarking its social media activities.

Table 2.1 Twitter Friends and Followers of BSchools in the Big XII

School	Joined	Friends	Followers	Reciprocity†	Tweets	Activity‡	Likes
Baylor_Business	4/9/2008	4,196	9,335	85%	5,535	1.63	679
ISU_CoB	5/20/2009	647	2,736	31%	5,648	1.89	2,826
KStateBusiness	7/2/2010	441	2,593	20%	2,714	1.05	475
KUBSchool	8/12/2009	797	6,862	15%	11,000	3.79	2,449
NeeleySchoolTCU	9/1/2011	294	1,728	9%	1,080	0.62	86
OUPriceCollege	3/2/2009	494	2,635	23%	2,417	0.96	94
SpearsSchoolOSU	2/20/2009	1,632	3,289	68%	3,463	1.31	1,334
TTURawlsCollege	3/31/2009	449	6,276	10%	6,263	2.14	1,654
UTexasMcCombs	8/28/2008	2,548	16,187	23%	9,547	3.26	4,312
WVUCoBE	5/11/2009	1,785	4,750	51%	8,729	3.47	3,918

†Percentage of a school's followers that are also its friends
‡Number of tweets per day

relationships within its community. Only by correctly benchmarking our reference group is this insight revealed. That said, we should be cautious about attributing too much confidence to findings based on our small sample of ten schools, particularly when we split them out into subsamples of four and six schools. Results based on such small samples are extremely sensitive to outliers.

Another critical decision is ***what to post***. Let's say we are starting a new Twitter feed for our casino. Benchmarking the Twitter feeds of the five largest casinos in the country (by gaming square footage) [30] can provide some inspiration for our own feed. Simple word clouds of more than three thousand tweets from each of these five casinos, depicted in Figure 2.4, show us that casinos primarily tweet about two forms of entertainment—shows and gambling. For two of the top five casinos, Foxwoods and Riverwind, tweets about shows and headlining performers dominate; for the remaining three, gambling-related tweets dominate. In Tutorial 8.2, we confirm this impression by examining the frequency counts of the words appearing most often in tweets emanating from the different casinos.

As we saw with our Big XII BSchools, benchmarking without understanding why some of our reference organizations behave differently from others is not enlightening. So why do some casinos emphasize performances over gambling? To answer this question, we can look at the casinos' seating capacity. Notably, Foxwoods's Fox Theater and Riverwind's Showplace Theater have the lowest seating capacity, at 1,932 and 1,500 persons, respectively [31, 32]. In contrast, Winstar's Colosseum and Mohegan Sun's Arena have theater seating capacities of 7,700 and 10,000 persons, respectively [33, 34]. San Manuel does not have a comparable theater; instead, musicians perform live at the casino's franchised Rock & Brews restaurant [35, 36]. Low seating capacity means that Foxwoods and Riverwind must do especially well on their ticket sales in order to cover their performers' costs. To understand the casinos' disparate strategies better, we look at ticket pricing for a random sample of their Friday and Saturday night events (between August and November 2017). Once again, with the lowest average differential of $61 and $10, respectively, between their top and lowest priced tickets, we find that Foxwoods and Riverwind behave similarly. In contrast, the average price differential for Winstar and Mohegan Sun is $121 and $216, respectively.

Our actionable insight? If our casino has a small theater, to which we are bringing star performers, we need to use social media to promote events to ensure they sell out. With larger auditoriums, underwriting performer

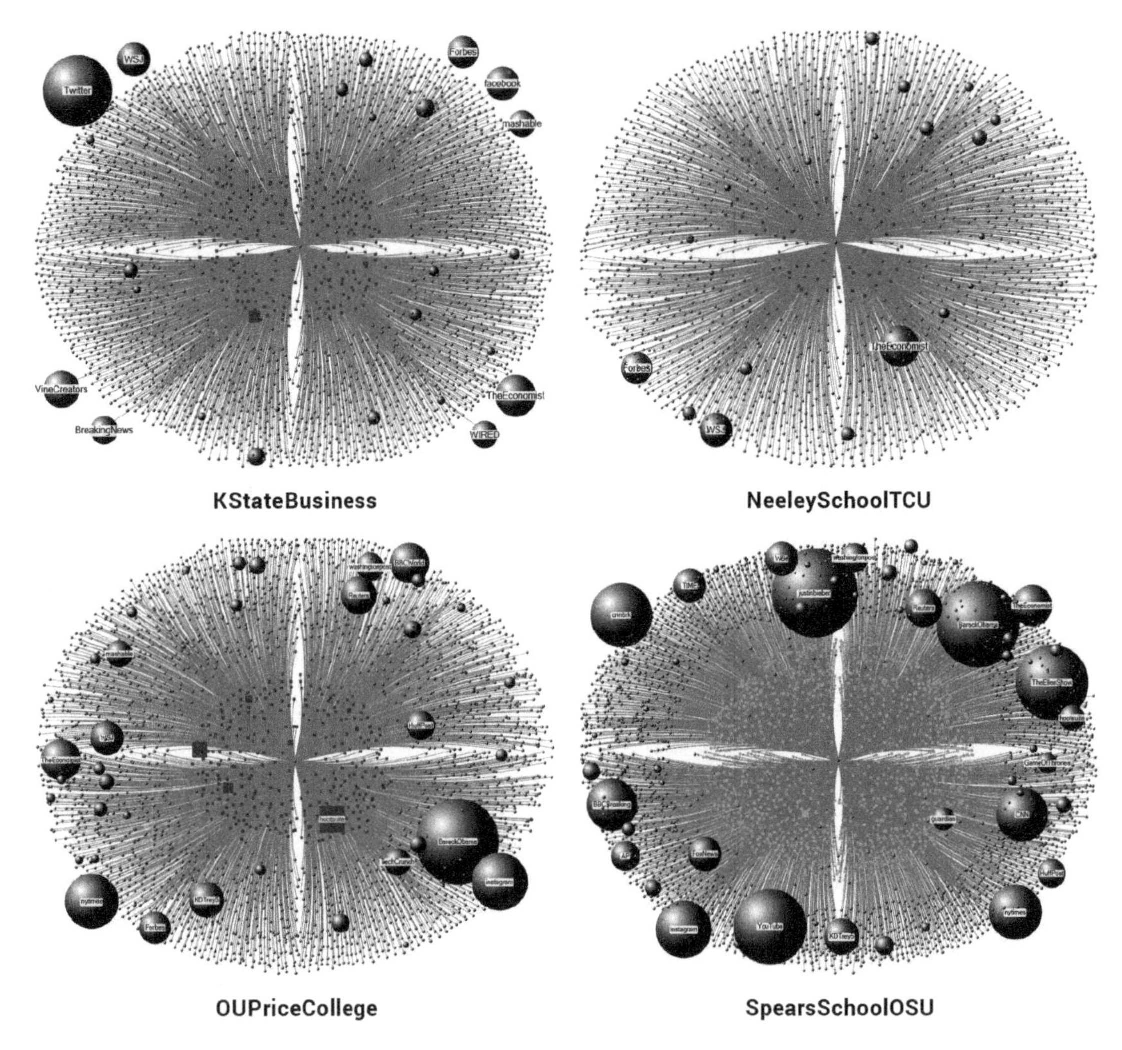

Note: Round vertices are reciprocated followers. Node size indicates number of followers. Labeled nodes indicate five million plus followers.

Figure 2.2 Reciprocation by Big XII Colleges with Less Than Five Thousand Tweets

expenses is easier. Therefore, if we have a larger auditorium or no auditorium, we can focus on promoting gambling via social media.

Social Analytics for Managing Conflicts

Social analytics can be used to resolve large-scale conflicts. First, it can be used to ***determine whether a social group is polarized.*** Such polarization tells us that there is a strong need to manage conflict within the group. In answering the third question in Tutorial 7.3 (Do ideological birds of a feather flock together?), we investigate the extent to which the public tweeting about/to Donald Trump polarizes between the period before the 2016 primaries and after the inauguration in 2017. The resulting insights once again are more diagnostic than actionable, telling us that we have a problem, but yielding little guidance on how to address it.

One way in which social analytics can be used to provide guidance on how to address conflict and polarization is to ***represent competing parties' semantic networks.*** This sheds light on such opposing perspectives. Without such understanding, conflicts persist—even escalate. A semantic network depicts the interrelationship

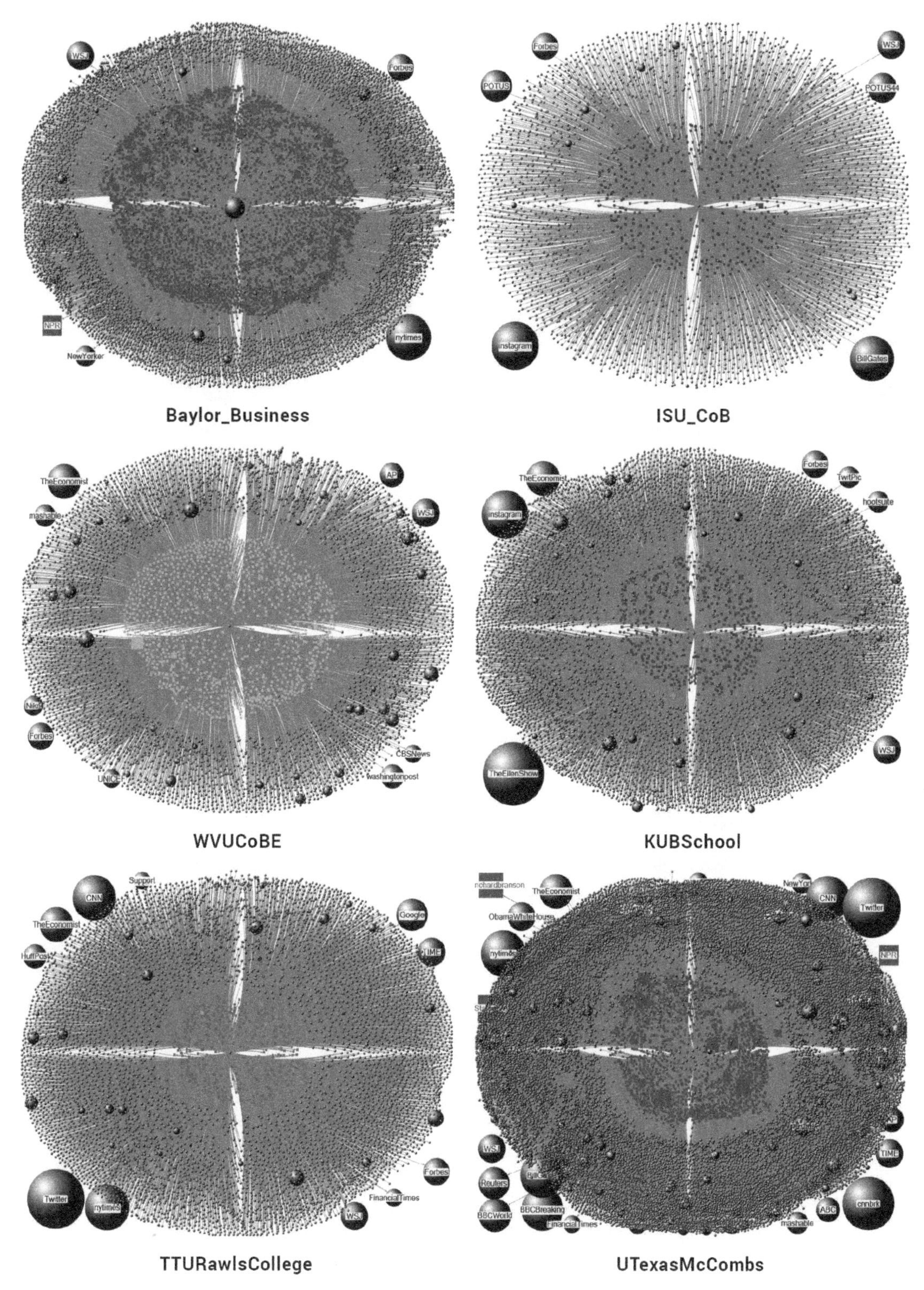

Note: Round vertices are reciprocated followers. Node size indicates number of followers. Labeled nodes indicate five million plus followers.

Figure 2.3 Reciprocation by Big XII Colleges with More Than Five Thousand Tweets

#5: Riverwind

Figure 2.4 Benchmarking Casino Twitter Posts

among concepts. Depending on what we wish to visualize, we can either map the semantic network around a focal concept of interest or map the semantic network of all concepts appearing in a text.

In 2009, India's Ministry of Electronics and Information Technology established the Unique Identification Authority of India (UIDAI), spearheaded by former CEO of Infosys, Nandan Nilekani. Over the next few years, the universal identifier initiative in India, branded as *Aadhaar* (meaning foundation [37]), came into being. By December 2017, the UIDAI has decreed that all bank accounts in India be validated with an Aadhaar card [38]. There was speculation that an Aadhaar card soon would become mandatory even to board a domestic flight [39] or book train tickets [40]. An August 2017 Supreme Court ruling that privacy is a fundamental right may challenge such mandates, though [37]. Given the widespread protests, the universal ID—or Aadhaar—clearly has very different meanings to the government and to citizens.

To understand what Aadhaar means to the Indian government and to the citizens it serves, we apply semantic network analyses in Tutorial 11.1. The first semantic network is based on 3,552 tweets collected from the UIDAI Twitter account between April and June 2017. This network sheds light on the government's portrayal of Aadhaar. The second semantic network is based on 35,780 tweets posted by 23,231 citizen accounts between January 2013 and June 2016. This network informs us about how citizens see Aadhaar.

The Indian government's conceptualization of Aadhaar, depicted in Figure 2.5, has three parts: promotional, legal, and procedural. The promotional part links the Aadhaar concept to the concept of "stardom." This is based on fifty-three tweets that promoted a social media contest in which parents were encouraged to film their children speaking about need the for and benefits of Aadhaar, or announcing contest winners [41]. Prizes of Rs. 5,000 (~$75) for the twenty best videos and of Rs. 1,000 (~$16) for the next fifty videos were to be credited directly to childrens' (or their parents') bank accounts, which were expected to be "linked by Aadhaar." The second part links Aadhaar to terms such as *entitled*, *section*, *apply*, *NRIs*, and *according*. This part of the government's Aadhaar conceptualization speaks to the legal meaning of Aadhaar, addressing sections of the legislation and how they apply to nonresident Indians (NRIs) versus resident citizens. It argues its legality and benefit in implementing a zero-tolerance policy toward corruption. It also exhorts the public not to share their Aadhaar details on social platforms. The third part links Aadhaar to terms such as update, post, and note, conveying procedural information about how citizens can obtain their Aadhaar card. This part details the registration process, discusses how citizens must generate the biometric identifiers required for the card, charges for citizens who wish to update their biometric or demographic information on existing cards, the lead time for the government to generate Aadhaar cards, and the benefits of Aadhaar to the Indian economy, as discussed at a recent conference.

Citizens' conceptualization of Aadhaar, depicted in Figure 2.6, has four parts: problems, disapproval, mandate scope, and procedural. The

Media and Political Polarization

Polarization is the situation wherein individuals hold and espouse increasingly extreme opinions [1]. Polarization is problematic because polarized people are less able to find the common ground that is necessary for collaboration within organizations, as well as for a functional democracy and a tolerant society [5].

Polarization has two related facets: The first is affective, where sentiment toward opposing policy and political parties becomes more negative [6]. The second is cognitive, where individuals' awareness and understanding of opposing perspectives decrease [7, 8]. Exposure to information consistent with one's perspectives increases one's affective polarization [11] and affective polarization prompts one to seek out and be receptive to information consistent with one's perspective [15]. Because we tend to selectively seek out relationships and information consistent with the views we hold, the internet and social media have actually exacerbated polarization, creating "echo chambers," within which only similar views are expressed and echoed [18].

Research has found that polarization can be decreased when individuals are exposed simultaneously to information that is consistent with and counter to the attitudes they hold [19]. Social analytics can help us visualize disparate ideologies simultaneously.

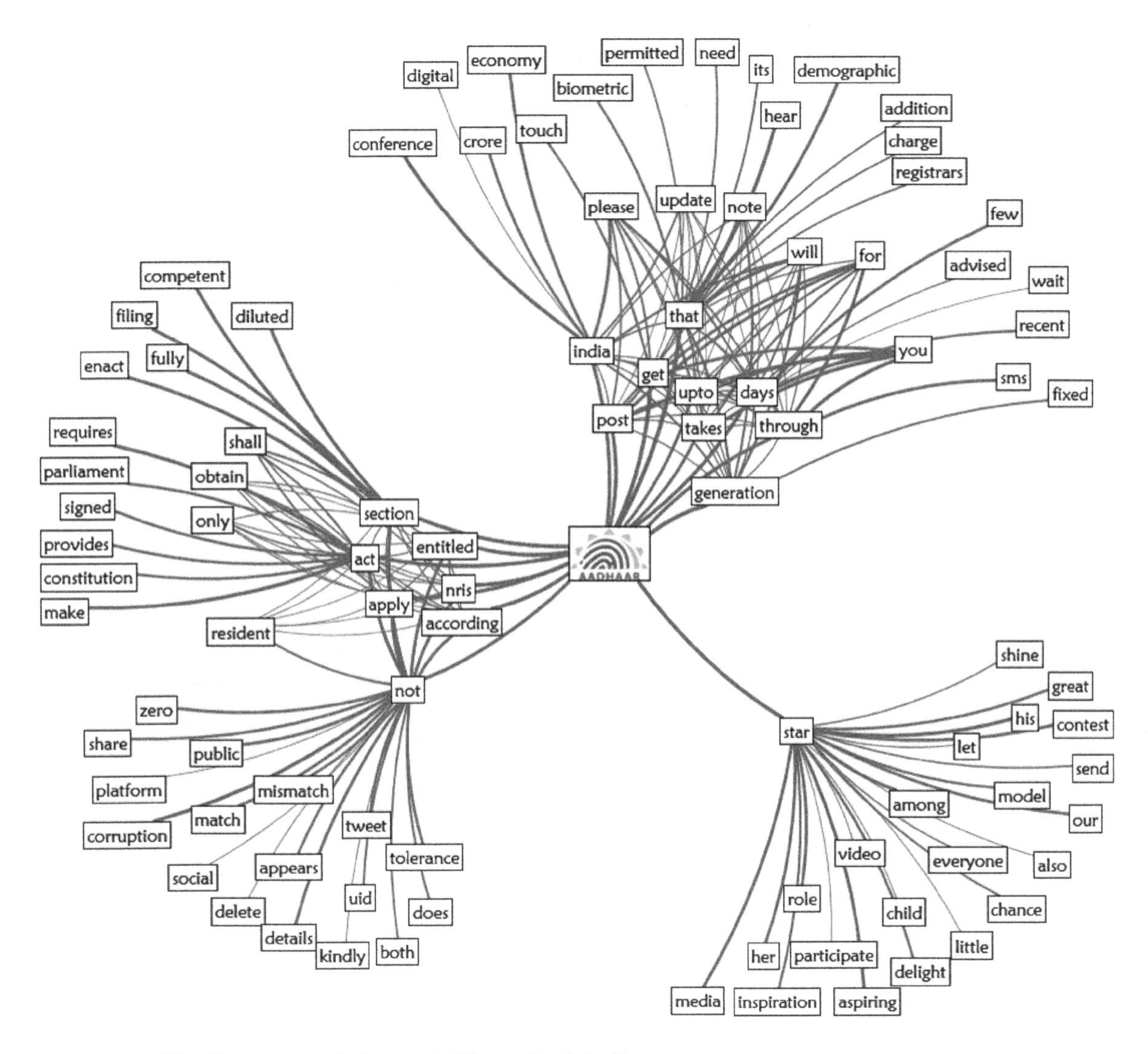

Figure 2.5 The Government's Semantic Network of Aadhaar

range of problems discussed included security, privacy, encroachment on individuals' civil liberties, and constitutionality. Citizens expressed their disapproval with the government, with Aadhaar, and with wireless carriers who deactivated phone numbers of clients who failed to link the Aadhaar cards to their wireless accounts, noting that they "sucked." Citizens noted that the Aadhaar mandate touched a wide range of services, including banking, medical care, and obtaining government assistance, even for NRIs. Finally, citizens raised the procedural challenges of linking Aadhaar cards and the PAN card previously required for identifying tax returns.

From a diagnostic perspective, a relatively naïve viewer of the two semantic networks can discern the different viewpoints advanced by the Indian government and its citizens. The Indian government is promoting the initiative so as to combat corruption—in the face of a significant "black market" or underground economy [42]—and join the global networked economy. Citizens, on the other hand, resent being coerced to compromise their security and cede their privacy to the government and to the technology firms that have arisen around the Aadhaar "technology stack" [43], just so they can live their daily lives. To the extent that the government uses Twitter and other social fora to address citizens' concerns about privacy, security, and information ownership, while also providing more information on how Aadhaar can elevate the economic well-being of all

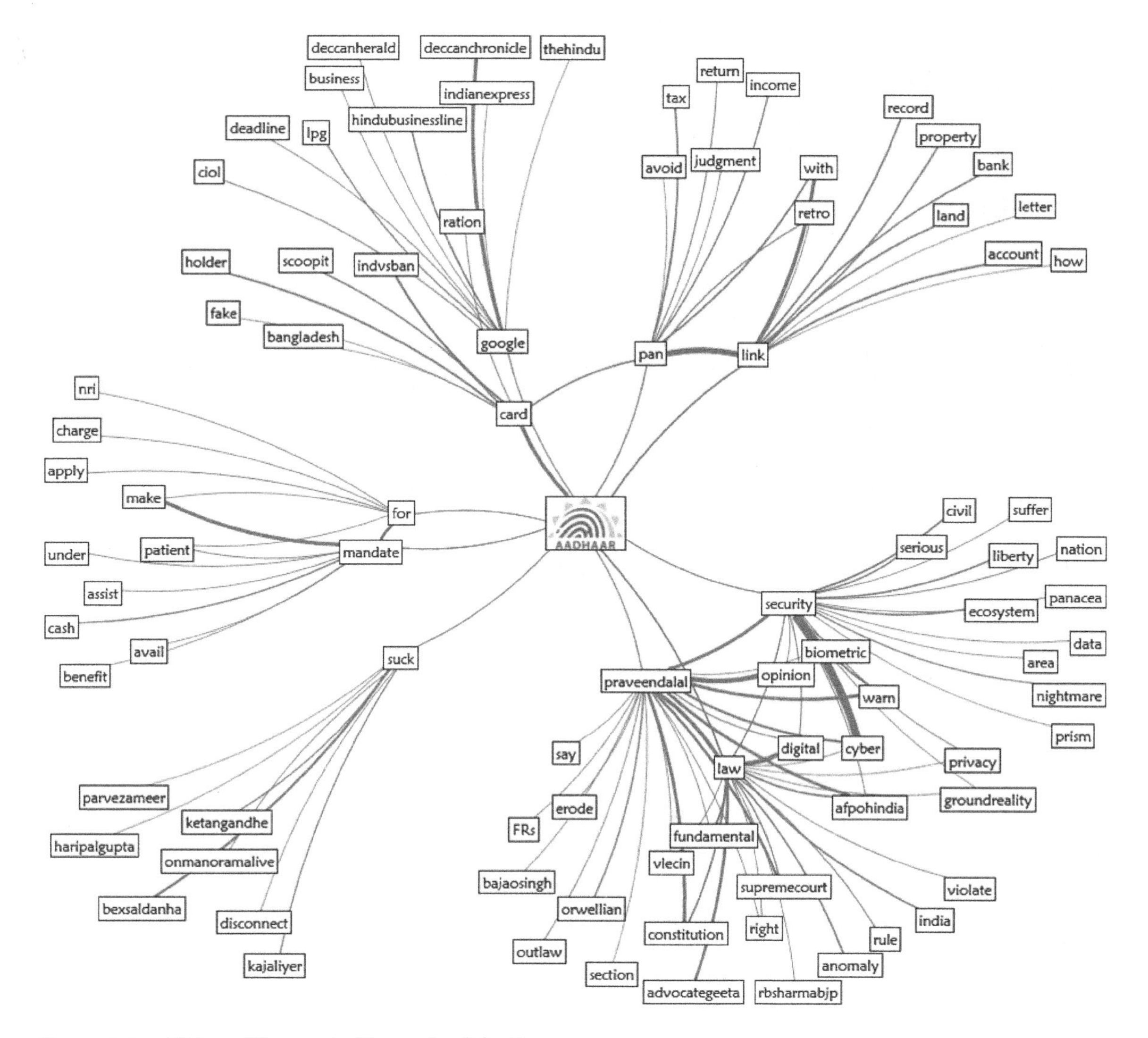

Figure 2.6 Citizens' Semantic Network of Aadhaar

citizens, not just big business interests, Indian citizens are more likely to buy into the new digital infrastructure. In this way, insights from the comparative semantic networks can be made actionable.

Conclusions

This chapter—in fact, this book—only begins to scratch the surface of what we can do with social analytics. Several of the tutorials referenced here require a combination of tool kits and skills. Technically the more adept we get with different tool kits and with combining different tools, the more problems we will be able to solve, and even forestall; the more opportunities we will be able to recognize; and the more actionable insights we will be able to glean.

In our quest for actionable insights, though, our ability to notice patterns and our persistence and diligence in digging for further information exist pays off. Rather than sticking with the data set we began analyzing—typically social media profiles or posts—we need to be willing to obtain and analyze additional data, as we saw when benchmarking casinos. This requires us to constantly ask questions: Why does this pattern occur? Why is this organization unlike others? Suddenly, an observation that seemed mildly interesting, at best, becomes the basis for an organizational strategy. This is what we will be striving for in our forays into social analytics. We also should ask ourselves follow-up questions like: Why might the results of this analysis be suspect? Under what conditions might we see a different result? Raising and addressing such questions will increase our confidence in our insights and help us craft a more appropriately tailored strategy.

Works Cited

1. Sunstein, C.R., "The Law of Group Polarization." *Journal of Political Philosophy*, 10(2; 2002): 175–95.
2. Ashforth, B.E., and R.H. Humphrey, "Emotional Labor in Service Roles: The Influence of Identity." *Academy of Management Review*, 18(1; 1993): 88–115.
3. Labianca, G., et al., "Emulation in Academia: Balancing Structure and Identity." *Organization Science*, 12(3; 2001): 312–30.
4. Lau, D.C., and J.K. Murnighan, "Demographic Diversity and Faultlines: The Compositional Dynamics of Organizational Groups." *Academy of Management Review*, 23(2; 1998): 325–40.
5. Lee, J.K., et al., "Social Media, Network Heterogeneity, and Opinion Polarization." *Journal of Communication*, 64(4; 2014): 702–22.
6. Iyengar, S., and S.J. Westwood, "Fear and Loathing across Party Lines: New Evidence on Group Polarization." *American Journal of Political Science*, 59(3; 2015): 690–707.
7. Stroud, N.J., "Polarization and Partisan Selective Exposure." *Journal of Communication*, 60(3; 2010): 556–76.
8. Reger, R.K., and A.S. Huff, "Strategic Groups: A Cognitive Perspective." *Strategic Management Journal*, 14(2; 1993): 103–23.
9. Hennig-Thurau, T., et al., "Are All Smiles Created Equal? How Emotional Contagion and Emotional Labor Affect Service Relationships." *Journal of Marketing*, 70 (July 2006): 58–73.
10. "7 Insane Airline Incidents Caught on Camera," Travel Safety, FoxNews, 2017, http://www.foxnews.com/travel/2017/05/09/7-insane-airline-incidents-caught-on-camera.html.
11. Lelkes, Y., G. Sood, and S. Iyengar, "The Hostile Audience: The Effect of Access to Broadband Internet on Partisan Affect." *American Journal of Political Science*, 61(1; 2017): 5–20.
12. DeSarbo, W.S., and R. Grewal, "Hybrid Strategic Groups." *Strategic Management Journal*, 29(3; 2008): 293–317.
13. Byron, K., "Carrying Too Heavy a Load? The Communication and Miscommunication of Emotion by Email." *Academy of Management Review*, 33(2; 2008): 309.
14. MacLennan, A., "How Did Delta Air Lines Blow Away Its Rivals in This Major Airline Survey?," The Motley Fool, September 7, 2014, https://www.fool.com/investing/general/2014/09/07/how-did-delta-air-lines-blow-away-its-rivals-in-th.aspx.
15. Jonas, E., et al., "Confirmation Bias in Sequential Information Search after Preliminary Decisions: An Expansion of Dissonance Theoretical Research on Selective Exposure to Information." *Journal of Personality and Social Psychology*, 80(4; 2001): 557.
16. Kramer, A.D., J.E. Guillory, and J.T. Hancock, "Experimental Evidence of Massive-Scale Emotional Contagion through Social Networks." *Proceedings of the National Academy of Sciences*, 111(24; 2014): 8788–90.
17. "Despite Inflammatory Incidents, Airline Customer Satisfaction Keeps Improving," JD Power Ratings 2017, July 17, 2017, http://www.jdpower.com/press-releases/jd-power-2017-north-america-airline-satisfaction-study.
18. Garrett, R.K., "Echo Chambers Online?: Politically Motivated Selective Exposure among Internet News Users." *Journal of Computer-Mediated Communication*, 14(2; 2009): 265–85.
19. Garrett, R.K., et al., "Implications of Pro-and Counterattitudinal Information Exposure for Affective Polarization." *Human Communication Research*, 40(3; 2014): 309–32.

20. Beveridge, A., and J. Shan, "Network of Thrones." *Math Horizons*, 23(4; 2016): 18–22.
21. Christakis, N.A., and J.H. Fowler, "Social Network Sensors for Early Detection of Contagious Outbreaks." *PloS one* 5(9; 2010): e12948.
22. Krebs, V.E., "Mapping Networks of Terrorist Cells." *Connections*, 24(3; 2002): 43–52.
23. McPherson, M., L. Smith-Lovin, and J.M. Cook, "Birds of a Feather: Homophily in Social Networks." *Annual Review of Sociology*, 27(2001): 415–44.
24. "Partisanship and Political Animosity in 2016, in U.S. Politics," Pew Research Center, 2016, http://www.people-press.org/2016/06/22/partisanship-and-political-animosity-in-2016/.
25. Burt, R.S., *Structural Holes: The Social Structure of Competition*. Cambridge, MA: Harvard University Press, 1995.
26. Mislove, A., et al., "You Are Who You Know: Inferring User Profiles in Online Social Networks," in *Proceedings of the Third ACM International Conference on Web Search and Data Mining*. New York: ACM, 2010.
27. "The Facebook Index: 83 Million Fake Accounts Don't Affect Most 'Liked' Stocks," Kapitall, 2012, http://wire.kapitall.com/investment-idea/the-facebook-index-83-billion-fake-accounts-dont-affect-most-liked-stocks/.
28. Belvedere, M.J., "Top 25 Stocks Based on Social Buzz: Index Creator," Exchange Traded Funds, http://www.cnbc.com/2016/04/21/top-25-stocks-based-on-social-buzz-index-creator.html.
29. DiMaggio, P.J., and W.W. Powell, "The Iron Cage Revisited: Institutional Isomorphism and Collective Rationality in Organizational Fields," *American Sociological Review*, 48(2; 1983): 147–60.
30. "Top Ten Biggest Casinos in U.S.—by Gaming Square Footage," Gamboool, 2017, http://gamboool.com/top-ten-biggest-casinos-in-u-s-by-gaming-square-footage.
31. "How Many Seats Are in the Foxwoods Theatre?," Google, 2017, https://www.google.com/search?q=fox+theater+foxwoods+seating+capacity&oq=fox+theater+foxwoods+seating+chart&gs_l=psy-ab.1.2.0i71k1l4.0.0.0.8324.0.0.0.0.0.0.0.0..0.0....0...1..64.psy-ab..0.0.0.aj9hgBMY0x4.
32. "Riverwind Casino," Indie on the Move, 2017, https://www.indieonthemove.com/venues/view/riverwind-casino-norman-oklahoma.
33. "Enjoy Sensational Performances," Winstar World Casino and Resort, 2017, https://www.winstarworldcasino.com/entertainment/.
34. "Mohegan Sun Arena," Wikipedia, 2017, https://en.wikipedia.org/wiki/Mohegan_Sun_Arena.
35. "San Manuel Casino," 2017, https://www.sanmanuel.com/.
36. "Rock & Brews," 2017, http://www.rockandbrews.com/.
37. "Indian Supreme Court in Landmark Ruling on Privacy," BBC, August 24, 2017, http://www.bbc.com/news/world-asia-india-41033954.
38. Dangwal, S., "Linking Aadhaar Number with Your Bank Account," India.com, June 18, 2017, http://www.india.com/business/linking-aadhaar-number-with-your-bank-account-last-date-december-31-2017-heres-how-you-can-link-2247180/.
39. "Aadhaar Could Soon Be Mandatory for Domestic Flights," Business Today Online, 2017, https://www.businesstoday.in/sectors/aviation/you-may-soon-have-to-get-aadhaar-for-flying-on-a-plane/story/249374.html.
40. "Soon, Aadhaar Card Will Be Must for Booking Train Tickets Online," Business Today Online, 2017, https://www.hindustantimes.com/mumbai-news/aadhaar-may-become-must-for-booking-train-tickets-online/story-kvp0SAeoW1LX9iQf4rKRtO.html.
41. "Participate in Aadhaar Stars Social Media Contest 2017 to Win Cash Prizes," Sarkari Yojana, 2017, http://www.sarkaridunia.in/participate-aadhaar-stars-social-media-contest-2017-win-cash-prizes/.

42. "Fight against Corruption and Black Money Will Continue: PM Narendra Modi," The Economic Times, April 6, 2017, http://economictimes.indiatimes.com/news/politics-and-nation/fight-against-corruption-and-black-money-will-continue-pm-narendra-modi/articleshow/58050110.cms.
43. Krishna, V., "India Stack—A Change Agent for Government, Startups and Corporates to Serve Citizens," 2016, https://yourstory.com/2016/07/india-stack/.

PART II

Social Network Analysis

CHAPTER 3

Introduction to Social Network Analysis

> **Learning Objectives**
>
> The purpose of this chapter is to familiarize you with:
>
> 1. the origins and applications of SNA;
> 2. vocabulary pertinent to social network analysis;
> 3. visualization approaches used in social network analysis; and
> 4. metrics used to represent social network data.

In the throes of the Cold War, the Stasi (East German secret police) constructed the graph (social network diagram) depicted in Figure 3.1. Data for the graph were obtained from surveillance of a targeted poet's mail and telephone conversations and from informants' reports of his meetings [2]. (The poet is believed to be Bernd Jentzsch. Restricted from traveling freely, he subsequently defected to West Germany in 1976.) The graph helped the secret police identify and then monitor other potential subversives, based on their affiliations with the initial target.

In her 2014 book *Dragnet Nation*, author Julia Angwin opines that modern-day surveillance—by governments, corporations, and individuals—is a high-tech version of the Stasi surveillance and social network analysis (SNA). The US government's short-lived Total Information Awareness Program (featured in the BBC television drama *The Last Enemy*) aimed to detect and classify foreign terrorists by mining data culled from e-mail communications and marriage and divorce records, in addition to credit card purchases, magazine subscriptions, Internet browsing histories, academic records, toll records, passport and driver's license applications, medical records, DNA, and so on.

Private sector mining and analysis of social network data is even more rampant. Consider, for example, the rendition of my LinkedIn connections, in Figure 3.2. Shape and shading depict my contacts' occupations, but I also could represent my contacts' home countries or locations. Imagine what else LinkedIn knows about us! To the extent that we are aware of these network data, not only can we make more informed choices about our own privacy, but we also can start to leverage network data, because analyzing each of these networks does have potential value.

SNA Origins and Applications

With theoretical roots in work by sociologist Georg Simmel, SNA methods emerged in the 1930s. The founder of what came to be known as the field of ***sociometry***—the study of social network phenomena—was Jacob Moreno [1]. One of Moreno's early insights was that social structure derived from individuals' personal preferences for affiliating with each other. Contracted by a New York girls' reformatory following a rash of runaways, he and his assistant—Helen Jennings—attempted to apply Moreno's ideas about preference-based social structures to the assignment of the girls to living cottages and dining room tables [5]. With each stage of their investigation, they painstakingly constructed social network diagrams—or ***sociograms***—depicting the

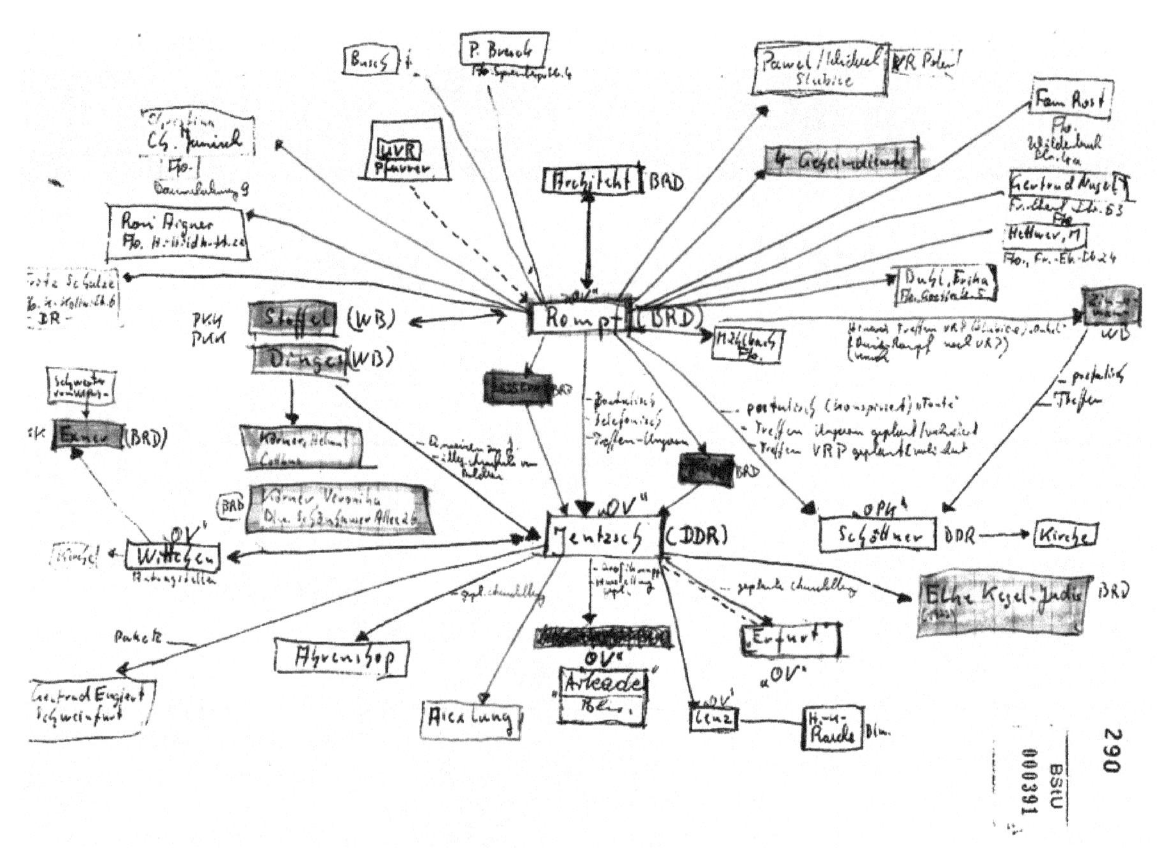

Figure 3.1 Stasi's Graph of an East German Poet's Network

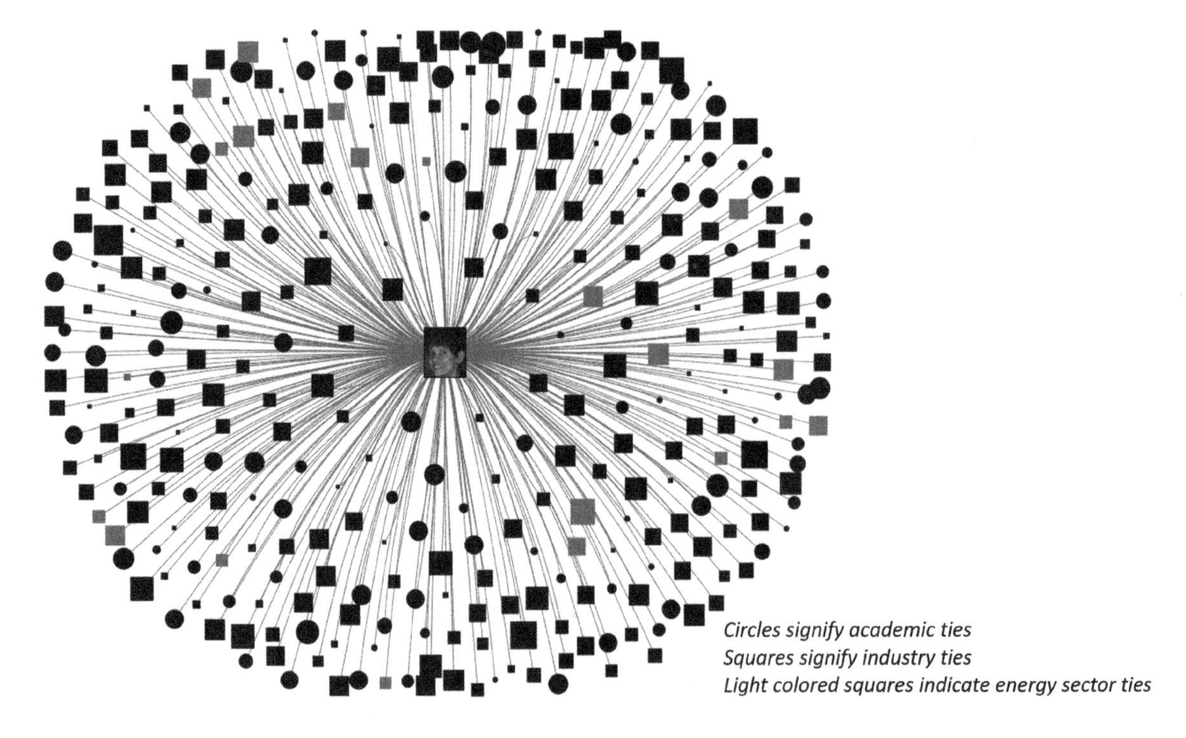

Figure 3.2 My LinkedIn Network

relationship preferences of the 505 girls at the reformatory. Some of these hand-drawn sociograms were published in the journal *Sociometry*, which Moreno founded in 1937.

"Every social group is composed of a number of interlocking atoms. The social atom is the smallest functional unit of any organization." (Moreno, cited in [1: 139])

A second landmark SNA study was Stanley Milgram's series of experiments in the 1960s that came to be known as the ***small world experiments***. His question was, "Given any two people in the world, person X and person Z, how many intermediate acquaintance links are needed before X and Z are connected?" [6: 62]. So he gave a folder to individuals located in Wichita, Kansas (because it seemed so remote!), and directed them to move the folder to the wife of a divinity student in Cambridge, Massachusetts, but only through people they knew personally. Each person through whom the folder moved added their name to a "tracer" card, enabling Milgram to construct the path through which the study participants in Kansas reached the target in Massachusetts. Replicating the study with participants in faraway Omaha, Nebraska, targeting a stockbroker, who worked in Boston, Massachusetts, and lived in Sharon, Massachusetts, Milgram found the number of intermediaries used to connect the source to the target ranged from two to ten, and averaged six [7]. This gave rise to the notion that, on average, there are ***six degrees of separation*** between any two randomly selected individuals. This notion later was popularized in the 1993 movie, starring Will Smith, and in the Kevin Bacon game!

A high-impact application of SNA came in the late 1970s and early 1980s. Desperate to forestall the spread of the dreaded AIDS virus, CDC researchers used SNA to identify an Air Canada flight attendant as patient zero in North America [8]. Subsequent biological evidence indicates that the AIDS epidemic in North America, in fact, preceded the flight attendants' contraction of the AIDS virus [9], highlighting the limits of SNA. However, early researchers traced the emergence and diffusion of different viral strains based on social network analyses of patients' symptoms.

Becoming increasingly mathematical, the field of sociometry grew through the influence of graph theory and matrix algebra, from where modern SNA borrows some terminology. Well into the 1980s, though, conducting SNA was a laborious process. Networks were hand-drawn or painstakingly rendered with a typewriter and later with rudimentary computer graphics software. Network metrics were simplistic and computed manually. Software for visualizing and analyzing social networks began to emerge in the 1990s [10, 11], popularizing the use of SNA and refining metrics available.

Today, organizations use social network analysis to visualize traffic on computer networks. For example, SolarWinds, a company that provides enterprise information technology infrastructure management software for IT professionals, offers software for computer network performance monitoring, and load balancing. A graph of an organization's computer resources produced by their software is depicted in Figure 3.3 [12].

Epidemiologists continue to use SNA to identify individuals at high risk for infection [13], and to determine the "threshold" level of virus penetration that would result in a full-blown epidemic [14]. Financial institutions can predict fraudulent behavior by tracing networks created through organizations' resource exchanges [15]. Researchers at MIT have developed a global language network, constituted by book, Wikipedia page, or Twitter post translations, as depicted in Figure 3.4 [16]. They found that the position of the language one speaks in this network affects one's visibility and the recognition one is likely to enjoy for one's contributions to the arts and sciences.

Some Social Network Terms

The basic building blocks of a social network are nodes and ties. A ***node*** usually represents a discrete actor (e.g., employees, patients, organizations, business units, and project groups), but may refer to any type of entity—a place, object, event, or abstract concept. In Figure 3.1, the actors are Jentzsch's family members, friends, and other acquaintances—presumed by the Stasi to be political affiliates. NodeXL refers to a node as a ***vertex***. We will use *node* and *vertex* interchangeably.

A focal node (i.e., a node of particular interest to the analyst) is termed an ***ego***. Nodes surrounding this ego are termed ***alters***. Sometimes, rather than being concerned with a ***complete network*** (i.e., the entire network of a particular social space), we are interested in the network surrounding a focal ego. Such a network is called

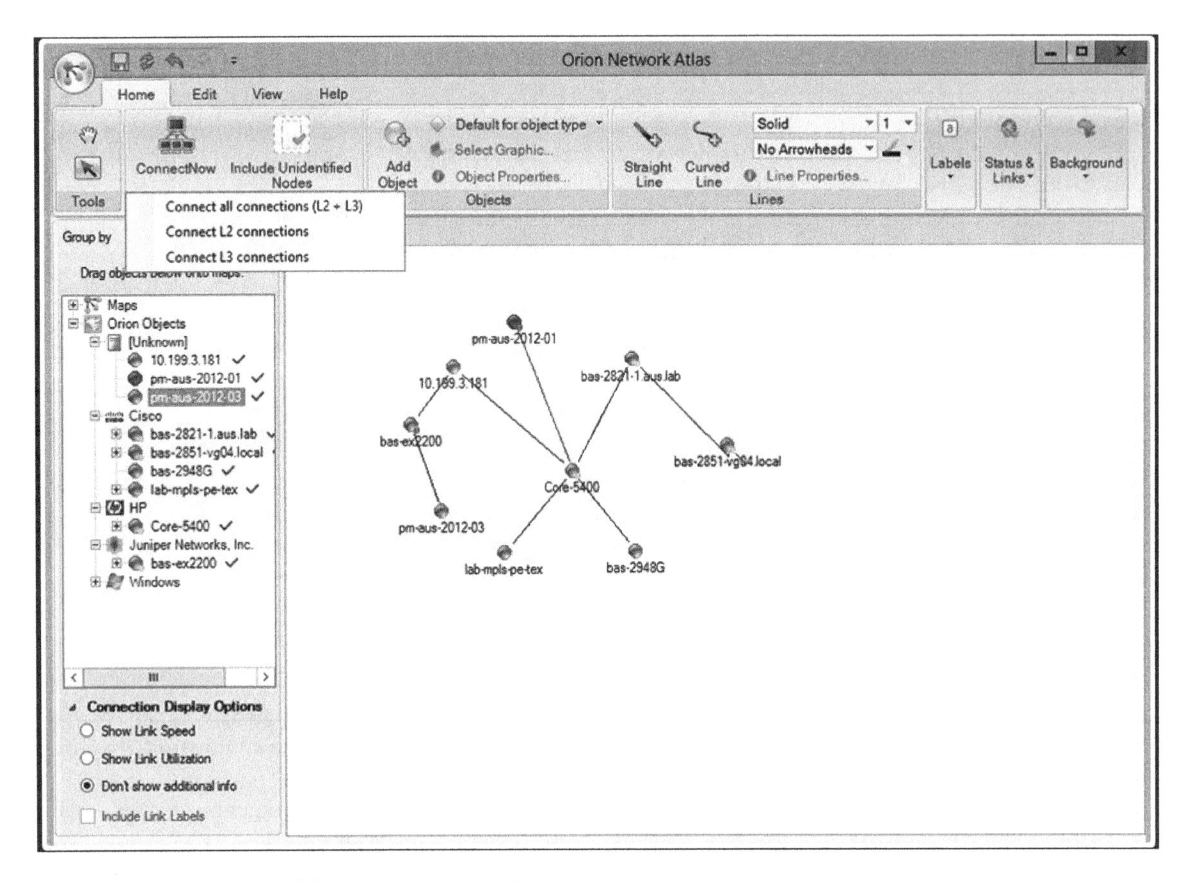

Figure 3.3 SolarWinds Traffic Monitoring System

is an ***ego network***. Figure 3.1 is an ego network, where the ego represented is Bernd Jentzsch, as is Figure 3.2, where the ego represented is me.

A ***tie*** is a link between nodes. Usually a tie represents an actual or latent interaction between two actors. In Figure 3.1, the ties represent Jentzsch's e-mail and phone communications and face-to-face meetings. NodeXL refers to a tie as an ***edge***. In social terms, ties capture a relationship. We will use *tie*, *edge*, and *relationship* interchangeably. In Chapter 1, we saw two types of relationships or ties—standing ties and interaction-based ties. Standing ties capture states such as kinship, role-based relationships, and cognitive/affective relationships [17]. Interaction-based ties are based on events such as communications or transactions [17].

Ties may be reciprocated or unreciprocated. ***Reciprocated ties*** are mutual. Reciprocation occurs when Gina and Max, for example, each select the other as their best friend. ***Unreciprocated ties*** are those that are not returned. If Sarah likes Julia, but Julia does not like Sarah, the liking tie between Sarah and Julia is unreciprocated.

Ties can be strong or weak. Positive affect between two people, repetitive engagements among them, or multiplexity (i.e., having many different types of relationships) create a ***strong tie***. Strong ties dispose people to trust one another and to act in a trustworthy fashion [18]. They are a source of social capital, permitting us to call on one another for assistance and receive recommendations and referrals from one another [19]. ***Weak ties*** such as those among acquaintances, who interact only occasionally, have informational advantages. For example, research has found that weak ties contribute more to a successful job search than strong ties [20].

The relationship between two nodes constitutes a ***dyad***. Relationships among three nodes constitute a ***triad***. When most ties seem to route through one network node, that node is considered to be ***central*** to a network. On the other hand, outlying nodes in a network are considered to be ***peripheral*** to the network. In organizations, those central to the network are considered "central connectors" or central information sources,

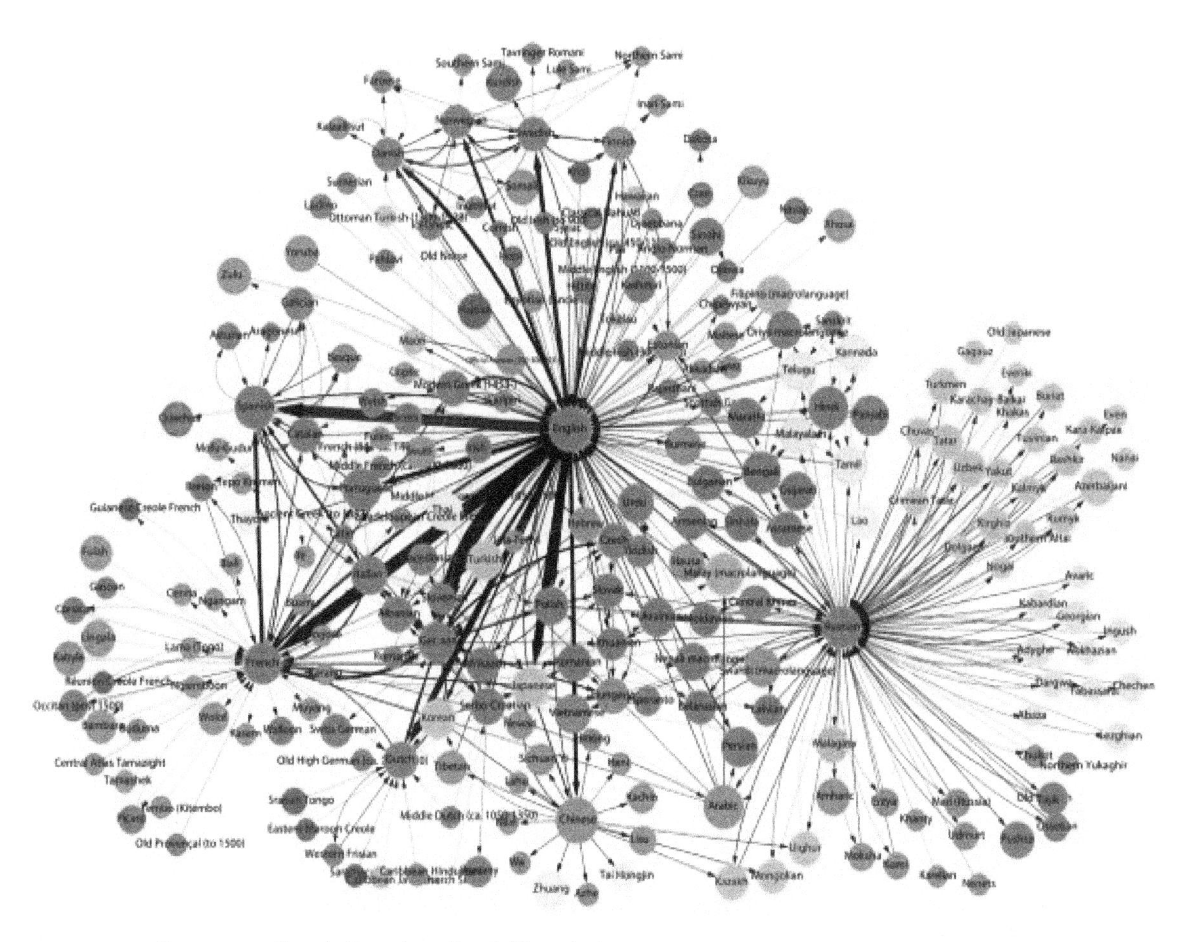

Figure 3.4 Language Graph Based on Book Translations

while those peripheral to the network are considered "peripheral specialists" because they tend to possess deep knowledge about a narrow area [21].

A ***component*** in a network is a node or collection of nodes that are separated from the rest of a network. A component may be an isolated node, a dyad, a triad, or a more complex network structure. In organizations, an individual who connects otherwise disconnected components is considered an ***information broker***, when all otherwise disconnected components are internal to the organization, and a ***boundary spanner***, when some otherwise disconnected components are external to the organization [21]. Information brokers and boundary spanners tend to be weak ties and thus are useful for apprising members of disconnected components of knowledge and opportunities they otherwise would not have [21].

Factors Accounting for Connections

In a collection of people, not every pair has an equal likelihood of connecting. What factors account for tie formation? The first factor researchers identified is *physical proximity* or ***propinquity***. In the 1930s, a third of married couples in Philadelphia were found to have lived within five blocks of each other prior to marriage, with the incidence of marriage decreasing as premarital physical distance increased [22]. More recently, people have been found to be more likely to seek information from proximate others than those who are more remotely located [23].

A second factor that promotes tie formation is ***homophily*** (i.e., demographic or other forms of similarity) [24]. Again, homophily accounts for a large number of marriages and long-term friendships [25]. In fact, a

New York Times article recently raised concerns that homophily in marriage—or assortative mating—promotes generational wealth inequalities as fiscally similar people marry [26].

The third factor accounting for ties is the principle of ***transitivity***, which is the tendency for ties to achieve balance and avoid dissonance. When person A is friends with B and C (i.e., two of the three possible ties are strong), the two other people (B and C) will develop strong ties. Likewise, if a person A strongly dislikes person B and likes person C, the principle of transitivity dictates that B and C will come to dislike each other. Or A will change his feelings toward B or C. Failure to do so would impose too much cognitive dissonance on every member of the triad. In larger networks, transitivity gives rise to ***network closure*** or a fully connected network (more on this later).

Types of Social Networks

There are two major types of networks—directed and undirected. A ***directed network*** is one in which a tie need not be reciprocated. For example, Bob seeks Emily's advice frequently, but Emily does not seek Bob's advice. On social media, Twitter instantiates a directed network of standing relationships, where I could, but do not, follow all my followers, and many I follow do not follow me! In a directed network, arrowheads depict the direction of the tie, and a reciprocated tie is designated with a two-way arrow.

An ***undirected network*** is one in which ties are, by definition, reciprocated or mutual. Example of inherently reciprocated networks include coauthors of articles, legislative bills, or books; members on advisory or corporate boards; and classmates. On social media, Facebook and LinkedIn instantiate undirected networks of standing relationships, where ties must be reciprocated. I cannot become your Facebook friend or LinkedIn connection without your consent.

Note that directed and undirected networks are not to be confused with unreciprocated or reciprocated ties. Reciprocation is an individual choice; network directedness is a function of the analyst's question (e.g., "Whom have you had a class with?" versus "Whom would you like to work with?") or, in the case of social media, a property of the platform.

In graphs of undirected networks, reciprocated ties will appear as a two-way arrow, while unreciprocated ties will appear as a one-way arrow. In Figure 3.1, we see a one-way arrow from Rompt to Jentzsch, likely indicating that Rompt contacted Jentzsch, but Jentzsch did not initiate contact with Rompt. On the other hand, the two-way arrow between Rompt and Stoffel (to Rompt's immediate left) suggests that each got in touch with the other.

Graphs often depict tie strength in the weight of edges. For example, in Figure 3.4, the heavy lines connecting English with French, Spanish, German, and Japanese suggest a higher incidence of books being translated from English to French, Spanish, German, and Japanese than from English to Russian or to Swedish.

Networks differ in the number of entities represented. ***One-mode networks*** capture ties among only a single type of entity. For example, a network representing which of your classmates have had classes together is a one-mode network. So, too, is the network of classmates who wish to work—or have worked—with each other on projects.

A ***two-mode network*** captures ties among different types of entities—typically actors and some type of event. In our network of classmates, if we wish to represent which classes tie together various groups of classmates, we would construct a two-mode network: one of the two modes would be classmates (actors) and the second would be classes (events). In our network of students (actors) who wish to work with each other, if we wished to depict the type of project (event) they wish to collaborate on—technical versus writing projects—project type would become the second mode in our network. Figure 3.5 represents a two-mode network of actors who worked on thirteen social media initiatives (events) at Ford Motor Company between 2009 and 2012 [27]. In constructing this network, we were interested in understanding how ideas about social media use diffused through the organization. Figure 3.5 depicts two different types of actors—Ford employees and PR agencies—involved in thirteen Ford Motor social media initiatives. While only a subset of more than fifty social media initiatives undertaken by Ford during the period, Figure 3.5 tells a story about how some of the initiatives might have emerged. Ford employees and PR agencies involved with the FiestaMovement—the first social media initiative—subsequently were involved with RoadTrip, RandomActsOfFusion, and the ElectrifiedVehicle.

Note that it is the two different social entities—actors and initiatives—that make Figure 3.5 a two-mode network, not the two different types of actors—Ford employees and PR agencies. Further, the distinction between one- and two-mode networks is a matter of analyst choice. If we need to represent only actors, we represent a one-mode actor network, as in Figure 3.6A; if we need to represent only social media initiatives, we would represent a one-mode initiative network, as in Figure 3.6B. In choosing between depicting one- and two-mode networks, analysts trade off information completeness and visual complexity.

Is a Group a Network?

A group is an organizationally or institutionally derived structure. You may be assigned to a group or self-select into a group. That group has a purpose, be it completing a project or nurturing a family unit. Groups meet.

A network is a latent social structure. It does not itself have a purpose, and it does not meet. Yet people often activate network ties by calling upon them. And networks do contribute to the purpose of many a group. For example, the informal networks of computer scientists and engineers in Silicon Valley are credited with solving many a technical problem encountered outside their own labs, thereby fostering the overall innovativeness of the region [3].

A group, thus, is one way of developing and activating network ties. Groups provide the glue that brings and holds together networks. In network terminology, a group may be viewed as one mode in a two-mode actor-group network—the event that ties together actors.

Setting Up Social Network Data

In preparation for visualizing or analyzing social networks quantitatively, we need to set up our data in accordance with the SNA package to be used. Reflecting the influence of matrix algebra on SNA, some software packages such as UCINet [28] require that you set up your data as an $n \times n$ matrix, where n is the number of nodes in your data set. This square matrix also is known as an ***adjacency matrix***. For example, to represent a group of five twelve-year-old girls, we would set up adjacency matrices as in Figure 3.7. Figure 3.7A is a symmetric matrix of girls who have been in a class together; Figure 3.7B is an asymmetric matrix of who likes whom. Note that the values above the diagonal in Figure 3.7A mirror those below the diagonal. In contrast, the values above and below the diagonal have no correspondence in Figure 3.7B, because while Agatha would like a sleepover with Catherine, Catherine would not like a sleepover with Agatha.

Other software packages such as NodeXL and R require an edge list. ***Edge lists*** are lists of connected node pairs. For example, Table 3.1A depicts the undirected network in Figure 3.7A, and Table 3.1B depicts the directed network in Figure 3.7B. In other words, the edge list for an undirected network will have a row for each 1 above (or below) the diagonal of an adjacency matrix—or half the number of 1s in the entire matrix; the edge list for a directed network will have as many rows as there are 1s in the adjacency matrix. While the ordering of the vertices in the edge list is irrelevant for an undirected network, the to/from ordering must be preserved with directed networks.

Visualizing Social Networks

Before getting into the mechanics of visualizing networks, let us consider the different topologies (i.e., configurations or combinations of tie patterns) we may encounter. In the 1950s, Bavelas and Leavitt—two MIT researchers interested in understanding communication efficiency—experimented with the four/five-person topologies depicted in the first four columns in Table 3.2 [29, 30]. The experimenters seated study participants alone in a room and permitted them to communicate with four other participants, also isolated in individual rooms, through slots permitting them to share notes with each other. Participants were tasked with identifying which two of the five of them shared a symbol given to them by the experimenter at the start of the study. Who could communicate directly with whom was determined by their designated topology.

The first topology (the ***star or wheel***) has a central node, node A, through whom all communications flow. In the second, the ***Y***, node A interfaces directly with B, C, and D, and D mediates between A and E. In this topology, A occupies a less central position than in the star. In the third, the ***line or chain***, node A interfaces directly with two other nodes, B and D, each of whom mediate node A's interaction with the two peripheral

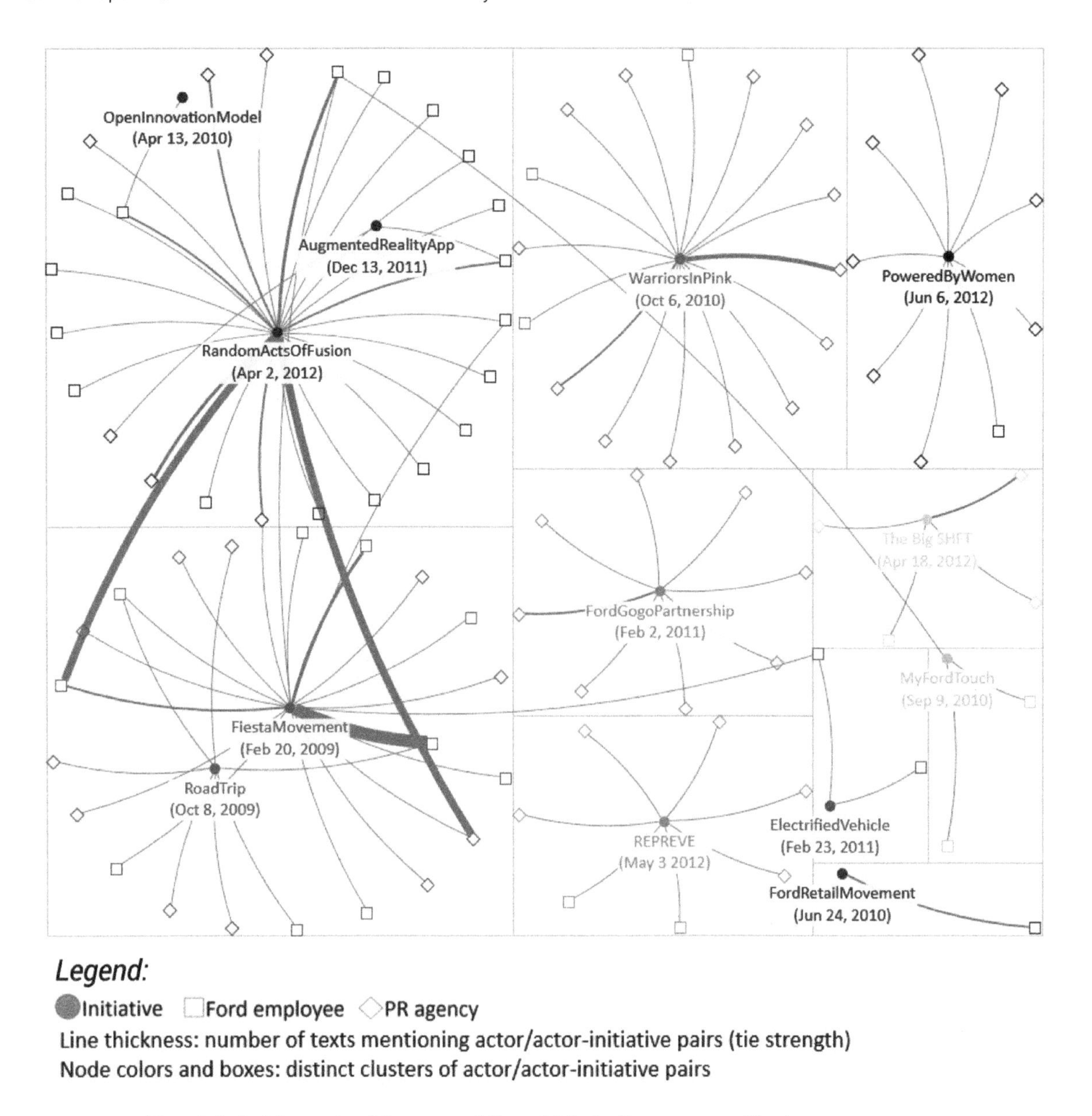

Figure 3.5 Two-Mode Network of Actors and Social Media Initiatives at Ford

nodes, C and E. In the fourth topology, the ***circle***, no single node is central and every node has two different pathways through which to reach every other node.

Unsurprisingly, the researchers found the star and the Y to be the most efficient topologies for the simple communication task, requiring the fewest messages and the least amount of time to complete; fewest errors occurred with the star, the Y, and the line. Leader emergence and agreement on who that leader was increased from circle, to line, to Y, to star. However, participants in the circle were most satisfied with the communication process. In addition to these four initially identified topologies, there is a fifth, a ***fully connected***—topology. Here, everyone is directly connected to everyone else. This topology, of course, offers both efficiency and social satisfaction, but incurs high costs in setting up and maintaining each tie.

Graph visualization has come a long way since those produced by early sociologists and the Stasi. A multitude of graphing tools now exists. These tools permit us to quickly and easily visualize complete networks

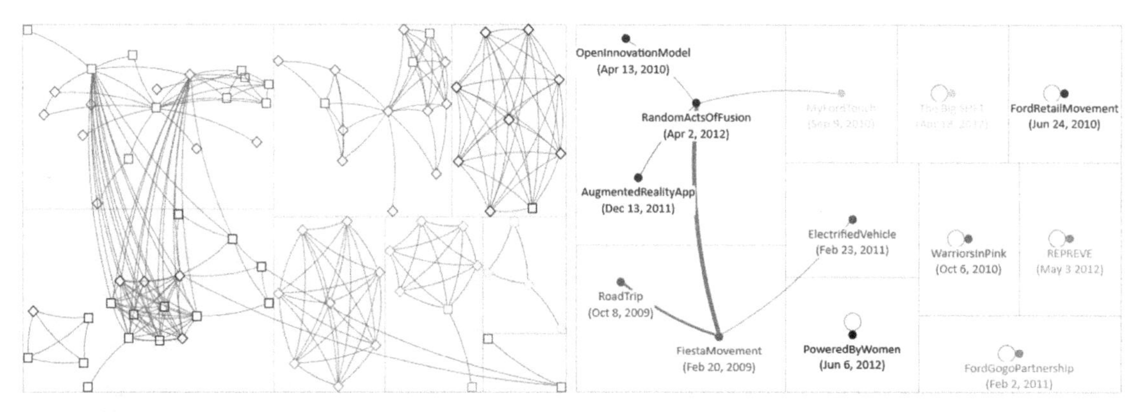

A. Employee and PR Agency Network **B. Social Media Initiative Network**

Legend:

Initiative Ford employee PR agency

Line thickness: number of texts mentioning actor/actor-initiative pairs (tie strength)

Node colors and boxes: distinct clusters of actor/actor-initiative pairs

Figure 3.6 One-Mode Networks of Ford Social Media Initiatives

	Agatha	Beatrice	Catherine	Daisy	Edith
Agatha		1	0	1	1
Beatrice	1		0	1	1
Catherine	0	0		1	1
Daisy	1	1	1		1
Edith	1	1	1	1	

A. Have you had a class with her?

	Agatha	Beatrice	Catherine	Daisy	Edith
Agatha		1	1	1	1
Beatrice	1		0	0	1
Catherine	0	0		1	0
Daisy	1	1	1		1
Edith	1	1	0	1	

B. Would you like a sleepover with her?

Figure 3.7 Two Adjacency Matrices for Five Girls

Table 3.1 Edge Lists for Figure 3.7

A: For Figure 3.7A	
Vertex 1	**Vertex 2**
Beatrice	Agatha
Daisy	Agatha
Edith	Agatha
Daisy	Beatrice
Edith	Beatrice
Daisy	Catherine
Edith	Catherine
Edith	Daisy

B: For Figure 3.7B	
Vertex 1	**Vertex 2**
Beatrice	Agatha
Daisy	Agatha
Edith	Agatha
Daisy	Beatrice
Edith	Beatrice
Daisy	Catherine
Edith	Daisy
Agatha	Beatrice
Agatha	Catherine
Agatha	Daisy
Agatha	Edith
Beatrice	Edith
Catherine	Daisy
Daisy	Edith

Table 3.2 Types of Network Topologies and Corresponding NodeXL Edge Lists

	Star/Wheel	Y	Line/Chain	Circle	Fully Connected
Graph	E, D, A, B, C	B, C, A, D, E	E, D, A, B, C	A, E, B, D, C	E, B, A, D, C
NodeXL Edge Lists	Vertex 1 – Vertex 2 A – B A – C A – D A – E	Vertex 1 – Vertex 2 A – B A – C A – D D – E	Vertex 1 – Vertex 2 A – D B – A C – B D – E	Vertex 1 – Vertex 2 A – B B – C C – D D – E E – A	Vertex 1 – Vertex 2 A – B A – C A – D A – E B – C B – D B – E C – D C – E D – E

Legend:
Node size is proportional to the number of ties
Lighter-colored node is most central to the network

Getting Started with NodeXL

As you get familiar with NodeXL, you will be able to interact with it more flexibly. To begin with, the following will keep you out of trouble.

Do:

1. Type or copy values for Vertex 1 and Vertex 2 (in columns A and B) on the EDGES sheet.
2. Let NodeXL automatically generate the Vertex list (in column A) on the VERTICES sheet.

Don't:

1. Use any columns before column N on the EDGES sheet, other than as prescribed in the comments and notes in rows 2 and 3.
2. Add any columns before column N on the EDGES sheet.
3. Use any columns before column AC on the VERTICES sheet, other than as prescribed in the comments and notes in rows 2 and 3.
4. Add any columns before column AC on the VERTICES sheet.
5. Add any new sheets before the OVERALL METRICS sheet.

as well as ego networks. One relatively easy-to-use tool is ***NodeXL***, which is an Excel template for SNA. Other commonly used tools include ***UCINet***, which has an excellent range of metrics and statistical analysis options; ***Pajek***, which has strengths similar to UCINet's; ***Gephi***, a beautiful visualization tool; and of course, SNA packages available for ***R***. These tools permit us to visualize the network constructed by the relationships among thousands—even millions—of nodes.

Visualization software offer a multitude of layout algorithms that enhance the clarity and aesthetic appeal of the graph. Different layout algorithms emphasize different aspects of the network and have different advantages. A ***random algorithm*** assigns each node to a random point on the screen in an effort to minimize collisions. The focus of this algorithm is to *avoid overlapping nodes*. ***Force-directed layout algorithms*** such as the Fruchterman-Reingold and Harel-Koren Fast Multiscale algorithms iteratively bring together connected nodes and push apart unconnected nodes. They also place connected nodes equidistant from each other. The emphasis of such algorithms therefore is on *proximity*. The Harel-Koren algorithm has the advantage of *speed*, relative to earlier force-directed alternatives such as the Fruchterman-Reingold, and therefore is particularly well-suited to visualizing large graphs [31]. ***Tree layout algorithms*** are ideal for depicting hierarchical social structures.

NodeXL is one of many social network analysis (SNA) tools we can use to visualize social networks and to conduct other types of analyses of the networks. The insert on "Getting Started with NodeXL" provides a few tips on what to do and what not to do when working with NodeXL. Be sure to acquaint yourself with these tips before beginning the tutorials.

When you open NodeXL, your screen should appear as in Figure 3.8. Explore the **NodeXL Tab** to see which options are available. We could use the Prepare Data button in the Data group—the first group on the **NodeXL Tab**—to obtain our list of vertices. You almost never should manually input this list. But the insert on "Specifying Edge Lists in NodeXL" describes how to set up edge lists from scratch. Make sure you are correctly displaying your graph as directed or undirected by setting the Graph Type in the Graph group—the second group on the **NodeXL Tab**. If you happen to lose your **Graph Pane**, you can click on the Show Graph button or the Refresh Graph button on the **NodeXL Tab**, depending on whether you previously have viewed a graph within that session, prior to losing the **Graph Pane**.

Specifying Edge Lists in NodeXL

To create the five simple graphs depicted in Table 3.2 using NodeXL, let's begin by opening up NodeXL; then copy the edge lists provided in the bottom of the table into the Vertex 1 and Vertex 2 columns on the Edges sheet in the Data Pane. Make sure you have no intermediate rows in which cells for either Vertex 1 or Vertex 2 are empty. Don't change anything else right now. Click the Show Graph button on the right Graph Pane of the NodeXL window. When you do so, NodeXL will automatically extract all unique vertices to the Vertex list on the Vertices sheet. Take a look at it. Note that once you have visualized a graph within a NodeXL session, the Show Graph button changes to a Refresh Graph button. See if you can produce the graphs shown.

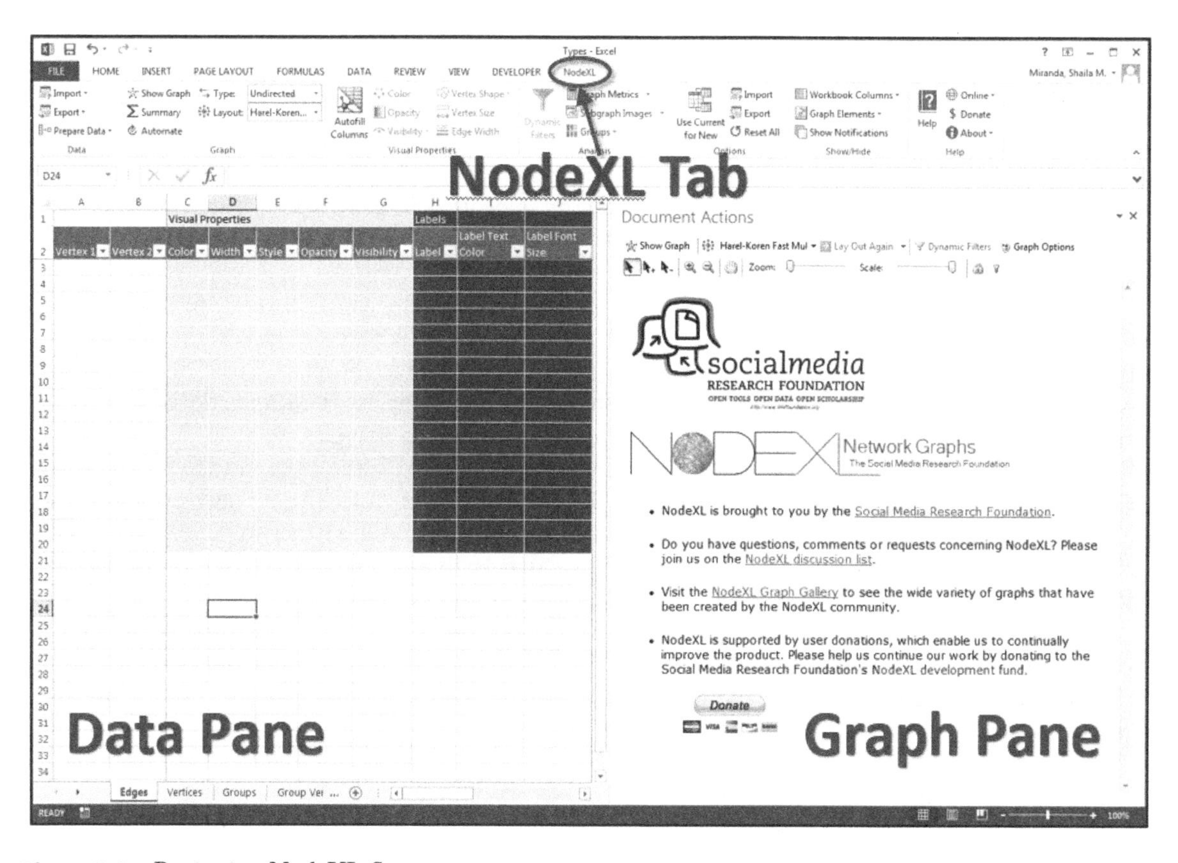

Figure 3.8 Beginning NodeXL Screen

Visualizing Node and Tie Properties

Instead of displaying all vertices and edges in exactly the same fashion, we can make our graph more informative by varying the formatting of edges on the EDGES sheet and of vertices on the VERTICES sheet. We can visualize ***node attributes*** by associating the color, size, and shape of the vertices on the VERTICES sheet with some data values. For example, the size of the nodes in the graphs in Table 3.2 reflect the number of ties in which they participate; blue nodes identify those that are most central to the network. In the graph of my LinkedIn network in Figure 3.2, the node colors reflect the industries in which my contacts work. Likewise, we can visualize ***edge attributes*** such as tie strength or sentiment reflected in a tie. In Figure 3.5, the weight of the edges (thickness of lines) reflects the number of times a particular Ford employee or PR agency was associated with a particular social media initiative in news articles or press releases about that initiative. In NodeXL, strong Excel skills help us provide meaningful visuals. (See the inset for some Excel functions that are useful in honing our graphs.)

Useful Excel Functions for Graphing Vertex and Edge Attributes

Function	Sample Use
=	Filter self-ties on EDGES sheet: *=[Vertex 1]=[Vertex 2]*
OR/AND/NOT	Filter data or set vertex or edge attributes based on whether certain conditions are met
COUNTIFS	Use to vary vertex size on VERTICES sheet based on the number of times the node appears in the edge list: *=COUNTIFS(Edges!A:B,[@Vertex])*
IF	Set vertex display features: *=IF([@Size]=MAX(D:D),"70,70,255","")*
VLOOKUP	Set vertex color or other display feature based on node attributes in the lookup table on the new data sheet
IFERROR	Handle data not found in lookup table

Tutorial 3.1. Does Pedagogy Change a Class's Network Structure?

The KMNetwork1 and KMNetwork2 files capture the network students' recognition and friendship ties at the start and midpoint of an 8-week Knowledge Management course. The class contained students from the Price College's MBA, MAcc, and MS-MIS program, as well as students from a few other majors. Some students were full-time students, while others were in the part-time program. Let's visualize each of the two networks and see how they have evolved over four weeks of class interaction.

Let's begin by opening up the KMNetwork1 file. The two vertices in the EDGES sheet represent recognition ties. First, notice the Graph Type on the **NodeXL Tab** indicates this is a directed network. This is because while Susan may know who John is (i.e., recognize him), John may not know who Susan is. Click "Show Graph" on the **Graph Pane**. Since this is a directed network, we see arrowheads on the lines indicating ties between nodes. Nodes are labeled for whether the student is full- or part-time. The solid triangles are the MBA students, the solid circles are accounting students, the solid diamonds are the MS-MIS students, and the hollow squares are industrial engineering students. Other majors are depicted as solid squares. The red nodes are the women in the class; the blue are the men. If you inspect the VERTICES sheet, you will see how we were able to do this. Scroll to the right of the VERTICES sheet, and you will see data beginning in column AC that describes each student—their gender, status, and major. To depict the student's full- or part-time status as a label, we simply set the Label column (column H) equal to the Status (i.e., *=[@Status]*). Since we are working in Excel, we can accomplish this using point and click or by typing the formula. We used an IF function to set the Color (column B) to Red if gender was "F" and to Blue if it was not: `=IF([@Gender]="F","Red","Blue")`. We used a nested IF to set the Shape (column C) relative to the major: `=IF([@ACCT]="x",2,IF([@IE]="x",10,IF([@[MS-MIS]]="x",7,IF([@MBA]="x",9,5))))`. I similarly could determine the visual appearance of the lines connecting the nodes by setting the values for the Visual Properties columns on the EDGES sheet.

In addition to setting the display options for vertices and edges within the graph via the Visual Properties, we also can set them via the Graph Options on the **Graph Pane**. Vertex formatting possibilities include changing the color, shape, and size of the vertices. Some edge formatting possibilities are to change the edge width and color or change edges from straight to curved lines. We also can set the font for labels displayed on the graph. Setting display options via the **Graph Pane** does not permit us to distinguish between different vertices or edges though. Use the Lay Out Again button to reorganize the graph until you are satisfied with its layout. Figure 3.9A depicts the starting recognition network for the Knowledge Management class. Experiment with the different visualization algorithms to see what they produce. Redoing these procedures on the KMNetwork2 file produces the network depicted in Figure 3.9B—a much more-densely connected network than in Figure 3.9A.

Now, scroll to the right of the EDGES sheet and you will see a Friendship column. Here, 1s represent the subset of recognized students who also are friends. Filter the data based on rows in which the Friendship column values on the Edges sheet are 1s. Then click the Refresh Graph button. You should see the network depicted in Figure 3.10A. Our later examination of network metrics revealed five network components—sets of ties that are unconnected. Click the Lay Out Again button to reorganize the graph till you are able to see the

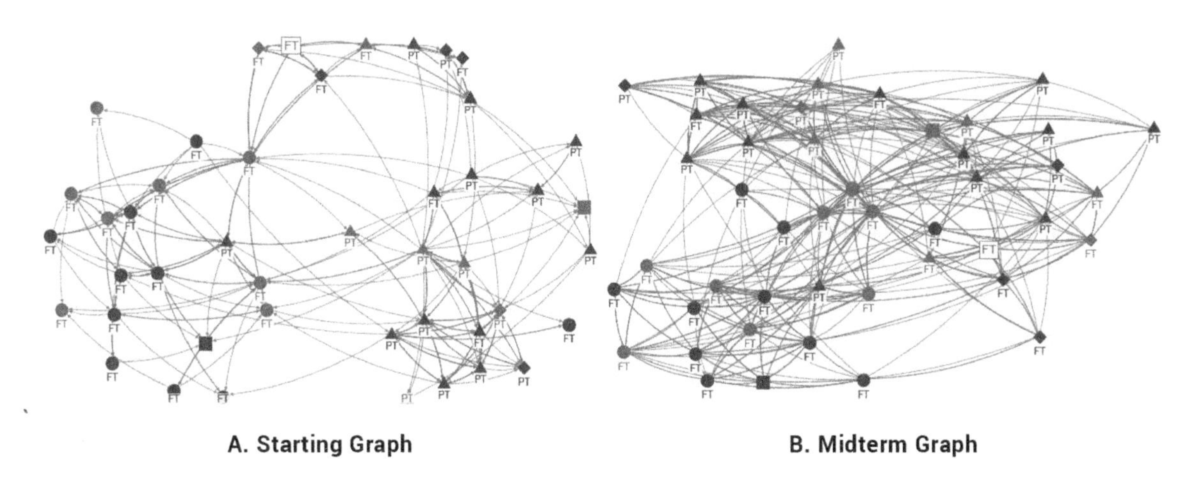

A. Starting Graph B. Midterm Graph

Figure 3.9 Evolution of Class Recognition Network

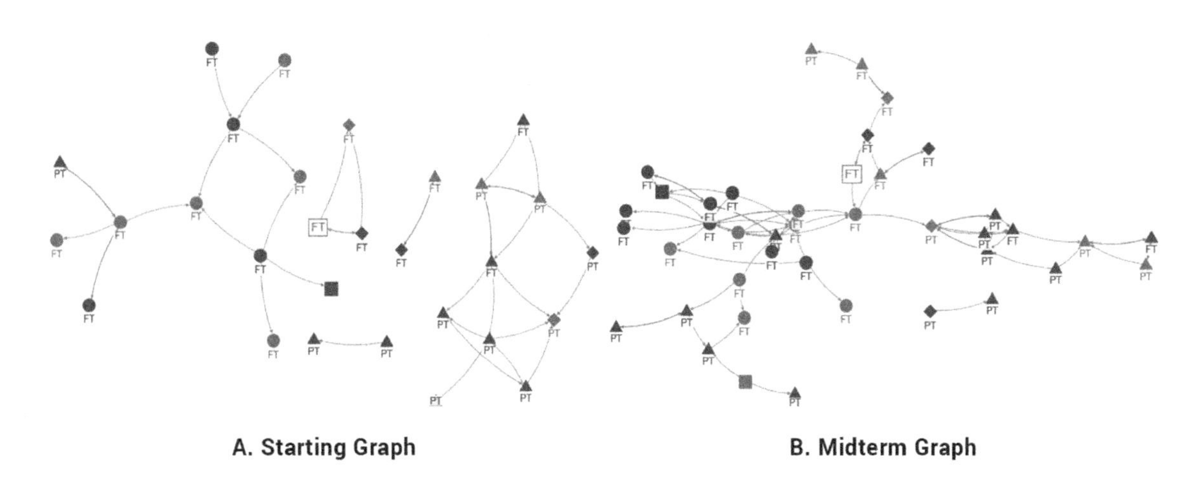

A. Starting Graph B. Midterm Graph

Figure 3.10 Evolution of Class Friendship Network

five different components. Figure 3.10B depicts the midterm friendship network, which, with two connected components, also is more connected than it was at the start of the class.

Social Network Metrics

Social network metrics provide information about the properties of an entire network or graph or of a specific ego (node) within the graph, beyond what we can visualize simply by looking at a graph. They describe a graph or sub-graph, or an ego. A ***subgraph*** is a subset of a graph that we wish to analyze.

Graph Metrics

Graph metrics provide the analyst with indicators of the properties of a given network—or subnetwork. Below, we consider the following graph metrics: connected components, geodesic distance, density, modularity, centralization, and clustering. Except for the modularity metric, these graph metrics can be also applied to a subgraph.

If a path between two nodes exists, then one node is considered ***reachable*** from the other node. A ***connected component*** contains either single node that is disconnected from the rest of the network (i.e., an ***isolate***), or multiple nodes that are connected among themselves, but disconnected or not reachable from the rest of the network. In Figure 3.9B, we can visualize two distinct components. In fact, graph metrics reveal twenty-six distinct connected components. ***Geodesic distance*** is the shortest path between two nodes. A graph's maximum geodesic distance is the largest of this shortest path within the network. Table 3.3 provides the maximum geodesic distances for the topologies in Table 3.2.

Geodesic distance speaks to ***communication efficiency***—the fewer the hops involved in communicating, the faster information moves through the network. Geodesic distance metrics also provide information on the cohesion or fragmentation of a graph. Graphs with high maximum or average geodesic distance have low ***cohesion*** because they are easier to fragment. In such graphs, removal of relatively few nodes results in a graph with multiple isolates or connected components.

The ***density*** of a graph is the proportion of all possible ties that exist or are realized. For an undirected graph, density is based on the possible combinations of ties, determined as:

$$\text{Possible ties} = \frac{n!}{2(n-2)!},$$ where n is the number of nodes in the graph/subgraph.

(Note that n always exceeds 1, because we don't have a network of one person. In fact, sociologists would argue that any social space smaller than three persons does not constitute a network [32].) In a directed graph or subgraph, density is based on the possible permutations of ties, determined as

$$\text{Possible ties} = \frac{n!}{2(n-2)!}.$$

Table 3.3 Graph Properties of Different Network Topologies

Topology	Max. Geodesic Distance	Density	Degree Centralization	Clustering
Star	2	0.40	1.00	0.00
Y	3	0.40	0.58	0.00
Line	4	0.40	0.17	0.00
Ring	2	0.50	0.00	0.00
Fully connected	1	1.00	0.00	1.00

In small graphs, density is readily visualized in the number of ties present. Table 3.3 gives the densities for the topologies in Table 3.2. The density of the first three topologies—the star, the Y, and the line—are equal, and slightly lower than that of the circle, which is less dense than the fully-connected topology, with a density of 1.0. Density also indicates cohesion, as denser graphs are less susceptible to fragmentation.

Graph ***modularity*** reflects the extent to which the network contains modules within which dense connections occur, but across which connections are sparse. Connected components are an extreme case of sparse intercomponent connections because of the absence of a path between components. Yet if connected components do not have dense within-component connections, modularity will be low. Modularity for a network depends on the grouping algorithm applied. Figure 3.11 provides three visualizations of the Fortune 100 companies' boards of directors' network based on two different grouping methods. Figure 3.11A separates groups based on a shared attribute—gender. Figure 3.11B separates groups based on connected components. Figure 3.11C separates groups based on naturally-occurring clusters (more on this later). Modularity for Figure 3.11A is 0.16, for Figure 3.11B is 0.35, and for Figure 3.11C is 0.43. Thus dense cross-group ties, as occur in Figure 3.11A and Figure 3.11C, or sparse within-group ties, as occur in Figure 3.11B, each reduce graph modularity. In contrast, the network surrounding the *#WhereIsRey* conversation (depicted in Figure 1.1B in Chapter 1), where intragroup ties are dense and intergroup ties are sparse, has a modularity of 0.88.

Network centralization refers to the extent to which information or other resource flows move through one node. Network centralization may be calculated based on any of the ego centrality metrics. The general computation of network centrality is the sum of the differences between the highest observed centrality and each node's centrality, normalized for the highest level of centralization possible in the given network. The numerator in the formula therefore represents the total disparities between each node's centrality and that of the most central node (i.e., the one with the highest centrality); the denominator represents the highest level of centralization possible. Thus the formula for computing degree centralization is:

$$\text{Centralization} = \frac{\sum_{i=1}^{n}\left(c_{max} - c(v_{(i)})\right)}{(n-1)(n-2)},$$

where

$cmax$ = the maximum degree centrality in the graph,
$c(v(i))$ = the degree centrality for each node in the graph, and
n = the number of vertices.

The centralization of the four topologies from Table 3.2 is provided in Table 3.3. As will be apparent from the table, centralization is highest for the star topology, followed by the Y. The ring and fully connected topologies are not at all centralized.

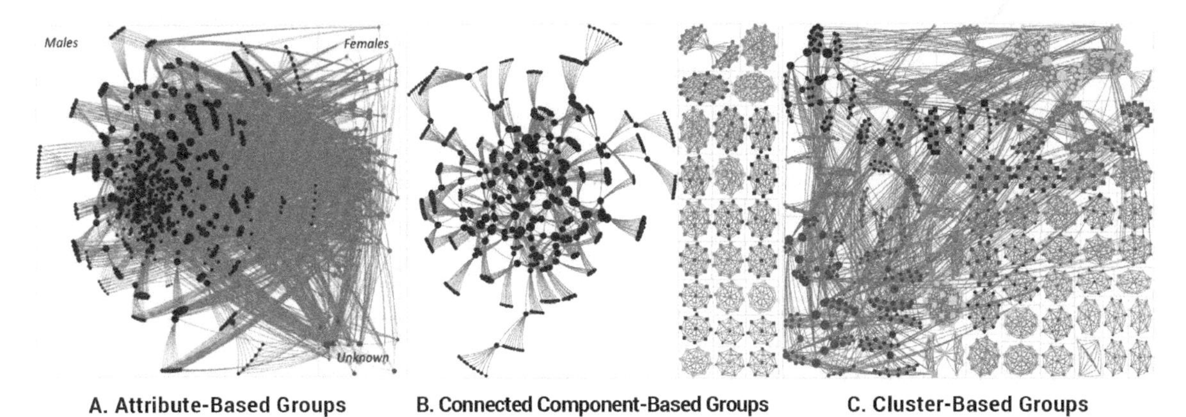

Figure 3.11 Three Groupings of the Interlocking Directorates Network

A graph also has a ***clustering*** coefficient, which is the proportion of cluster members who are tied to each other. The clustering coefficient for a graph is the average clustering coefficients for its nodes. (See the clustering coefficient discussion in the "Ego Metrics" section below. We will cover clustering in further detail in Chapter 5.) Clustering coefficients capture the ***cliquishness*** of a graph. Table 3.3 reports the clustering coefficient for the topologies in Table 3.2. As will be apparent in Table 3.3, clustering or cliquishness is nonexistent in star, Y, line, and ring topologies, and is optimized in the fully connected topology.

Ego Metrics

Ego metrics provide the analyst with different indicators of the connectedness and structural equivalence of each ego within the network. Connectedness, as you might imagine, indicates the extent to which an ego is linked to other egos within the network. Structural equivalence speaks to the extent to which egos have similar ties.

Centrality speaks to the prominence of a node [33]. A node may attain prominence in one of three main ways, giving rise to three key centrality metrics—degree centrality, betweenness centrality, and closeness centrality. (See the "Computing the Three Key Centrality Metrics" insert for computations. Also, while we will encounter other centrality metrics, such as eigenvector centrality, they typically are extensions of one of these three metrics.) In Table 3.2, node A is the most prominent across the first three topologies based on all three metrics. That different nodes may attain prominence or centrality based on each of these metrics, though is visible in Figure 3.12 as a special type of network topology known as *Krackhardt's kite* [34]. We now examine each of these three forms of centrality.

Degree centrality is the count of an ego's direct connections. It is a function of activity—nodes that are the most active attain the highest degree centrality. In Figure 3.12, node D has a total of six direct ties, more than any other node, and therefore enjoys the highest degree of centrality. In undirected networks, such as Figure 3.12, we have only a single measure of degree centrality. In directed networks, we separate ***in-degree centrality***, which assesses an ego's popularity as its number of inbound ties, from ***out-degree centrality***, which assesses ego's proactiveness or extraversion as its number of outbound ties. To account for network size, the tie count sometimes is standardized by dividing the count by the number of nodes in the network. While NodeXL does not perform this standardization, we should if our objective is to compare networks of different sizes.

Betweenness centrality assesses the number of indirect ties a node mediates (i.e., is on the geodesic path between). As such, betweenness centrality captures the frequency with which a node acts as a ***bridge*** (i.e., connects unconnected components) within its network. In the star topology in Table 3.2, node A has a betweenness centrality of 6 because it mediates six indirect ties: B-C, B-D, B-E, C-D, C-E, and D-E. All other nodes in the star topology have a betweenness of zero, since they do not mediate any other indirect ties. In the Y topology in Table 3.2, node A has a betweenness of 5; node D has betweeness of 3; and B, C, and E have a betweeness of zero. In the line topology, node A has a betweenness of 4, B and C have a betweenness of 3, and D and E have a betweenness of zero. In the ring, each node has a betweeness centrality of 1, mediating between exactly one indirect tie.

In Krackhardt's kite in Figure 3.12, node H has the highest betweenness of 14—in other words, being on 14 geodesic paths. Node H is a beneficial position for a person to occupy, since the person in that position brokers or intermediates between otherwise disconnected components of the network. From an organizational perspective, node H is a boundary spanner or broker, bridging different network components. However, node H also represents a single point of failure to the organization—if the person in position H becomes unavailable, the network falls apart.

Closeness centrality is related to a node's geodesic distance from other nodes in the network. With this metric, prominence is a function of a node's proximity to other nodes in a graph. A proximate position is advantageous in terms of monitoring, as information tends to flow through these positions. Since distance is inversely related to closeness, closeness centrality is the inverse of the sum of a node's geodesic distances from all other nodes in the network. In other words, a node's closeness centrality is computed as the reciprocal of the total number of hops from that node to each other node. In Figure 3.12, nodes C and G have the highest closeness centrality. These two nodes are immediately proximate to five of the nine other nodes, and are only three hops away from the farthest node—node J. In contrast, node D, which is immediately proximate to six

Computing the Three Key Centrality Measures

To understand how the different centrality metrics are computed, let us consider a small four-person graph:

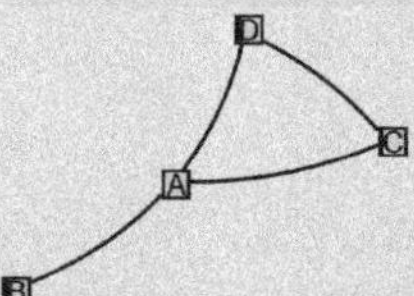

Degree Centrality:

Count all edges associated with node.

A: 3	B: 1	C: 2	D: 2

Note: For directed graphs, we would count all the inbound ties to obtain in-degree centrality and all the outbound ties to obtain out-degree centrality for each node.

Betweenness Centrality:

Step 1:	Identify all node pairs not involving the node for which betweenness is being calculated.
Step 2:	For each node pair, identify the geodesic path.
Step 3:	Determine the fraction of geodesic paths for each node pair that contains that node.
Step 4:	Sum the geodesic fractions to obtain betweenness.

(1) Pairs without Node	(2) Geodesic Path	(3) Fraction with Node
For Node **A**		
BC	B-**A**-C	1/1
BD	B-**A**-D	1/1
CD	C-D	0
(4) Sum of fractions		2
For Node **D**		
AB	A-B	0
AC	A-C	0
BC	B-A-C	0
(4) Sum of fractions		0

Closeness Centrality:

Step 1:	Identify geodesic path from node for which closeness is being computed to every other node.
Step 2:	Compute distance of the node from every other node.
Step 3:	Compute node's "farness" as a sum of its distances.
Step 4:	Compute closeness as the reciprocal of "farness."

(1) Geodesic Path	(2) Distance
For Node **A**	
A-B	1
A-C	1
A-D	1
(3) "Farness"	3
(4) Closeness	1/3=0.33
For Node **D**	
D-A	1
D-A-B	2
D-C	1
(3) "Farness"	4
(4) Closeness	1/4=0.25

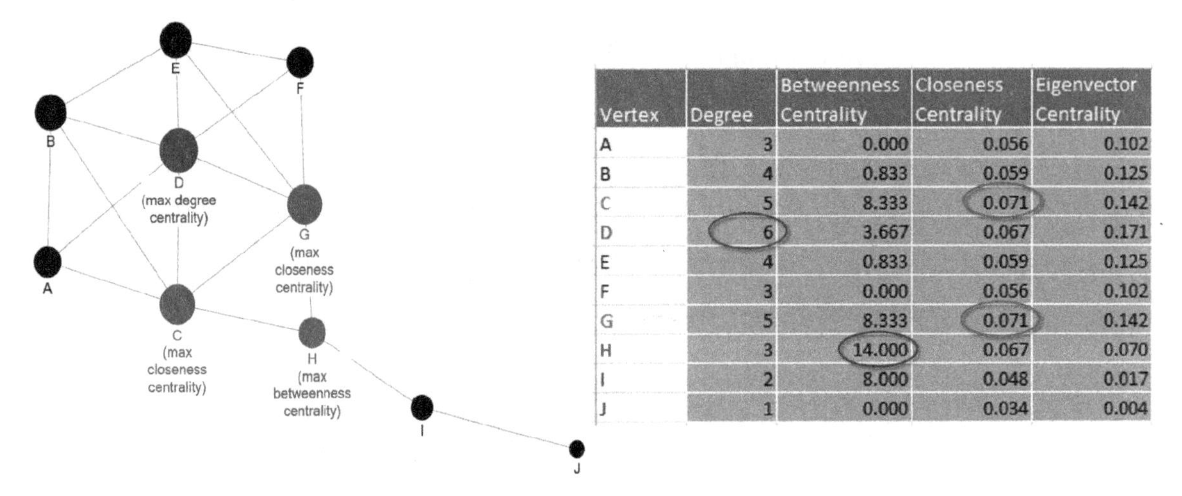

Vertex	Degree	Betweenness Centrality	Closeness Centrality	Eigenvector Centrality
A	3	0.000	0.056	0.102
B	4	0.833	0.059	0.125
C	5	8.333	0.071	0.142
D	6	3.667	0.067	0.171
E	4	0.833	0.059	0.125
F	3	0.000	0.056	0.102
G	5	8.333	0.071	0.142
H	3	14.000	0.067	0.070
I	2	8.000	0.048	0.017
J	1	0.000	0.034	0.004

Figure 3.12 Krackhardt's Kite

nodes, takes four hops to reach node J; node H, which intermediates fourteen ties, is two or more hops away from six other nodes.

Because a node's geodesic distance to an unconnected node is infinitely long, graph-wide closeness centrality cannot be determined for networks with unconnected components. In NodeXL, isolates have a closeness centrality of zero; for nodes in connected components of size greater than one, closeness centrality is based only on a node's proximity to the other nodes within its connected component (i.e., with which it is directly or indirectly connected). Thus a pair of connected nodes that are unconnected with the rest of the network have a closeness centrality of 1, while nodes in the larger connected component have lower closeness centrality scores if they are not fully connected.

Related to degree centrality is ***eigenvector centrality***, which adjusts a node's prominence based on the relative prominence of the nodes to which it is tied. In Figure 3.12, node D has the highest degree centrality and, with four ties each, D's direct ties convey the indirect advantage of these ties to D. In Table 3.2, node A in the Y topology has the highest degree, betweenness, and closeness centrality, but has the same eigenvector centrality as node D. This is because D and A each are connected to the remainder of their network directly or through each other.

Thus with the eigenvector centrality, metric prominence is attributed not just to the most active nodes, but to those undertaking strategic or efficient activity. Implied in this metric is the recognition that direct ties are costly to form and to maintain. Robin Dunbar theorized a cortical limit on our information-processing ability, which permitted us to maintain a limited number of social connections [35]. Among humans, based on a study of Christmas cards sent, he estimated this number to average 150 connections [36], which has come to be called *Dunbar's number*.

Computing eigenvector centrality is nontrivial. It involves an iterative process of computing the eigenvector centrality of each node's neighbors and deducing the node's eigenvector centrality based on its neighbors' eigenvector centrality. Unlike the other three centrality measures covered, eigenvector centrality also is nonstandard—meaning that there are different algorithms for performing the iterative computation. Thus the eigenvector centrality scores computed by different software packages, while highly correlated, will not be the same. In NodeXL, eigenvector centralities for a graph add up to 1. This will not be the case with R.

The ***clustering coefficient*** is related to the proportion of one's ties that also are tied to each other. It speaks to the extent to which the social structures surrounding the egos in the network are structurally-equivalent. In Krackhardt's kite in Figure 3.12, nodes A and F have perfect clustering coefficients of 1.0. As apparent in the figure, each of the nodes with which A and F are tied also share ties with each other. Nodes C and G have clustering coefficients of 0.50. Of the ten possible ties among each of the nodes and their neighbors (as per formulas in discussion of density above), only five are realized. Nodes I and J have clustering coefficients of 0.0, as none of the nodes neighboring each of them are adjacent to each other. Nodes with a high clustering coefficient tend to form a clique with their proximate nodes. A ***clique*** is a fully connected subgroup within the network.

What Does High Degree and Low Eigenvector Centrality Reveal?

Consider the 11-person graph below. Nodes B and G enjoy the highest degree centrality—5 each. In contrast, node A has a degree centrality of only 2. Yet node A has the highest eigenvector centrality at 0.161, compared to the eigenvector centrality of 0.097 for nodes B and G. Why is this?

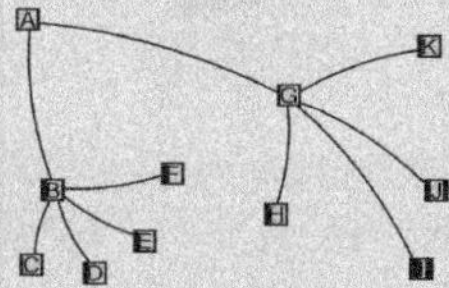

Unlike other centrality metrics, eigenvector centrality accounts for the network properties of one's neighbors. The eigenvector centrality of node A thus is a function of the very degree centrality of nodes B and G that overshadows its own degree centrality. Put another way, node A is able to enjoy the benefits of connecting to nodes C, D, E, F, H, I, J, and K without having to invest in maintaining those ties. All it needs to do to maintain its ties to those peripheral nodes is to maintain its ties to nodes B and G. Its relationship management strategy thus is vastly more efficient than the strategy employed by node B and node G, who each have to maintain five ties. Node A's ties are more efficient than node B's and node G's ties in one other way. In two hops, node A can reach every other network node (e.g., A-B-C and A-G-K). In contrast, nodes B and G take as much as three hops to reach their most distant neighbors (e.g., B-A-G-K and G-A-B-C).

Generating Network Metrics with NodeXL

NodeXL produces most, but not all, of the metrics discussed above. To obtain graph/subgraph or ego metrics, select the Graph Metrics button on the Analysis group—the fourth group on the **NodeXL Tab**. Check the metrics you want NodeXL to generate. Below, we first consider graph/subgraph metrics (i.e., those representing the entire network or subgroups within the network) and then ego metrics.

NodeXL provides graph metrics on the OVERALL METRICS sheet. The initial information provided on this sheet is whether a directed or undirected graph was assumed, the total number of vertices in the graph, the unique and total edges in the graph, and the number of self-ties or self-loops. Relevant to directed graphs, NodeXL then informs us of the level of reciprocation in terms of vertices and edges.

Next, NodeXL provides information on the number of connected components, the number of single-vertex connected components (or isolates), and the maximum vertices and edges within a connected component. NodeXL provides the maximum geodesic distance and average geodesic distance within the graph. In the presence of unconnected components, NodeXL computes the maximum geodesic distance of each of the unconnected components and sets the maximum geodesic distance of the graph to the highest of these values. Next, NodeXL provides an index of density. Finally, NodeXL provides an index of modularity. NodeXL will provide the modularity index of a graph only after you have applied a grouping algorithm. (See the "Sub-Group and Cluster Analysis" in Chapter 5.)

NodeXL provides several ego metrics on the VERTICES sheet. Among others, they include four measures of centrality and nodes' clustering coefficient.

Tutorial 3.2. Who Are the Most Influential Students in My Class?

While it does seem like both recognition and friendship ties in my knowledge management class got substantially denser within the four-week period of intense interaction among students, can we quantify the changes?

Let's reopen the KMNetwork1 file. To examine how the overall network has changed, we select the Graph Metrics button on the Analysis group on the **NodeXL Tab** and check the first option—Overall Graph Metrics—and click Calculate Metrics. This produces the output depicted in Figure 3.13A on the OVERALL METRICS sheet. Redoing these steps for the KMNetwork2 file produces the output in Figure 3.13B, permitting us to compare the starting and midterm networks.

	A	B
1	Graph Metric	Value
2	Graph Type	Directed
3		
4	Vertices	45
5		
6	Unique Edges	225
7	Edges With Duplicates	0
8	Total Edges	225
9		
10	Self-Loops	0
11		
12	Reciprocated Vertex Pair Ratio	0.388888889
13	Reciprocated Edge Ratio	0.56
14		
15	Connected Components	1
16	Single-Vertex Connected Components	0
17	Maximum Vertices in a Connected Component	45
18	Maximum Edges in a Connected Component	225
19		
20	Maximum Geodesic Distance (Diameter)	4
21	Average Geodesic Distance	2.185679
22		
23	Graph Density	0.113636364

A. Starting Graph

	A	B
1	Graph Metric	Value
2	Graph Type	Directed
3		
4	Vertices	46
5		
6	Unique Edges	501
7	Edges With Duplicates	0
8	Total Edges	501
9		
10	Self-Loops	0
11		
12	Reciprocated Vertex Pair Ratio	0.605769231
13	Reciprocated Edge Ratio	0.754491018
14		
15	Connected Components	1
16	Single-Vertex Connected Components	0
17	Maximum Vertices in a Connected Component	46
18	Maximum Edges in a Connected Component	501
19		
20	Maximum Geodesic Distance (Diameter)	3
21	Average Geodesic Distance	1.724953
22		
23	Graph Density	0.242028986

B. Midterm Graph

Figure 3.13 Graph Metrics for the Knowledge Management Class Recognition Network

From row 4, we see that the number of vertices went up from 45 to 46 because one student added the class late. Row 6 shows us that the number of edges increased from 225 to 501, indicating a 123% increase in students' recognition of one another. The reciprocated vertex pair ratio in row 12 also increased from 0.3889 to ~0.6058, indicating a 58% improvement in a student's ability to recognize another student who recognized him/her. Similarly, the reciprocated edge ratio in row 13 increased 35% from 0.56 to ~0.7545. The number of connected components depicted in row 15 was 1 for both time periods, indicating that the class recognition network was unfragmented from the start. The maximum geodesic distance depicted in row 20 decreased from 4 to 3 hops, reflecting a 25% improvement in efficiency. Average geodesic distance depicted in row 21 decreased from a little over 2 hops to a little under 2 hops, reflecting a 21% improvement. Network density—the ratio of realized to possible ties—doubled between the start and the middle of the term. All of these metrics point to increasing students' familiarity with one another.

How about the friendship network? Begin by filtering the Friendship column on the EDGES sheet for 1s. Then regenerate the overall metrics. In Figure 3.14, we see that we began the class with only 29 students who indicated that they were friends with someone or were claimed as a friend. By the middle of the term, this was up to 41 students. The number of friendships claimed (row 6) went up from 39 to 74. Reciprocation of friendship ties (rows 12 and 13) improved only modestly. From row 15, we see fragmentation decreased considerably from 5 islands of ties to only 2. The density of friendship ties, however, remained relatively unchanged.

What were the major changes to the individual students' ego networks? To examine how the students' networks have changed, we once again select the Graph Metrics button on the Analysis group on the **NodeXL Tab**. Now, we check the third option (Vertex in-degree) through tenth options (Edge reciprocation) and click Calculate Metrics. (Note that because we are dealing with directed graphs, we select the in-degree and out-degree centrality metrics. If these were undirected graphs, we would select only the degree metric—second option from the list.) Once calculated, NodeXL places the ego metrics on the VERTICES sheet. Let's focus on MH, a full-time, dual-degree (MBA/MS-MIS) student.

	A	B
1	Graph Metric	Value
2	Graph Type	Directed
3		
4	Vertices	45
5		
6	Unique Edges	225
7	Edges With Duplicates	0
8	Total Edges	225
9		
10	Self-Loops	0
11		
12	Reciprocated Vertex Pair Ratio	0.388888889
13	Reciprocated Edge Ratio	0.56
14		
15	Connected Components	1
16	Single-Vertex Connected Components	0
17	Maximum Vertices in a Connected Component	45
18	Maximum Edges in a Connected Component	225
19		
20	Maximum Geodesic Distance (Diameter)	4
21	Average Geodesic Distance	2.185679
22		
23	Graph Density	0.113636364

A. Starting Graph

	A	B
1	Graph Metric	Value
2	Graph Type	Directed
3		
4	Vertices	41
5		
6	Unique Edges	74
7	Edges With Duplicates	0
8	Total Edges	74
9		
10	Self-Loops	0
11		
12	Reciprocated Vertex Pair Ratio	0.193548387
13	Reciprocated Edge Ratio	0.324324324
14		
15	Connected Components	2
16	Single-Vertex Connected Components	0
17	Maximum Vertices in a Connected Component	39
18	Maximum Edges in a Connected Component	73
19		
20	Maximum Geodesic Distance (Diameter)	11
21	Average Geodesic Distance	4.116721
22		
23	Graph Density	0.045121951

B. Midterm Graph

Figure 3.14 Graph Metrics for the Knowledge Management Class Friendship Network

For the initial network in the KMNetwork1 file, MH was the student with the highest in-degree centrality (in column S)—who is recognized by the most students, a total of 12 other students. MH has the second-highest out-degree centrality (in column T)—the person who recognizes the highest number of other students, with a score of 11. He also has the second-highest betweenness centrality score, indicating his ability to broker relationships among his classmates, and the highest closeness centrality score, indicating highest proximity to others in the class network. His eigenvector centrality is only fourth-highest, though, indicating his tendency to connect both with high- and low-connection classmates—a high-effort network maintenance strategy. MH has the seventh-lowest clustering coefficient, indicating few closed triads around him and confirming that he therefore is among the best-positioned to broker relationships among other subgroups within the class. Twelve of the students have a reciprocated vertex pair ratio of zero at this time, indicating that no one whom they recognize recognizes them.

For the midterm network in the KMNetwork2 file, MH has the second-highest in-degree centrality score of 22, being recognized by 10 more students than at the start of the class. MH now is the student with the highest out-degree centrality, which has increased to 25. MH's betweenness centrality also is highest. He also enjoys the highest closeness and eigenvector centrality. A relatively low clustering coefficient tells us that he continues to be surrounded by unconnected triads. The number of students with a reciprocated vertex pair of zero now has dropped to only one—BG, a part-time MBA student.

Tutorial 3.3. Whose Friending Do We Imitate?

"The Wired-Kapitall and the Buzz Insights Indices" insert provides the Twitter account names for each of the twenty-seven organizations listed on these indices [37, 38]. In the CorporateFriends.xlsx file, the EdgeList sheet lists the accounts friended by each of these twenty-seven accounts (obtained via R's twitteR package). The FriendCharacteristics sheet lists the accounts friended by the twenty-seven index accounts, the number of followers that each of these accounts has, the number of status updates (tweets) posted by each friended

Table 3.4 Correlating Friending by Top Brands with Account Characteristics

Characteristic	Formula	Correlation
Popularity	=CORREL(FriendCharacteristics!$B:$B,FriendCharacteristics!C:C)	0.32
Activity	=CORREL(FriendCharacteristics!$B:$B,FriendCharacteristics!D:D)	0.13
Gregariousness	=CORREL(FriendCharacteristics!$B:$B,FriendCharacteristics!E:E)	0.10

account, and the number of accounts each of these friended accounts have themselves friended. These last three characteristics represent the friended account's popularity, activity, and gregariousness, respectively. Using Excel's CORREL function, we can determine the extent to which organizations on the social media index funds tend to friend accounts high in popularity, activity, and gregariousness. Table 3.4 depicts the correlation between the extent to which the top social media brands friend an account and the account's popularity, activity, and gregariousness.

While we see a moderate positive correlation between the number of times an account is friended by the top social media brands and the popularity of those accounts (r = 0.32), the correlation of the level of activity and gregariousness of those brands with the number of times an account is friended by the top social media brands is very low. We can conclude that the top social media brands appear to favor popular others (i.e., accounts with a large number of followers) when deciding which accounts to friend. This suggests that the top social media brands may be more concerned with leveraging the influence of their friends than obtaining information from them.

The Wired-Kapitall and Buzz Insights Indices

The Wired-Kapitall index fund lists nine organizations. For organizations with Twitter accounts, these accounts are depicted below.

CocaCola	Disney	Viacom
Nike	Starbucks	McDonalds
TheLimited	Monster Beverage†	Walmart

The Buzz Social Media Insights index lists twenty-four organizations. For organizations with Twitter accounts, these accounts are depicted below.

Google	Apple†	Alcoa
Disney	GileadSciences	Abbvie
Opko Health†	TeslaMotors	Ford
SiriusXM	Facebook	Valeant Pharmaceuticals†
Celgene	Intel	Twitter
JNJCares	ATT	JetBlue
Nike	AltriaNews	Biogen
Visa	Yahoo	Freeport-McMoRaN†

†Does not have a Twitter account.

Conclusion

Social network analysis can provide insights into the dynamics of social milieus with which we personally are unfamiliar. Our visualization of the start and midterm class networks in Tutorial 3.1b and the subsequent analyses of graph metrics in Tutorial 3.2 suggest that the knowledge management class provided students with many opportunities for interaction, increasing and deepening their familiarity with one another. In fact, by the middle of the term, students already had completed three homework team assignments and three in-class team assignments. Students were permitted to reconstitute teams, increasing their opportunities for networking across the class.

If our analyses of ego metrics in Tutorial 3.2 led you to believe that MH was an extremely gregarious individual, you are correct. Notably, MH was the only student in that class who made a conscious effort to change teams across the various in-class and homework assignments. Similar analyses of CB's metrics might reveal a shy but highly socially aware student. We can glean these insights about the class several years after students have passed through the University of Oklahoma.

Examining organizations' connections is similarly insightful. Through our analysis of the friending patterns of top social media brands, we were able to deduce their social media strategy via-à-vis friending Twitter accounts. Specifically we saw a tendency for them to friend popular, rather than active or gregarious, others. Rather than simply friending the accounts these brands friend most frequently—i.e., Forbes, Mashable, NY Times, Red Cross, and WSJ (as noted in Chapter 2)—other organizations wishing to learn from the top social media brands can apply the popularity rule in deciding whom to friend.

Exercise: Interlocking Directorates

The MS Excel file, *Board of Directors.xlsx*, contains information on the board members of the 2012 Fortune 100 companies on five sheets. Use this information to develop the following graphs:

1. One-mode director network
2. One-mode company network
3. Two-mode network

Each network should be a separate NodeXL file. You will need to copy the appropriate information from the *Board of Directors.xlsx* file into your NodeXL files in order to create the required graphs. The first three sheets in the *Board of Directors.xlsx* file provide you with the vertices for the three required networks. You may copy these directly into the Vertex 1 and Vertex 2 columns in the EDGES sheet of your NodeXL file.

The last two sheets of the *Board of Directors.xlsx* file provide you with attribute data to enable you to develop more meaningful visuals. To use these data, add a new sheet at the very end of your NodeXL workbook—after the OVERALL METRICS sheet—using the ⊕ button.

The ONE-MODE DIRECTOR NETWORK sheet contains the following information:

[A] Director1: Name of first director.
[B] Director2: Name of second director. This director serves on a board with Director 1.

The ONE-MODE COMPANY NETWORK sheet contains the following information:

[A] Company1: Name of first company.
[B] Company2: Name of second company, linked to Company1 through one or more shared directors.

The TWO-MODE NETWORK sheet contains the following information:

[A] Company: Name of company.
[B] Director: Name of director affiliated with the company.
[C] Title: Director's title on company board. This was used to derive the next two columns. You probably will not use this directly, but I have left it in just in case you notice information you can extract.
[D] Chairman: Whether or not the director serves as chairman on that board.
[E] CEO: Whether or not the director serves is CEO of the company.
If you use data beyond columns A and B from this sheet, be sure to copy them after column N on the EDGES sheet.

The DIRECTOR ATTRIBUTES sheet contains the following information:

[A] Director: Name of director.
[B] AdvDegree: Whether or not the director has an MD or PhD.
[C] Gender: Whether the director is *M*ale, *F*emale, or gender *U*nknown.
[D] Chairman: Whether or not the director serves as chairman on any board.
[E] CEO: Whether or not the director serves as CEO of any company.

The COMPANY ATTRIBUTES sheet contains the following information:

[A] Company: Name of the company.
[B] Industry: Industry in which the company operates.

Team Assignment Part 1

Decide who will develop each of the three graphs. Every team must have at least two versions of each graph.

Individual Assignment

Develop your graph, providing the viewer with as much information as possible. Produce multiple visuals of the same graph to highlight different information. Experiment with different layouts. Use your judgment to filter self-ties as appropriate. Save each visual to an MS Word file. Submit the Word and NodeXL files.

Team Assignment Part 2

Put together your team's graphs into a PowerPoint that tells a story about the Fortune firms and their boards. Your first slide should name all team-members. Your story should reveal at least five insights that explain or predict and lead you to tangible recommendations for corporate strategy or public policy.

Works Cited

1. Nolte, J., *The Philosophy, Theory and Methods of JL Moreno: The Man Who Tried to Become God*. New York: Routledge, 2014.
2. Angwin, J., *Dragnet Nation: A Quest for Privacy, Security, and Freedom in a World of Relentless Surveillance*. New York: Macmillan, 2014.
3. Saxenian, A., *Regional Advantage: Culture and Competition in Silicon Valley and Route 128*. Cambridge, MA: Harvard University Press, 1996.
4. Tutterow, C., "Socilab," January 16, 2016, http://socilab.com.
5. Moreno, J.L., and H.H. Jennings, *Who Shall Survive? Foundations of Sociometry, Group Psychotherapy, and Sociodrama*. Beacon, NY: Beacon House, 1934.
6. Milgram, S., "The Small World Problem." *Psychology Today*, 2(1; 1967): 60–67.
7. Travers, J., and S. Milgram, "An Experimental Study of the Small World Problem." *Sociometry*, 32 (4; 1969): 425–43.
8. Auerbach, D.M., et al., "Cluster of Cases of the Acquired Immune Deficiency Syndrome: Patients Linked by Sexual Contact." *The American Journal of Medicine*, 76(3; 1984): 487–92.
9. Worobey, M., et al., "1970s and 'Patient 0' HIV-1 Genomes Illuminate Early HIV/AIDS History in North America." *Nature*, 539(7627; 2016): 98–101.
10. Borgatti, S., M. Everett, and L. Freeman, "UCINET IV Network Analysis Software." *Connections*, 15(1; 1992): 12–15.
11. Batagelj, V., and A. Mrvar, "Pajek—Program for Large Network Analysis." *Connections*, 21(2; 1998): 47–57.
12. SolarWinds, "Automated Network Mapping for Network Visualization," January 16, 2016, https://www.solarwinds.com/topics/network-visualization.
13. Christley, R.M., et al., "Infection in Social Networks: Using Network Analysis to Identify High-Risk Individuals." *American Journal of Epidemiology*, 162(10; 2005): 1024–31.
14. Klovdahl, A., et al., "Networks and Tuberculosis: An Undetected Community Outbreak Involving Public Places." *Social Science & Medicine*, 52(5; 2001): 681–94.
15. Baesens, B., V.V. Vlasselaer, and W. Verbeke, *Fraud Analytics Using Descriptive, Predictive, and Social Network Techniques: A Guide to Data Science for Fraud Detection*. Hoboken, NJ: Wiley, 2015.

16. Ronen, S., et al., "Links That Speak: The Global Language Network and Its Association with Global Fame." *Proceedings of the National Academy of Sciences*, 111(52; 2014): E5616–E5622.
17. Borgatti, S.P., and D.S. Halgin, "On Network Theory." *Organization Science*, 22(5; 2011): 1168–81.
18. Krackhardt, D., "The Strength of Strong Ties," in *Networks in the Knowledge Economy*, edited by R. Cross, A. Parker, and L. Sasson, 82–108. Oxford: Oxford University Press, 2003.
19. Burt, R.S., *Structural Holes: The Social Structure of Competition*. Cambridge, MA: Harvard University Press, 1995.
20. Granovetter, M.S., "The Strength of Weak Ties." *American Journal of Sociology*, 78 (6; 1973): 1360–80.
21. Cross, R., and L. Prusak, "The People Who Make Organizations Go—Or Stop." *Harvard Business Review*, 80(6; 2002): 104–12.
22. Bossard, J.H., "Residential Propinquity as a Factor in Marriage Selection." *American Journal of Sociology*, 38 (2; 1932): 219–24.
23. Borgatti, S.P., and R. Cross, "A Relational View of Information Seeking and Learning in Social Networks." *Management Science*, 49(4; 2003): 432–45.
24. McPherson, M., L. Smith-Lovin, and J.M. Cook, "Birds of a Feather: Homophily in Social Networks." *Annual Review of Sociology*, 27(2001): 415–44.
25. Suitor, J., and S. Keeton, "Once a Friend, Always a Friend? Effects of Homophily on Women's Support Networks across a Decade." *Social Networks*, 19(1; 1997): 51–62.
26. Cowen, T., "The Marriages of Power Couples Reinforce Income Inequality," *New York Times*, December 26, 2015, https://www.nytimes.com/2015/12/27/upshot/marriages-of-power-couples-reinforce-income-inequality.html.
27. Miranda, S.M., I. Kim, and J. Summers, "Jamming with Social Media: How Cognitive Structuring of Organizing Vision Facets Affects IT Innovation Diffusion." *MIS Quarterly*, 39(3; 2015): 591–614.
28. Borgatti, S.P., M.G. Everett, and L.C. Freeman, *UCINET 6 for Windows: Software for Social Network Analysis*. Cambridge, MA: Analytic Technologies, 2002.
29. Bavelas, A., "Communication Patterns in Task-Oriented Groups." *Journal of the Acoustical Society of America*, 22(6; 1950): 725–30.
30. Leavitt, H.J., "Some Effects of Certain Communication Patterns on Group Performance." *The Journal of Abnormal and Social Psychology*, 46(1; 1951): 38.
31. Harel, D., and Y. Koren, "A Fast Multi-scale Method for Drawing Large Graphs," in *Proceedings of the International Symposium on Graph Drawing*. New York: Springer, 2000.
32. Simmel, G., "The Triad," in *The Sociology of Georg Simmel*, 145–69. New York: The Free Press, 1950.
33. Wasserman, S., and K. Faust, *Social Network Analysis: Methods and Applications*. Cambridge: Cambridge University Press, 1994.
34. Krackhardt, D., "Assessing the Political Landscape: Structure, Cognition, and Power in Organizations." *Administrative Science Quarterly*, 35(1990): 342–69.
35. Dunbar, R.I., "Neocortex Size as a Constraint on Group Size in Primates." *Journal of Human Evolution*, 22(6; 1992): 469–93.
36. Hill, R.A., and R.I. Dunbar, "Social Network Size in Humans." *Human Nature*, 14(1; 2003): 53–72.
37. "The Facebook Index: 83 Million Fake Accounts Don't Affect Most 'Liked' Stocks," Kapitall, 2012, http://wire.kapitall.com/investment-idea/the-facebook-index-83-billion-fake-accounts-dont-affect-most-liked-stocks/.
38. Belvedere, M.J., "Top 25 Stocks Based on Social Buzz: Index Creator," Exchange Traded Funds, 2016, http://www.cnbc.com/2016/04/21/top-25-stocks-based-on-social-buzz-index-creator.html.

CHAPTER 4

Visualizing Networks and SNA with R

In Chapter 3, we learned about SNA concepts, visualization techniques, and metrics. This chapter introduces you to conducting SNA with R. We will find that most of the R SNA functions parallel the SNA tools available in NodeXL. With R, however, we can generate many more metrics, gain scalability, and combine our network analysis with statistical analysis of network properties alone, or analyze network properties in conjunction with other social, political, and/or economic data. While only introductory, the chapter resources should provide you with sufficient background to tackle more intricate problems on your own.

Learning Objectives

The purpose of this chapter is to introduce you to social network analysis with R. It covers R commands required to:

1. load the appropriate packages necessary for SNA;
2. open, prepare, and inspect network data;
3. graph networks;
4. obtain metrics for entire network; and
5. obtain metrics for specified vertices.

SNA Packages

To perform SNA in this chapter, we will need the R **igraph** package. The igraph package is a key package required for every aspect of SNA—from creating the network data object, to visualizing the network and calculating network metrics. There is quite a bit more functionality associated with the igraph than is covered in this chapter. Run *install.packages()* and *load library()* for the package.

While igraph is used extensively for SNA, it is not the only SNA package available. A group out of the University of California, Irvine, also developed an SNA package called **network**, and recently released another package—**sna**—for R. A group at Stanford is working on another package called **SoNIA**. Others worth investigating include **visNetwork**, for visualizing networks, and **ndtv**, for dynamic network visualizations over time.

Opening, Preparing, and Inspecting SNA Data

As with most analytics jobs in R, we begin by reading in our data. Once we have done so, we will need to create a graph data frame—a special purpose data object needed for network analysis. Recall from our work with NodeXL that there were two portions to graph data—an edge list and a vertex list. We create our graph data object by optionally combining a data frame containing the edge list with a data frame of vertex attributes using the ***graph_from_data_frame(EDGEDATAFRAME, vertices=VERTEXDATAFRAME, directed=T/F)*** command. The "directed=" argument lets R know whether we are working with a directed or undirected graph.

Next, we wish to inspect the set of egos and edges present in the graph. As with examining the rows and columns of a regular data frame, this helps us understand our network data and ensures we imported it correctly. We can examine egos using the ***V(GRAPHFRAME)*** or the ***get.vertex.attribute(GRAPHFRAME,'NAME')*** command. Besides permitting us to determine the ordering of the vertices in the graph data frame, the V() function permits us to interact with and set vertex attributes such as node color, as we will see below. Using

E(GraphFrame) allows us to inspect and set edge attributes such as edge weight and is equivalent to ***get.edge.attribute(GraphName)***. Finally, using the ***simplify(GraphName)*** command eliminates self-ties or loops from or graph data frame.

Tutorial 4.1. Setting Up the Social Network of Legislative Bills

We will be working with two files—see the "Bills Data" insert for descriptions of the two files and of what they capture. We will import it into a named storage location called *CoSponsors*, keeping in mind that the file has headers, using

> **The Bills Data**
>
> In this tutorial, we use a data set about co-sponsorship of legislative bills by thirty-five members of Congress. The *cosponsors.csv* file provides an edge list of the thirty-five Congress members who co-sponsored a recent bill. (Let's see whether we can tell *how many* bills through our analyses.) Each legislator is represented by their initials (followed by a number, if two or more legislators share the initials). The *legislators.csv* file provides Congress members' names, party affiliation, gender, and tenure in Congress at the time of the bills.

```
CoSponsors=read.csv('cosponsors.csv',header=T)
```

Being a simple edge list, this file has only the two columns and is very similar to the edge lists we used in NodeXL.

We create the graph data frame using

```
CoSponsorGraph=graph_from_data_frame(CoSponsors, directed=F)
```

The "directed=" argument lets R know whether our graph is directed or undirected. Since ties are mutual in the bill co-sponsorship relationship, we set "directed=F".

To list all egos, we use

```
V(CoSponsorGraph)
```

This provides us with a list of the thirty-five legislators in the data set. This list is important because we will want to ensure our vertices are ordered accordingly in the legislators.csv file.

```
## + 35/35 vertices, named:
##  [1] BF1 BF2 BG  BL  CC  CH  CM  DE  DJ  EC  EJ  JB  JC1 JC2 JK  JR  KB
## [18] KG  LB  LS  MC  MM1 MM2 PK  PO  PS  RB  RN  RW  SP1 SP2 TP  WH  MB
## [35] PG
```

This tells us that the first legislator R expects to find in the legislators.csv file is BF1, the fifth is CC, and the last is "PG". The ordering is not alphabetic, but rather based on the order in which a legislator appears in an edge in the cosponsors.csv file. Once we are sure the order of our legislators in the cosponsors.csv file matches the order of our legislators in the legislators.csv file (see the insert on "Matching Vertex to Edge Files"), we can import our legislators data using

```
Legislators=read.csv('legislators.csv', header=T)
```

Then, we add a "vertices=" argument to the graph_from_data_frame(). This permits R to incorporate vertex attributes into the analysis. So reassigning the CoSponsorGraph graph data frame as

```
CoSponsorGraph=graph_from_data_frame(CoSponsors, directed=F, vertices=Legislators)
```

Matching Vertex to Edge Files

In order to analyze node attributes correctly, it is important that the ordering of vertices in our vertex file (here legislators.csv) match up with the ordering of the edges in the edge file (here cosponsors.csv). If they do not, many of our visuals and computations will be incorrect.

To ensure correctly matched vertex and edge files, I used V() with the column $name to ensure the legislators' names and not just IDs were output, used cbind() to convert the individual name values to a column, and data.frame() to convert the column to a data frame. I then assigned the data frame a name (Legislators) and output the data frame to a file (*legOrder.csv*) using the code below. After that, I opened up both files in Excel to ensure that the vertices order in the legislators.csv file matched the vertices order in the legOrder.csv file.

```
LegOrder=data.frame(cbind(V(CoSponsorGraph)$name))
write.csv(LegOrder,file='legOrder.csv')
```

allows us to use the gender and party-affiliation data from the legislators.csv file in our visualizations and metrics of the cosponsors.csv file.

We now can produce the edge list using

```
E(CoSponsorGraph)
```

To eliminate self-ties (a.k.a. loops) or duplicate edges, we use

```
CSG=simplify(CoSponsorGraph)
```

This also creates a new graph data frame called CSF. We will find no difference in the visuals and metrics on the CSG graph data frame and the CoSponsorGraph graph data frame, though, because our bill's data set does not contain self-ties or repeated edges.

Graphing Networks

We use R's ***plot(GRAPHNAME)*** command visualize the network graph. This sends the output to the RStudio IO panel. We can use the standard set of plot() options available. For example, using '***margin=PROPORTION***', where positive proportion values increase margins and negative values shrink them, gives us a handle on the whitespace around our graph and permits us to zoom in. In addition to these, we have some options specific to plotting networks that permit us to get a handle on displays of the vertices and edges. See the "Network-Specific plot() Options" insert for some of the more useful plot options. To use these options in our plot() function, we set vertex options with ***vertex.OPTION=''*** (e.g., vertex.shape='circle') and edge options with ***vertex.OPTION=''*** (e.g., edge.color='darkred'). We can link some—not all—display options to vertex and edge attributes—for example, a demographic variable such as gender or a network attribute such as centrality, permitting us to vary vertex and edge display properties relative to the underlying data.

We can route this output to a PDF, BMP, JPEG, PNG, or TIFF file, by preceding our plot() and related commands with a ***pdf('FILE.pdf')***, ***bmp('FILE.pdf')***, ***jpeg('FILE.pdf')***, ***png('FILE.pdf')***, or ***tiff('FILE.pdf')***, respectively, and terminating the command block with ***dev.off()***. Or, we simply can get a screenshot of the output from the IO panel and paste that into our report.

An alternative to a simple plot() is ***tkplot(GRAPHNAME)***. This command sends the output to an interactive output window. The *Tk* window, permits us to move around vertices for easier inspection, change layout algorithms (though fewer layout options are provided here than via the layout command), fit, center, or rotate the graph, toggle labels on/off, and export the graph to a postscript file. **Note, though, that the tkplot() command does not route titles (main or subtitles) to the *Tk* window. Nor are all plot() vertex and edge options available with *Tk*.**

R's igraph package provides many more layout algorithms than NodeXL. Recall that a layout algorithm determines the placement of each node on the graph. Some layout algorithms target overall aesthetics. Other algorithms attempt to optimize some specific dimension of aesthetics such as edge crossings. A final set—the force-directed, spring-based, and multidimensional scaling algorithms attempt to optimize node placement relative to proximity to other nodes. We use ***layout_ALGORITHM(GRAPHNAME)*** to specify our desired layout for the plot, where "ALGORITHM" is replaced with the desired layout. If no layout is specified, the default for graphs with fewer than one hundred vertices is *layout_with_kk*. If dissatisfied with the layout, we can try any of the alternatives noted in the "igraph Layout Algorithms" insert. When choosing a layout, consider what you are trying to communicate. For example, using *layout_in_circle*, *layout_on_grid*, *layout_randomly*, and *layout_as_star* may produce pretty pictures, but communicates little about distance. The *layout_with_mds* tends superimpose nodes on one another, making the graph difficult to read.

Network-Specific plot() Options

Vertex Options	
size	Sets the vertex size; valid values are nonzero numbers; default is *15*
color	Sets the vertex color; valid values are any R palette specification format; default is *SkyBlue2*
shape	Sets the vertex shape; valid shapes are *circle*, *square*, *csquare*, *rectangle*, *crectangle*, *vrectangle*, *pie*, *sphere*, and *none* (which omits drawing the vertices); default is *circle*
label	Specifies the text to be used to label vertices; default is vertex ID
label.family	Sets the font family to be used for vertex labels; valid values are *serif*, *sans*, or *mono*; default is *serif*
label.font	Specifies the font type to use; valid values are *1* for plain, *2* for bold, *3* for italic, *4* for bold italic, and *5* for symbol; default is *1*
label.cex	Specifies the scaling size for the labels; default is *1*; 1.5 requests a size that is 50% larger; 0.5 requests a size that is 50% smaller
label.dist	Specifies distance of label from vertex center; default is 0, placing the label at the center of the node; distances greater than 1 position the label above the vertex; distances less than 1 position the label below the vertex
label.color	Specifies the color for the label text; default value is *black*
Edge Options	
color	Specifies edge color; default is *darkgrey*
width	Specifies edge thickness; default is *1*
arrow.size	Specifies size of arrowheads; default is *1*
arrow.width	Specifies width of arrowheads; default is *1*
lty	Specifies line type for edges; valid values are *0* for no edges (blank), *1* for solid line, *2* for dashed, *3* for dotted, *4* for dot-dash, *5* for long-dash, and *6* for two-dash; default is *1*
label	Specifies text to be used to label edges; default is to omit labels
label.family	Sets the font family to be used for edge labels; see above for valid values
label.cex	Specifies the scaling size for the edge labels; see above for valid values and default
label.color	Specifies the color for the edge labels; see above for default value
curved	Specifies whether or not edges should be curved; valid values are *TRUE* or *FALSE*; default is *FALSE*

Tutorial 4.2. Visualizing the Social Network of Legislative Bills

igraph Layout Algorithms

as_bipartite	Two-row layout for bipartite graphs
as_star	Places one vertex in the center of a circle and the rest on a perimeter, at equidistant intervals
as_tree	Uses the Reingold-Tilford algorithm, which displays graph as a hierarchy [1]
in_circle	Positions vertices in a circle
nicely	Automatically chooses a suitable layout for the graph
on_grid	Positions nodes on a grid
on_sphere	Positions nodes on the surface of a sphere
randomly	Positions nodes randomly in 3D space
with_dh	Uses Davidson-Harel simulated annealing algorithm to optimize aesthetic quality; competitive with the Spring algorithm for graphs of "modest" size [2]
with_drl	Uses DrL iterative, multilevel, force-directed algorithm; suitable for large-scale graphs [3]
with_fr	Uses the Fruchterman-Reingold force-directed algorithm to position vertices on a plane [4]
with_gem	Uses the GEM (graph embedder) force-directed algorithm to iteratively position nodes in 3D space [5]
with_graphopt	Uses the GraphOpt force-directed algorithm; performs relatively well with large graphs
with_kk	Uses the Kamada-Kawai model, based on physical springs, to position vertices in 2D or 3D space
with_lgl	Uses the Large Graph Layout generator
with_mds	Uses a multidimensional scaling model, based on a distance matrix of nodes, to lay out the graph
sugiyama	Uses the Sugiyama algorithm, which minimizes edge crossings

To obtain a quick visualization of the simplified network of co-authors of legislative bills, we can use

```
plot(CSG)
```

This produces the graph depicted in Figure 4.1A. Running

```
tkplot(CSG)
```

instead opens up a new, interactive window, as depicted in Figure 4.1A. Either output depicts one group of tightly connected individuals, another group of four individuals connected to one in the first group, and one individual connected to one in the first group. **If what you see looks like a scatterplot matrix rather than a network graph, you forgot to create the graph object using the graph_from_data_frame() command.**

Try a few different layouts, though, and check that what they do communicate is accurate. For example, we can use

```
plot(CSG, layout=layout_as_tree(CSG))
```

and

```
plot(CSG, layout=layout_with_gem(CSG))
```

to produce the graph layouts depicted in Figures 4.2A and 4.2B, respectively. Both layouts appear to elevate one of the legislators. The Reingold-Tilford layout gives prominence to BF1 (Bill Flores), who simply happens to be the first legislator in the data set. The Gem layout somewhat emphasizes RN (Randy Neugebauer). While he cosponsored two of the three bills in the data set, so too did SP2 (Steven Palazzo). In fact, from Figure 4.1, we see that both RN and SP2 seem to occupy privileged positions. And through our later analyses of ego metrics, we will see that it is SP2 who is best positioned. So, elevating BF1 and RN in Figure 4.2A and Figure 4.2B, respectively, is misleading. In this case, we would prefer our original Kamada-Kawai layout from Figure 4.1, which also was more readable. Keep in mind, though, that as with NodeXL, we can lay out the graph repeatedly by rerunning the lines of code that generated it or by rerunning the layout algorithm in the *Tk* plot window.

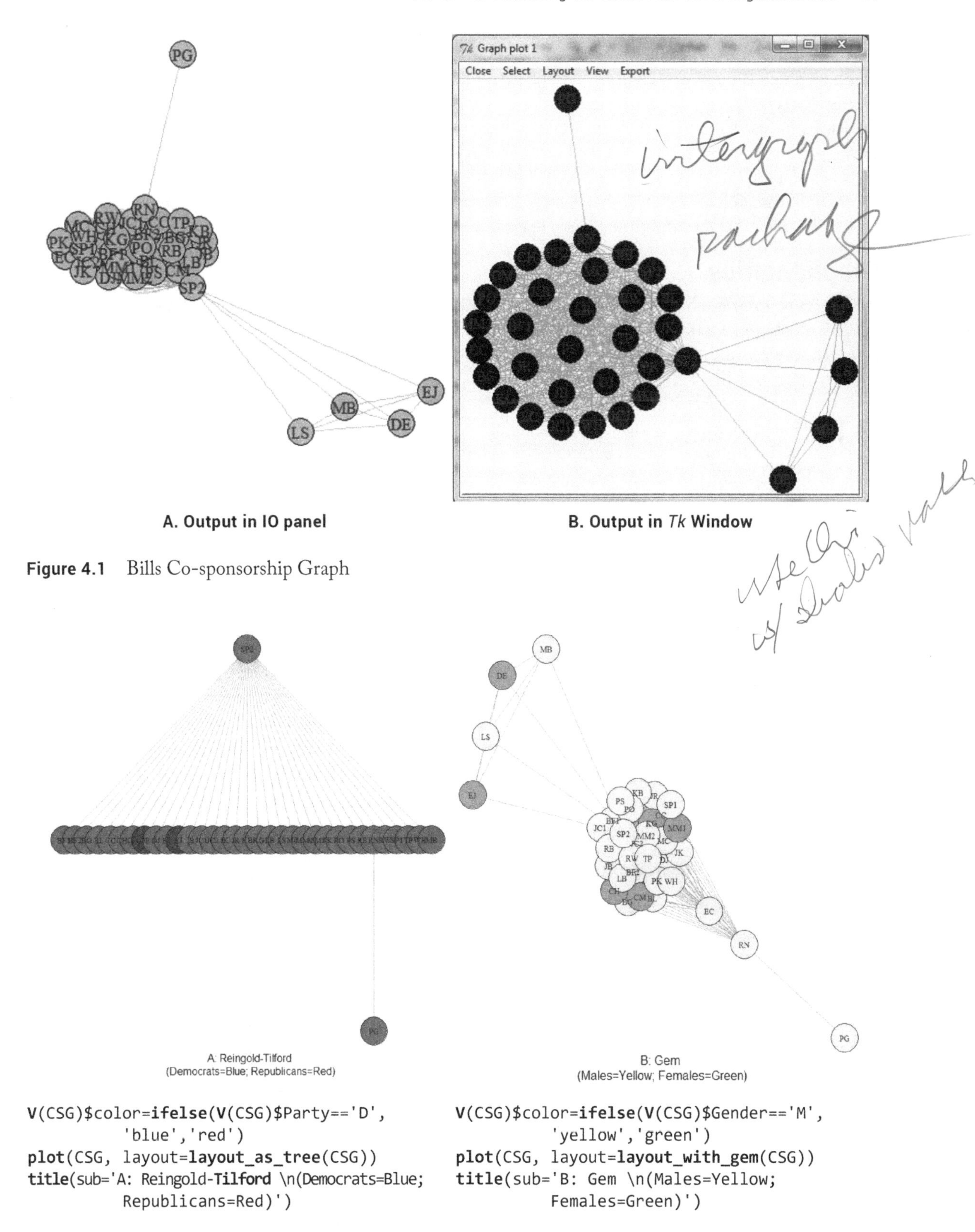

Figure 4.1 Bills Co-sponsorship Graph


```
V(CSG)$color=ifelse(V(CSG)$Party=='D',
          'blue','red')
plot(CSG, layout=layout_as_tree(CSG))
title(sub='A: Reingold-Tilford \n(Democrats=Blue;
          Republicans=Red)')
```

```
V(CSG)$color=ifelse(V(CSG)$Gender=='M',
          'yellow','green')
plot(CSG, layout=layout_with_gem(CSG))
title(sub='B: Gem \n(Males=Yellow;
          Females=Green)')
```

Figure 4.2 Legislators' Networks and Associated Code

We associated node color with a vertex attribute through the V() function. This allows us to create a new graph attribute (i.e., $color). To produce the graph in Figure 4.2A, we set values of this attribute to depend on the legislators' party affiliation—that is, values of the Party column that the CSG graph frame obtained from the legislators.csv file. To produce the graph in Figure 4.2B, we set values of the $color attribute to depend on the legislators' gender (i.e., values of the Gender column from the legislators.csv file). Note that the V() needs to precede the plot() in order for the plot() to know what colors to use. We conclude the batch with the title() command. Instead of using the "main=" argument that we used in Chapter 3, we use the "sub=" argument. This places our title at the bottom of the chart, instead of at the top.

Graph Metrics

We begin by examining igraph functions that provide us with the basic dimensions of the graph. We can get the number of vertices with the ***vcount(GraphFrame)*** function. We can get a count of the edges with ***ecount(GraphFrame)***. As with NodeXL, we also can obtain graph density with the ***graph.density(GraphFrame)*** function. This function accepts the "loops=" boolean argument, which permits us to determine the density of the network, with or without self-ties.

The ***diameter(GraphFrame)*** provides the longest geodesic distance on the graph. The function accepts an "unconnected=" argument, which permits us to determine how unconnected components should be handled. If set to TRUE, diameter() of the largest connected component will be returned; if FALSE, diameter() will be set to the number of vertices plus 1. The ***farthest.nodes(GraphFrame)*** returns the vertex numbers connected by the diameter. If many are found with the same diameter, R returns the first such path.

Besides the above metrics that parallel those offered by NodeXL, R provides several more. On directed graphs, we can determine the level of reciprocity in the graph with the ***reciprocity(GraphFrame)*** function. This reciprocity metric is not meaningful on undirected graphs. On directed graphs with self-ties, we can direct R to ignore self-ties with the "ignore.loops=T" argument when computing reciprocity. We also can obtain a ***transitivity(GraphFrame)***.

Ego Metrics

Ego metrics available through R parallel the ones we see on NodeXL's Vertices sheet. We can obtain degree centrality using ***degree(GraphFrame)***, with the "mode='in'" or "mode='out'" argument for in- and out-degree on directed graphs. For undirected graphs, we leave off the "mode=" argument or, if used, it is ignored. We can compute closeness with the ***closeness(GraphFrame)*** function, which also will accept the "mode=" argument. Similarly, ***betweenness(GraphFrame)*** provides a vector of betweenness centrality metrics and the ***evcent(GraphFrame)*** a vector of eigenvector centrality metrics for each vertex.

Burt's [6] constraint metric can be obtained using ***constraint(GraphFrame)***. This metric indicates the extent to which each node is constrained by other nodes in the graph or operates as a structural hole. High values suggest high constraint; low values indicate a node that occupies a structural hole, bridging sections of the network.

To obtain the shortest—or geodesic—distance between every pair of vertices in our network, we use the ***shortest.paths(GraphFrame)*** function. Unlike the centrality and constraint functions, which produce vector outputs, shortest.paths() produces an adjacency matrix. We can determine which vertices are "reachable" from a specified vertex in the graph with the ***subcomponent(GraphFrame, VertexID)*** function. For directed graphs, we can specify whether we wish in- or out-reachability to/from the vertex using "mode=" followed by "in" or "out".

Tutorial 4.3. Obtaining Metrics on the Legislative Bills Network

To obtain the number of vertices in the legislative bills network, we use

```
vcount(CSG)
```

This tells us we have 35 vertices or legislators in the data set. To obtain a count of the edges, we use

```
ecount(CSG)
```

This indicates that our network has 446 edges or ties. To obtain the density of the network, we use

```
graph.density(CSG)
```

This produces a density measure of ~0.75. Since our graph does not contain loops, we can omit the "loops=" argument. To determine the maximum geodesic distance on our network, we use

```
diameter(CSG)
```

This tells us that the maximum geodesic distance is 3. Using

```
farthest.nodes(CSG)
```

tells us this diameter is constituted by nodes DE (Donna Edwards) and PG (Paul Gosar), and also reminds us that the geodesic distance between these nodes is 3. In fact, in Figure 4.1 we observe four such paths with a geodesic distance of 3; later analyses of ego networks will confirm this observation.

Because CSG is an undirected graph,

```
reciprocity(CSG)
```

is a perfect 1, but not meaningful. Running

```
transitivity(CSG)
```

tells us that transitivity is high (~0.99) in our graph of legislators.

Next, we look at ego metrics within our graph. For our undirected graph,

```
degree(CSG)
```

produces the following vector, as will **degree**(CSG, mode='in') or **degree**(CSG, mode='out').

```
## BF1 BF2  BG  BL  CC  CH  CM  DE  DJ  EC  EJ  JB JC1 JC2  JK  JR  KB  KG
##  29  29  29  29  29  29  29   4  29  29   4  29  29  29  29  29  29  29
##  LB  LS  MC MM1 MM2  PK  PO  PS  RB  RN  RW SP1 SP2  TP  WH  MB  PG
##  29   4  29  29  29  29  29  29  29  30  29  29  33  29  29   4   1
```

The

```
evcent(CSG)
```

command provides more than just the vector of centrality metrics, though—see the following output. We can limit the output using

```
evcent(CSG)$vector
```

which lets R know that we are interested only in the $vector portion of the output. (See the "Collating Metrics for Further Analyses" insert.)

```
##        BF1        BF2         BG         BL         CC         CH
## 0.99487411 0.99487411 0.99487411 0.99487411 0.99487411 0.99487411
##         CM         DE         DJ         EC         EJ         JB
## 0.99487411 0.03845222 0.99487411 0.99487411 0.03845222 0.99487411
##        JC1        JC2         JK         JR         KB         KG
## 0.99487411 0.99487411 0.99487411 0.99487411 0.99487411 0.99487411
##         LB         LS         MC        MM1        MM2         PK
## 0.99487411 0.03845222 0.99487411 0.99487411 0.99487411 0.99487411
##         PO         PS         RB         RN         RW        SP1
## 0.99487411 0.99487411 0.99487411 0.99601847 0.99487411 0.99487411
##        SP2         TP         WH         MB         PG
## 1.00000000 0.99487411 0.99487411 0.03845222 0.03433800
```

As we saw with NodeXL, we also can use this output in our visualization. For example, the code below resizes the vertices relative to their eigenvector centrality—specifically, (eigenvector centrality*5)$^{1.5}$, producing the output in Figure 4.3. (I like using power, rather than straight multiplicative, functions to emphasize central nodes better.)

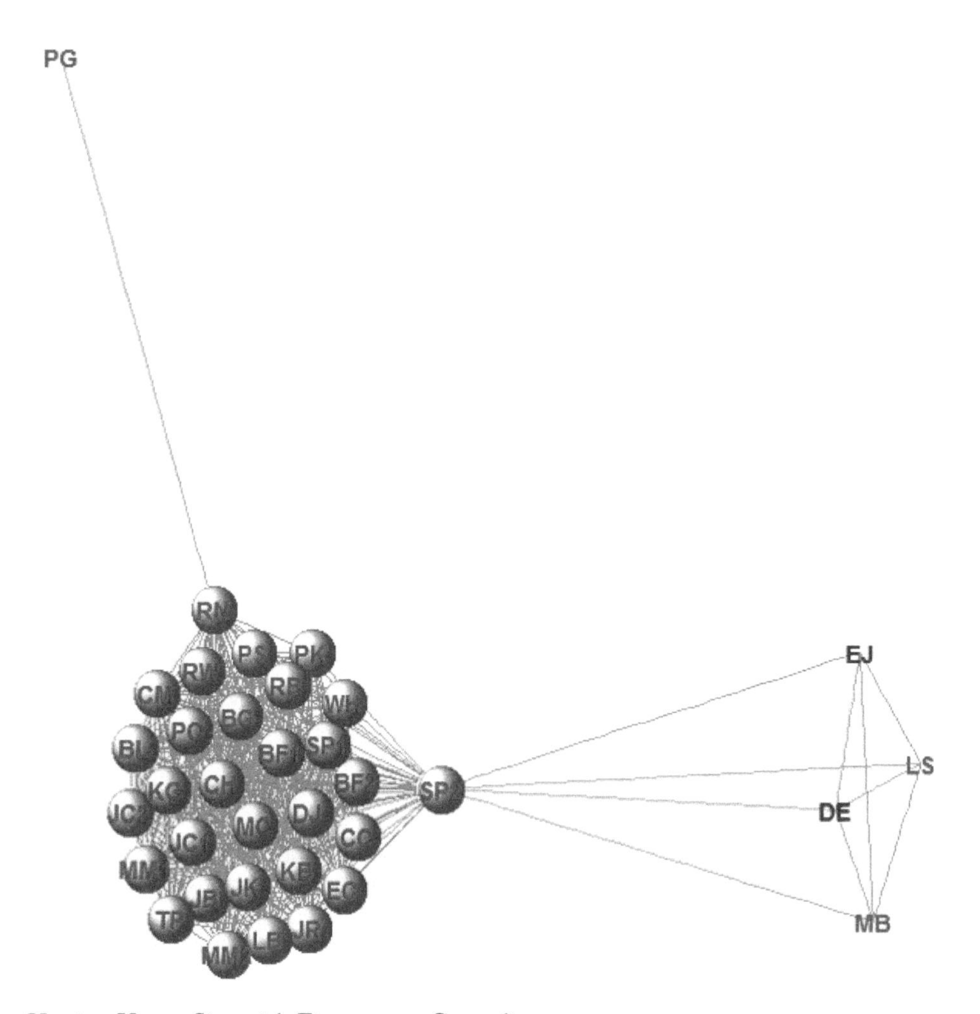

Figure 4.3 Varying Vertex Size with Eigenvector Centrality

```
plot(CSG, vertex.size=evcent(CSG)$vector*5^1.5, vertex.shape='sphere',
    vertex.label.color=ifelse(V(CSG)$Party=='D','blue','red'),
    vertex.color='white', vertex.label.family='sans',
    vertex.label.cex=.95, vertex.label.font=2, margin=-.35)
```

Running

```
constraint(CSG)
```

reveals the most highly constrained legislator to be PG, with a constraint of 1.00; the least constrained is SP2, with a constraint score of ~0.11. To obtain an adjacency matrix of the shortest paths between every node pair, we can run

```
shortest.paths(CSG)
```

```
    BF1 BF2 BG BL CC CH CM DE DJ EC EJ JB JC1 JC2 JK JR KB KG LB LS MB MC MM1 MM2 PG PK PO PS RB RN RW SP1 SP2 TP WH
BF1   0   1  1  1  1  1  1  2  1  1  2  1   1   1  1  1  1  1  1  2  2  1   1   1  2  1  1  1  1  1  1   1   1  1  1
BF2   1   0  1  1  1  1  1  2  1  1  2  1   1   1  1  1  1  1  1  2  2  1   1   1  2  1  1  1  1  1  1   1   1  1  1
BG    1   1  0  1  1  1  1  2  1  1  2  1   1   1  1  1  1  1  1  2  2  1   1   1  2  1  1  1  1  1  1   1   1  1  1
BL    1   1  1  0  1  1  1  2  1  1  2  1   1   1  1  1  1  1  1  2  2  1   1   1  2  1  1  1  1  1  1   1   1  1  1
CC    1   1  1  1  0  1  1  2  1  1  2  1   1   1  1  1  1  1  1  2  2  1   1   1  2  1  1  1  1  1  1   1   1  1  1
CH    1   1  1  1  1  0  1  2  1  1  2  1   1   1  1  1  1  1  1  2  2  1   1   1  2  1  1  1  1  1  1   1   1  1  1
CM    1   1  1  1  1  1  0  2  1  1  2  1   1   1  1  1  1  1  1  2  2  1   1   1  2  1  1  1  1  1  1   1   1  1  1
DE    2   2  2  2  2  2  2  0  2  2  1  2   2   2  2  2  2  2  2  1  1  2   2   2  3  2  2  2  2  2  2   2   1  2  2
DJ    1   1  1  1  1  1  1  2  0  1  2  1   1   1  1  1  1  1  1  2  2  1   1   1  2  1  1  1  1  1  1   1   1  1  1
EC    1   1  1  1  1  1  1  2  1  0  2  1   1   1  1  1  1  1  1  2  2  1   1   1  2  1  1  1  1  1  1   1   1  1  1
EJ    2   2  2  2  2  2  2  1  2  2  0  2   2   2  2  2  2  2  2  1  1  2   2   2  3  2  2  2  2  2  2   2   1  2  2
JB    1   1  1  1  1  1  1  2  1  1  2  0   1   1  1  1  1  1  1  2  2  1   1   1  2  1  1  1  1  1  1   1   1  1  1
JC1   1   1  1  1  1  1  1  2  1  1  2  1   0   1  1  1  1  1  1  2  2  1   1   1  2  1  1  1  1  1  1   1   1  1  1
JC2   1   1  1  1  1  1  1  2  1  1  2  1   1   0  1  1  1  1  1  2  2  1   1   1  2  1  1  1  1  1  1   1   1  1  1
JK    1   1  1  1  1  1  1  2  1  1  2  1   1   1  0  1  1  1  1  2  2  1   1   1  2  1  1  1  1  1  1   1   1  1  1
JR    1   1  1  1  1  1  1  2  1  1  2  1   1   1  1  0  1  1  1  2  2  1   1   1  2  1  1  1  1  1  1   1   1  1  1
KB    1   1  1  1  1  1  1  2  1  1  2  1   1   1  1  1  0  1  1  2  2  1   1   1  2  1  1  1  1  1  1   1   1  1  1
KG    1   1  1  1  1  1  1  2  1  1  2  1   1   1  1  1  1  0  1  2  2  1   1   1  2  1  1  1  1  1  1   1   1  1  1
LB    1   1  1  1  1  1  1  2  1  1  2  1   1   1  1  1  1  1  0  2  2  1   1   1  2  1  1  1  1  1  1   1   1  1  1
LS    2   2  2  2  2  2  2  1  2  2  1  2   2   2  2  2  2  2  2  0  1  2   2   2  3  2  2  2  2  2  2   2   1  2  2
MB    2   2  2  2  2  2  2  1  2  2  1  2   2   2  2  2  2  2  2  1  0  2   2   2  3  2  2  2  2  2  2   2   1  2  2
MC    1   1  1  1  1  1  1  2  1  1  2  1   1   1  1  1  1  1  1  2  2  0   1   1  2  1  1  1  1  1  1   1   1  1  1
MM1   1   1  1  1  1  1  1  2  1  1  2  1   1   1  1  1  1  1  1  2  2  1   0   1  2  1  1  1  1  1  1   1   1  1  1
MM2   1   1  1  1  1  1  1  2  1  1  2  1   1   1  1  1  1  1  1  2  2  1   1   0  2  1  1  1  1  1  1   1   1  1  1
PG    2   2  2  2  2  2  2  3  2  2  3  2   2   2  2  2  2  2  2  3  3  2   2   2  0  2  2  2  2  1  2   2   2  2  2
PK    1   1  1  1  1  1  1  2  1  1  2  1   1   1  1  1  1  1  1  2  2  1   1   1  2  0  1  1  1  1  1   1   1  1  1
PO    1   1  1  1  1  1  1  2  1  1  2  1   1   1  1  1  1  1  1  2  2  1   1   1  2  1  0  1  1  1  1   1   1  1  1
PS    1   1  1  1  1  1  1  2  1  1  2  1   1   1  1  1  1  1  1  2  2  1   1   1  2  1  1  0  1  1  1   1   1  1  1
RB    1   1  1  1  1  1  1  2  1  1  2  1   1   1  1  1  1  1  1  2  2  1   1   1  2  1  1  1  0  1  1   1   1  1  1
RN    1   1  1  1  1  1  1  2  1  1  2  1   1   1  1  1  1  1  1  2  2  1   1   1  1  1  1  1  1  0  1   1   1  1  1
RW    1   1  1  1  1  1  1  2  1  1  2  1   1   1  1  1  1  1  1  2  2  1   1   1  2  1  1  1  1  1  0   1   1  1  1
SP1   1   1  1  1  1  1  1  2  1  1  2  1   1   1  1  1  1  1  1  2  2  1   1   1  2  1  1  1  1  1  1   0   1  1  1
SP2   1   1  1  1  1  1  1  1  1  1  1  1   1   1  1  1  1  1  1  1  1  1   1   1  2  1  1  1  1  1  1   1   0  1  1
TP    1   1  1  1  1  1  1  2  1  1  2  1   1   1  1  1  1  1  1  2  2  1   1   1  2  1  1  1  1  1  1   1   1  0  1
WH    1   1  1  1  1  1  1  2  1  1  2  1   1   1  1  1  1  1  1  2  2  1   1   1  2  1  1  1  1  1  1   1   1  1  0
```

This tells us that BF1 (Bill Flores) is one step away from everyone, except from DE (Donna Edwards), EJ (Eddie Johnson), LS (Lamar Smith), MB (Mo Brooks), and PG (Paul Gosar), from whom he is two steps removed. The greatest geodesic distance in the graph is three steps, confirming what we saw earlier with *farthest.nodes(CSG)*. But we see here that there are four paths of this diameter: PG to DE, PG to EJ (Eddie Johnson), PG to LS, and PG to MB. In other

Collating Metrics for Further Analyses

In order to analyze our ego metrics further, it is helpful to collate the different metrics into a single data frame. To do so, we can bind together the columns of vector outputs generated by the individual functions. The code below collates our degree, betweenness, and eigenvector centrality, and constraint metrics into a single data frame named CSGMetrics. After collating these metrics, we relabel the columns to be more accessible, and write it out to a file.

```
CSGMetrics=data.frame(cbind(degree(CSG)))
CSGMetrics=cbind(CSGMetrics, data.frame(cbind(betweenness(CSG))))
CSGMetrics=cbind(CSGMetrics, data.frame(cbind(evcent(CSG)$vector)))
CSGMetrics=cbind(CSGMetrics, data.frame(cbind(constraint(CSG))))
colnames(CSGMetrics)=c('Degree','Betweenness','Eigenvector','Constraint')
write.csv(CSGMetrics,'BillMetrics.csv',header=T)
```

words, the paths from the uppermost node in Figure 4.1 to any of the four nodes in the bottom right group constitute the graph's diameter.

We ascertain the reachability for Bill Flores (id=1 from results of the V() or get.vertex.attribute() functions from earlier in the chapter), we can use

```
subcomponent(CSG, 1)
```

For Donna Edwards (id=8 from V() function earlier in the chapter), we can use

```
subcomponent(CSG, 8)
```

Conclusion

As we have seen, R's igraph offers a range of metrics not available with NodeXL. Initially, it may seem that the network visualizations created in R cannot approach the sophistication and aesthetics of those created in NodeXL. As we gain greater command of R, though, this will cease to be the case. Experiment with controlling the different graph attributes in the plot() function. We will see a complete list of these in Chapter 6.

Exercise: Analyzing a Committee's E-mail Communications

The *CommitteeEMail.csv* file documents 129 email communications for a particular committee assignment over a three-month period and involving a total of 29 people. The file provides you with information on who each e-mail was **From**, whom the e-mail was directed **To**, and the **Date** of the e-mail. The *Members.csv* file notes the **Discipline** and **Role** of each **Person** participating in the communications. Disciplines are *BUS*iness or *NON*business. Roles include *F*aculty, *S*taff, and *A*dministrator. Complete the following tasks to analyze the network underlying the email communications.

1. Using two different algorithms, provide two visualizations of the network needed to complete the committee's tasks. Color code for discipline in one and for role in the other.
2. Obtain graph density and reciprocity metrics.
3. Obtain degree, closeness, betweenness, and eigenvector centrality for each graph ego.
4. Provide a "key actor" analysis:
   - Develop a scatterplot of actors' betweenness and eigenvector centrality.
   - Develop a scatterplot matrix of actors' degree, closeness, betweenness, and eigenvector centrality.

Comment on the results of your analysis. Be sure to use appropriate titles for your graphical displays. Copy all your code and output into a Word file named with your first and last name.

Works Cited

1. Supowit, K.J., and E.M. Reingold, "The Complexity of Drawing Trees Nicely." *Acta Informatica*, 18(4; 1983): 377–92.
2. Davidson, R., and D. Harel, "Drawing Graphs Nicely Using Simulated Annealing." *ACM Transactions on Graphics (TOG)*, 15(4; 1996): 301–31.
3. Martin, S., W.M. Brown, and B.N. Wylie, *DrL: Distributed Recursive (Graph) Layout*. Albuquerque, NM: Sandia National Laboratories, 2007.
4. Fruchterman, T.M., and E.M. Reingold, "Graph Drawing by Force-Directed Placement." *Software: Practice and Experience*, 21(11, 1991): 1129–64.

5. Frick, A., A. Ludwig, and H. Mehldau, "A Fast Adaptive Layout Algorithm for Undirected Graphs," in *Proceedings of the DIMACS International Workshop on Graph Drawing*, 388–403. Princeton, NJ: Springer-Verlag, 1995.

6. Burt, R.S., *Structural Holes: The Social Structure of Competition*. Cambridge, MA: Harvard University Press, 1995.

CHAPTER 5

Advanced SNA Concepts

> **Learning Objectives**
>
> The purpose of this chapter is to familiarize you with:
>
> 1. concepts underlying subgroup analyses;
> 2. visualizing subgroups;
> 3. subgroup metrics;
> 4. distributional properties of networks; and
> 5. harvesting social media data.

In Chapter 1, we considered shoppers' dismay at the absence of the popular Star Wars character Rey from the lineup of toys available for the 2015 holiday season. We saw that if Disney and Hasbro had been monitoring social media feeds assiduously, the conversation around the *#WhereIsRey* hashtag could have prompted a more timely response. In fact, neither Hasbro nor Disney participated in the conversation. When Hasbro did release a statement in January 2016, it did so to *Entertainment Weekly* [2]. How could Disney and Hasbro have responded differently?

In Chapter 1, Figure 1.3 depicted the social networks of fans participating in the *#WhereIsRey* conversation. We noted that Disney, Hasbro, or other retail organizations could have used social network analysis to change the conversation. In Figure 5.1, we present two graphs of the social network surrounding the *#WhereIsRey* conversation. Let us consider the insights offered by these graphs and how they could inform the strategic action taken by the retail and entertainment companies. Figure 5.1A highlights the position of Disney and Hasbro in the conversation. Our first observation is the extremely marginal position of these two companies. Neither company participated in the conversation, thereby foregoing the opportunity to have their voice heard on the issue and shape the conversation. Second, only a handful of fans referred explicitly to the two companies. This represents a missed opportunity for the companies to enhance brand recognition and reputation within the community. Figure 5.1A depicts the profile pictures of the ten (actually eleven, because of a tie) individuals with the highest in-degree centrality. Presumably these are the ten individuals to whom other fans pay the most attention. One option available to Hasbro and/or Disney is to attempt to change the conversation by targeting these ten individuals and co-opting them to disseminate a message more favorable to the companies—the social media equivalent of an emergency phone tree. But how do we know that the ten/eleven individuals are sufficient? Do we need to reach out to all of them?

A second approach is for us to identify the distinct communities or cliques—or subgroups—within our network. We then can identify the individual most central to each of those cliques. This is what we see in Figure 5.1B. We see twenty, relatively well-contained cliques containing at least four members. Note that Disney does not show up because the company was referenced by only a single fan. Most of these cliques have a well-defined central player, on whom we can rely to disseminate a message—if persuaded of its value. This provides us with better guidance for constructing our ***emergency digital communication tree*** than simply targeting the individuals most central to the entire network. This is one example of a use case for subgroup analyses. Below, we examine the different types of subgroup analyses. We then explore how we can visualize and quantify subgroups in NodeXL.

Network data are subject to certain anomalies that preclude conventional statistical analyses. We briefly consider these anomalies. Of course, all our analyses abilities would be worth very little if we were unable to

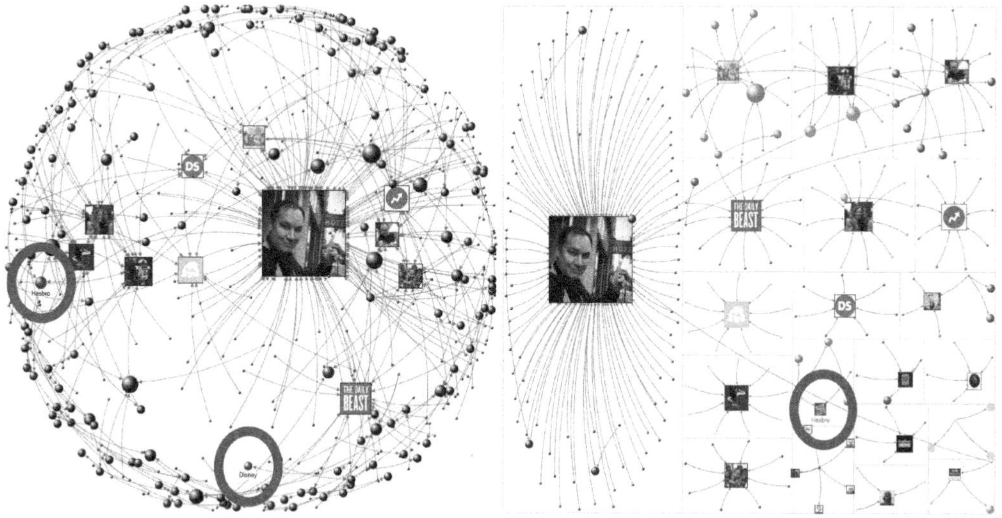

A. Unpartitioned Network

B. Partitioned Communities of 4+ Members

Figure 5.1 The *#WhereIsRey* Social Network

harvest social media data. The latter part of this chapter therefore will examine how we can use NodeXL to import data—profiles and posts—from Twitter and Facebook.

What Is Subgroup Analysis?

Based on their interaction patterns, social networks can organize themselves into subgroups or cliques. Subgroup analysis can help us determine the extent to which homophily has influenced tie formation and/or tie deletion. When homophily relates to demographics such as gender, age, race, religion, education, social class, or occupation, it is easily understood. Contextual commonalities such as geographic location, family ties, and organizational membership facilitate such forms of homophily [3]. Sometimes the nature of the homophily can be opaque. This is especially true when homophily relates to shared attitudes or ideology.

We can detect the subgroups underlying social networks in one of two ways. The first approach—***attribute-based partitioning***—entails partitioning the network based on a specified node attribute. This approach enables us to visualize and quantify a specified basis of homophily—that is, some specific demographic attribute or collection of attributes that constitute fault lines across which individuals are less likely to affiliate. For example, partitioning a network based on gender would permit us to visualize homophily in the density of ties among people of the same gender versus the density of ties among people of different genders.

The second approach, which applies ***clustering*** or ***community detection*** algorithms, is to discover the natural fault lines in the network—that is, boundaries across which no (or relatively few) ties exist and within which ties are relatively dense. The more stringent variation of this approach looks for distinct ***connected components*** (i.e., fault lines across which *no* ties exist). The second variant approach permits few ties across fault lines and highlights cliques and ***small-worlds*** (i.e., subgroups that are not perfectly interconnected but have a high clustering coefficient and low geodesic distance) [4].

Every SNA tool typically makes available several different ***clustering algorithms***. These algorithms vary in their partitioning approach and the speed with which they work. Consequently, algorithms such as the Girvan-Newman are not recommended for analyzing large networks. Nodes within a cluster are considered to be ***structurally-equivalent*** (i.e., possessing similar patterns of ties). This form of subgroup analysis, by itself, sheds little light on the nature of the fault lines or why the cliques or small-worlds exist.

In NodeXL, we identify subgroups by selecting the Groups button on the Analysis group on the **NodeXL Tab**. Then, depending on the subgroup analysis approach we wish to take, we select the Group by Vertex

Attribute (for attribute-based analysis), Group by Connected Component (for analysis of unconnected subgroups), or Group by Cluster (for discovering cliques or small-worlds) from the drop-down menu. For the last of these three options, NodeXL offers three clustering options: the Clauset-Newman-Moore algorithm, the Wakita-Tsurumi algorithm, and Girvan-Newman algorithm. Personally, I like to see how sensitive my graph is to different clustering algorithms. But keep in mind the speed constraints of the different algorithms, relative to your network size.

Once we have partitioned our network into subgroups, we compute graph and subgroup metrics and can visualize the subgroups. We now examine these SNA tasks.

Subgroup Metrics

Once we have identified groups via one of the three methods, we can obtain graph modularity and subgroup metrics. In Chapter 3, we defined ***modularity*** as the extent to which the network contains modules within which dense connections occur, but across which connections are sparse. Note that we cannot compute modularity until we have partitioned our network. Further, different network partitions yield different modularity values, providing a quick benchmark for which partitioning approach was the most meaningful.

For each subgroup, we also can compute several different metrics (e.g., density, geodesic distance). In fact, each subgroup functions as a distinct network. Therefore, most SNA metrics that can be computed for the entire graph can be computed for each subgroup.

Visualizing Subgroups

We can manipulate three aspects of the graph to optimize visualization of subgroups. First, in addition to using attribute information associated with vertices and edges as we did with analyses of the full graph, we also can use ***attribute information that describes groups***. For NodeXL, these attributes must be located on the VERTICES sheet. Second, we can ***display each group in its own box*** as depicted in Figure 5.1B. This enables us to quickly see which nodes cluster together. To so in NodeXL, select Layout Options from either the **Graph Pane** or from the Layout Options of the Graph group on the **NodeXL Tab**, as shown in Figure 5.2. Then, select the *Lay out each of the graph's groups in its own box* option, as depicted in Figure 5.3.

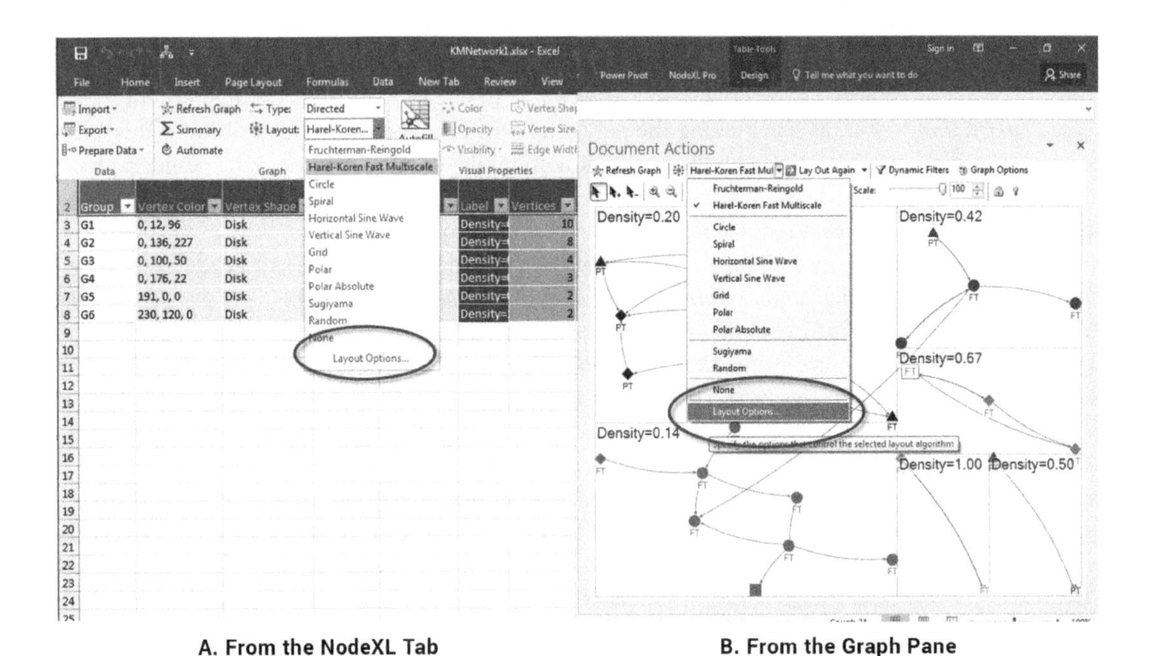

Figure 5.2 Setting Up the Subgroup Visual

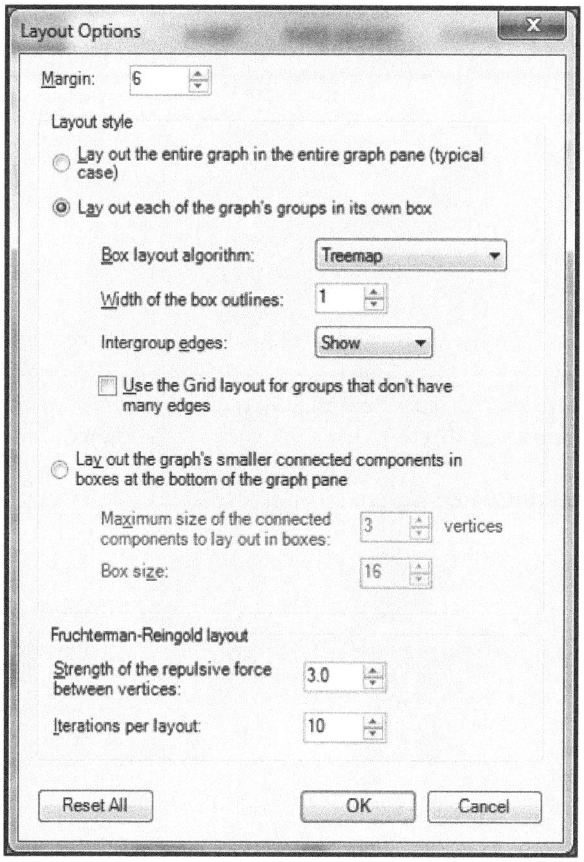

Figure 5.3 Selecting Layout Options

Third, once we have derived subgroup metrics, we can ***conditionally display specific subgroups*** relative to the value of a specific subgroup metric. This is done on the GROUPS sheet in NodeXL. We now can use different Excel formulas to relate the graph attributes to vertex or group attributes from the VERTICES or GROUPS sheets. See the "Some Excel Formulas for Setting Graph Attributes" insert.

Tutorial 5.1. What Explains the Fragmentation of Our Class Network?

We want to examine our first KM class recognition network (KMNetwork1.xlsx) for fault lines and the basis for fault lines. (Be careful that you are not filtering for any edge attributes right now [e.g., friendship ties] or node attributes.)

We have three demographic attributes—gender, status (full- versus part-time), and major. Let's begin with gender. To do so, we partition based on the node attribute—gender. In NodeXL, select the Groups button on the Analysis group on the **NodeXL Tab**, and then Group by Vertex Attribute from the drop-down menu. We select the Gender attribute and indicate that it is a categorical variable as depicted in Figure 5.4A. (We also could group by a continuous variable such as a vertex's degree centrality. To do so, we need to specify the break points for the different groups. See, for example, the groups specified in Figure 5.4B.)

Some Excel Formulas for Setting Graph Attributes

We can set the Size column on the VERTICES sheet to the number of times a vertex shows up in an edge using *=COUNTIFS(Edges!A:B,[@Vertex])*, We can set the shape of large nodes to a square and small nodes to a disk by setting the formula in the Shape column on the VERTICES sheet to *=IF([@Size]>20,5,2)*. Finally, we can display the vertex name for large nodes by setting the formula of the Label column to *=IF([@Shape]=5,[@Name],"")*. Remember to change the cell format from Text to General if the formula does not work.

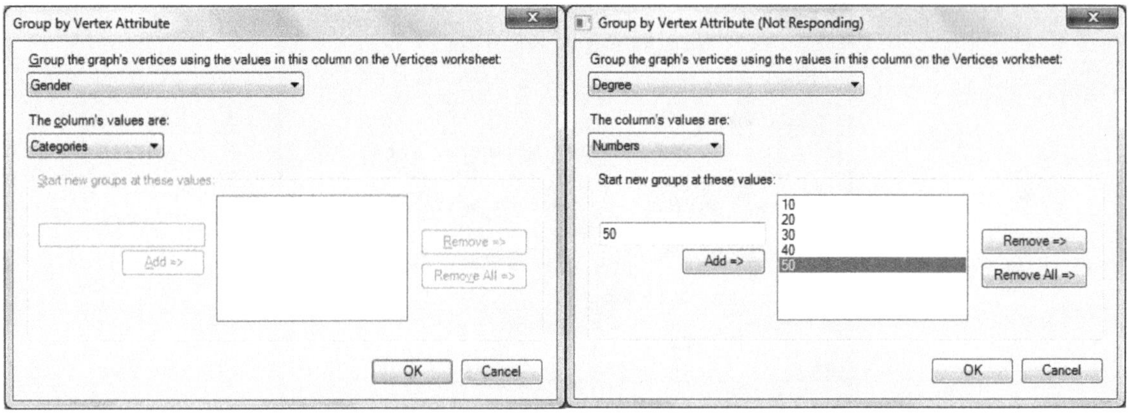

Group by Vertex Attribute

Group the graph's vertices using the values in this column on the Vertices worksheet:
Gender
The column's values are:
Categories
Start new groups at these values:
Add => Remove => Remove All =>
OK Cancel

Group by Vertex Attribute (Not Responding)

Group the graph's vertices using the values in this column on the Vertices worksheet:
Degree
The column's values are:
Numbers
Start new groups at these values:
50
Add =>
10
20
30
40
50
Remove => Remove All =>
OK Cancel

A. On a Categorical Variable **B. On a Continuous Variable**

Figure 5.4 Specifying Attribute-Based Groups

	A	B	C	D	E	F	K	L
1		Visual Properties				Labels	Graph Metrics	
2	Group	Vertex Color	Vertex Shape	Visibility	Collapsed?	Label	Vertices	Unique Edges
3	M	0, 12, 96	Disk			Male		
4	F	0, 136, 227	Disk			Female		

Figure 5.5 Population of GROUPS Sheet

After we click OK, we will see output to the GROUPS sheet as depicted in Figure 5.5. Note that I have added labels for each gender, but we have not as yet calculated group metrics.

Let's calculate graph modularity and the subgroup metrics. To do so, select Graph Metrics from the Analysis group of the **NodeXL Tab**. Then, select the options to display the *Overall graph* metrics and *Group metrics.* Note that if you had generated the *Overall graph* metrics before identifying subgroups, group modularity would not have been computed. You must redo the *Overall graph* metrics after having identified the subgroups in order to obtain the modularity coefficient associated with that particular grouping method. Graph modularity based on gender is a very low 0.072, suggesting gender plays little, if any, role in my class fault lines. We see the following metrics for each gender on the GROUPS sheet: number of vertices, number of edges, maximum and average geodesic distance, and graph density.

Let's repeat this process now for status. We should see modularity go up to 0.247, suggesting that full- and part-time status do account for fault lines in our class network. Somewhat counterintuitively, the subgroup density—seen on the GROUPS sheet—is higher for part-time students (0.225) than for full-time students (0.145).

Now, we repeat the process for major. Modularity here is comparable to modularity for the status-based partitioning (0.235). We see that the densest subgroup is our Accounting majors; MBAs and MS-MIT student subgroups are of comparable density at 0.187 and 0.191, respectively. Does this suggest to you which specific major is most responsible for the Majors fault line? Can you confirm your hunch?

Tutorial 5.2. How Do Students Tend to Aggregate?

For this tutorial, we once again will use the KMNetwork1.xlsx file. This time, we will focus on the friendship network, though. So let's begin by filtering the Friendship column on the EDGES sheet—excluding the 0 values and leaving only the 1s.

First, we want to see the distinct connected components. To do so, we select the Groups button, and then *Group by Connected Component* from the drop-down menu. Then, we can regenerate our graph and group metrics. Both the GROUPS and the OVERALL METRICS sheets tell us we have five distinct connected components—the five different groups identified on the GROUPS sheet and row 15 on the OVERALL METRICS sheet. Modularity is relatively high at 0.576. This is because one factor contributing to modularity—the connections across subgroups—essentially is zero. Graph density for the five subgroups ranges from a relatively low 0.106 for the largest group of twelve students to 1.000 for the smallest group of two.

Next, we look for naturally occurring clusters. We select the Groups button, and then *Group by Cluster* from the drop-down menu. Since we have a relatively small graph, we choose the Girvan-Newman from the three algorithms provided. This produces six subgroups. Rerunning the graph and group metrics tells us that network modularity based on this new partition is 0.589—the highest we have seen so far. This is because one of our larger subgroups of connected components from above has been broken out into two subgroups here, as depicted in Figure 5.6. Notice each subgroup appears in its own pane; the shape of each node still depicts the different majors, but all vertices within a subgroup have a distinct color; and each subgroup pane is labeled with the subgroup density, rounded to two decimal places.

How do we accomplish this? First, to situate each group in its own pane, we select Layout Options from either the Layout option of the Graph group on the **NodeXL Tab** or from the **Graph Pane**, as shown in Figure 5.2. Then, select the *Lay out each of the graph's groups in its own box* option, as depicted in Figure 5.3.

Second, we designate which vertex attributes are to be drawn from the VERTICES sheet versus the GROUPS sheet by selecting the Groups button on the **NodeXL Tab** Analysis group, and then Group Options from the drop-down menu. To set the shape of our nodes based on attributes on the VERTICES sheet and the colors based

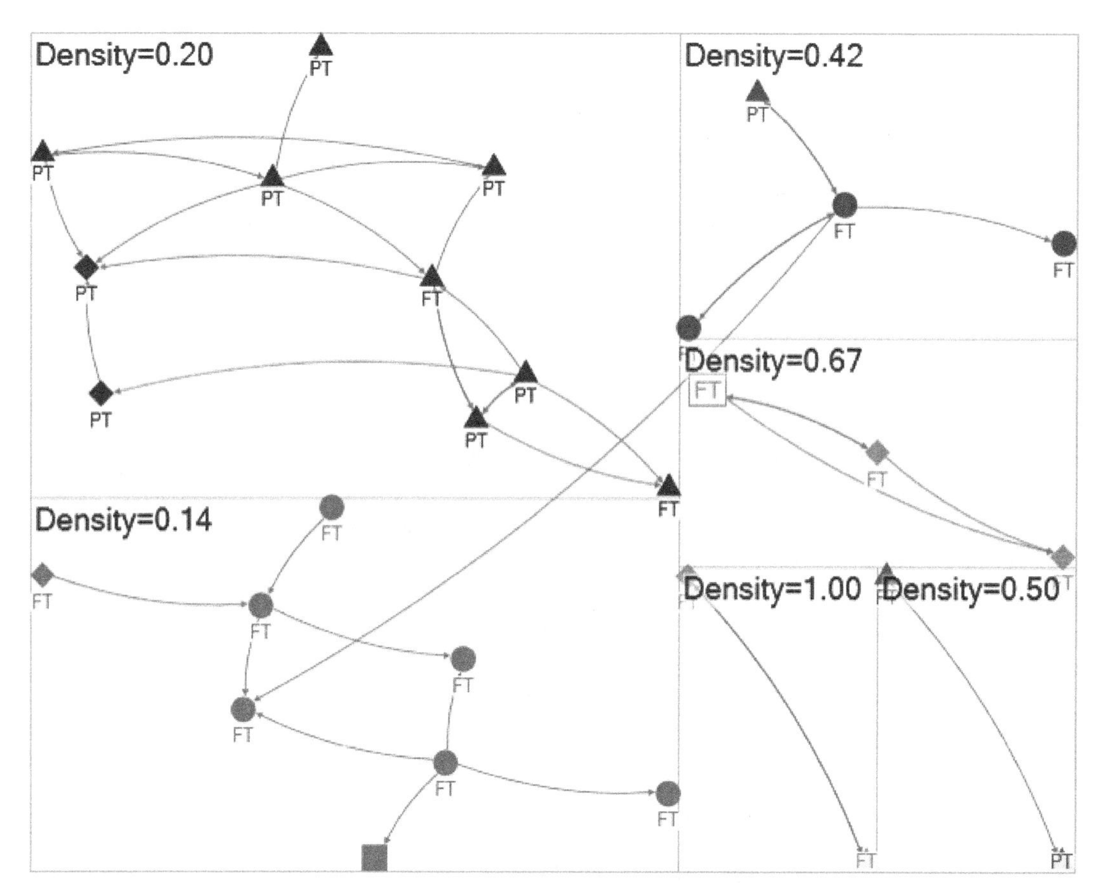

Figure 5.6 Cluster-Based Subgroup Analysis of the Friendship Network

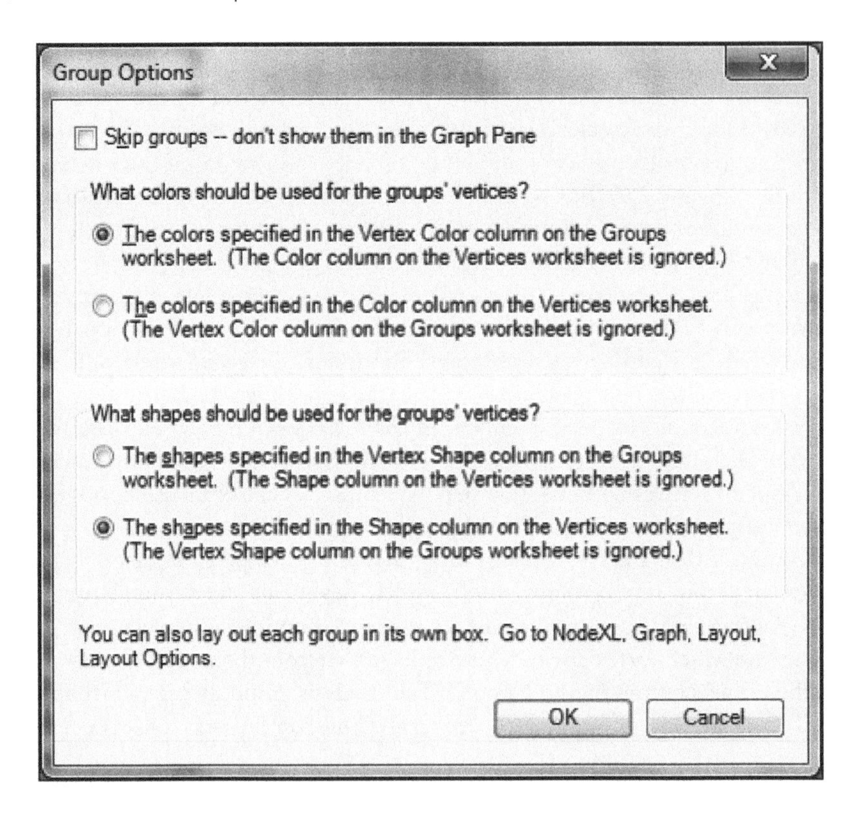

Figure 5.7 Determining Data Sources for Graph Attributes

on attributes from the GROUPS sheet, we leave the answer to the first question, "What colors should be used for the groups' vertices?," to the first option and change the answer to the second question, "What shapes should be used for the groups' vertices?," from the first option to the second, as shown in Figure 5.7.

Third, we can specify what the group labels are and how they are to be displayed. For our labels, we will use the formula:

="Density="&TEXT([@[Graph Density]],"0.00")

This formula concatenates the text "Density=" with the value of the graph density metric, formatted to two decimal places and formatted as text—so it can be concatenated easily with the "Density=" prefix. To position the label at the upper left of each pane (instead of dead center), select the Graph Options button from the **Graph Pane**, as shown in Figure 5.8A. Then, select the Other tab on the Graph Options dialog box, and then Labels, as in Figure 5.8B.

From here, we can set the font size and color for any of our labels, as depicted in Figure 5.9. We select the Font button associated with the *Group box labels* and set the font size to 12 and font style to boldface. We also can set the label position to the top left of the respective group boxes.

Now, click Refresh Graph from the **Graph Pane** or from the Graph group of the **NodeXL Tab**. This should produce the graph in Figure 5.6.

Distributional Properties of Network Data

Early social network analysts found that as network size increased, the distribution of ties was unlike the distribution of other social data. For example, in the school of 505 girls, Moreno found girls' rooming preferences were not uniformly or normally distributed; rather, most girls received few votes, and a few girls were extremely popular. In our data on the 1,034 directors on 100 boards, we notice a similar phenomenon in the distributions of board size and boards served in Figure 5.10. While the distribution of board size (or the number of directors firms have) approximates a normal distribution, the distribution of directors' firm ties (or the number of boards on which they serve) does not. As with tie distributions in other large networks, the distribution of the number of boards assumes a ***power law function***—a hockey-stick shape—also known as a ***long-tail distribution***.

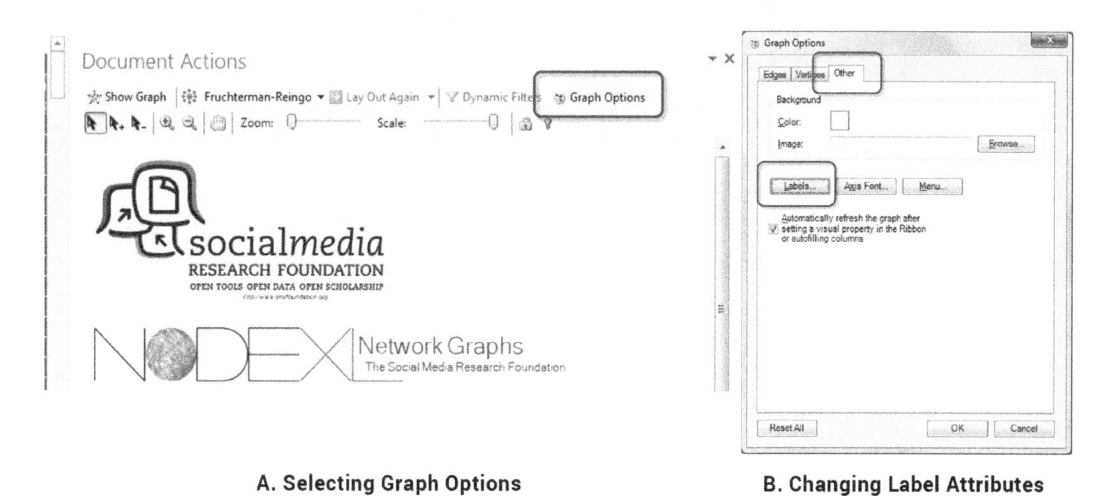

A. Selecting Graph Options

B. Changing Label Attributes

Figure 5.8 Setting Graph Options

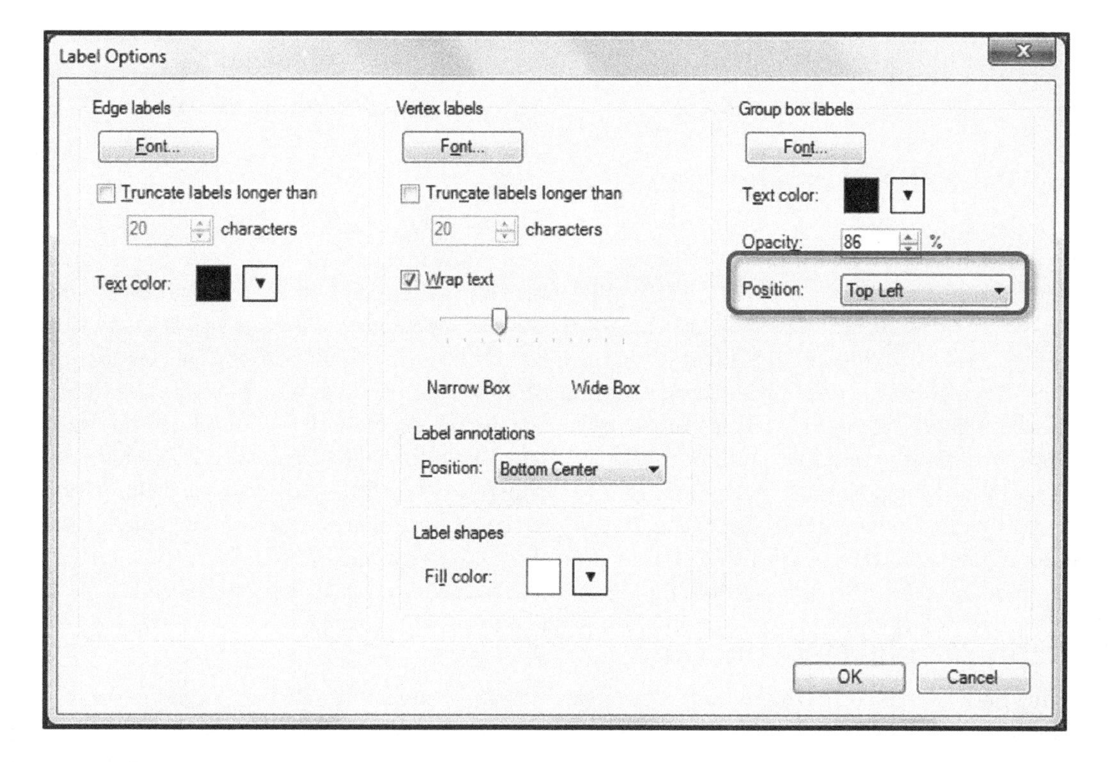

Figure 5.9 Setting Label Properties

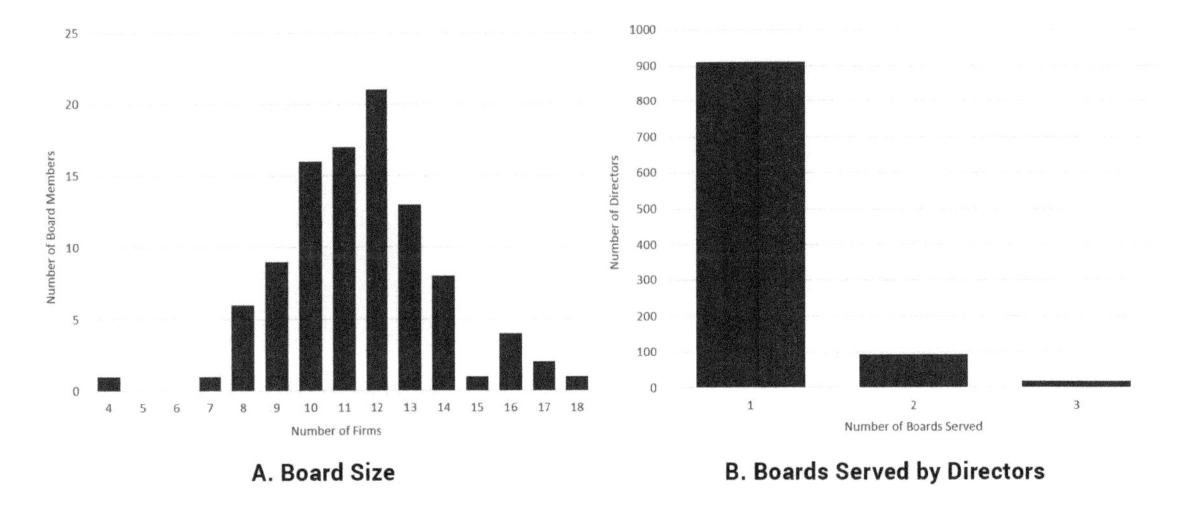

Figure 5.10 Distribution of Firms' Board Size and Directors' Boards Served

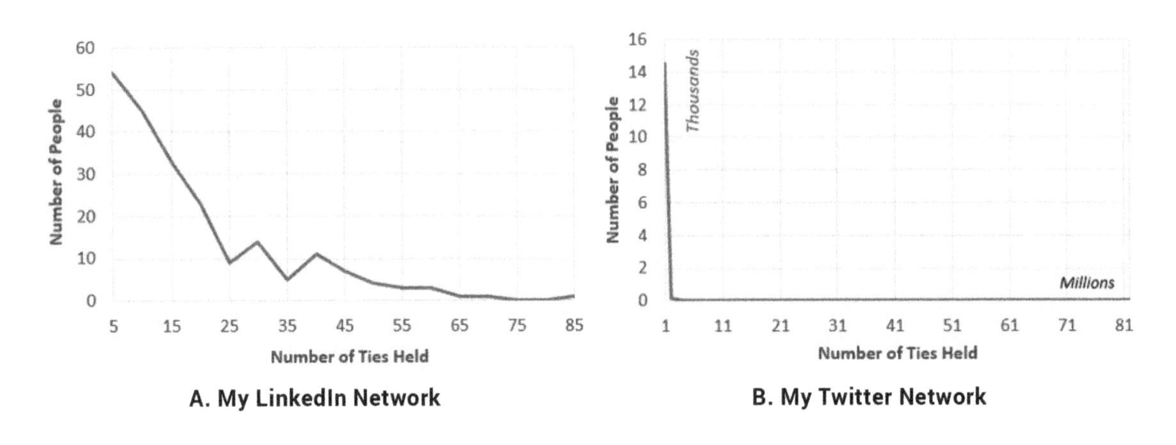

Figure 5.11 Distributions of Social Media Ties

Networks in which the distribution of ties follows a power law function are called ***scale-free networks*** [5]. This distribution characterizes the World Wide Web, where some sites/pages receive a great deal of attention, whereas others receive very little [5]. It also characterizes social media networks, as is visible in my LinkedIn and Twitter networks in Figure 5.11. What factors give rise to the hockey-stick distribution? Researchers have suggested that preferential attachment accounts for the distinctive distribution of ties in large networks. ***Preferential attachment*** refers to individuals' preference for affiliating with those rich in social ties—a sort of "the rich get richer" process applied to social ties. Other researchers have found that ***reciprocity*** mitigates scale-freeness in social networks and online communities [6]. Moreno noted little mutuality or reciprocity in the schoolgirls' rooming preferences, giving rise to the hockey-stick distribution of rooming preferences. Platforms that enforce reciprocity (e.g., LinkedIn) certainly have a less anomalous distribution. Notice the hockey stick is more pronounced in my Twitter network (in Figure 5.11B) than in my LinkedIn network in (Figure 5.11A).

Gathering Social Network Data

Collecting network data is fraught with decision points [7]. How should we select the nodes to study? What qualifies as a tie? How do we know a tie exists between two nodes? We briefly consider these generic issues that social network researchers face. We then see how NodeXL permits us to harvest social network data from social media.

Authorizing NodeXL to Harvest Twitter Data

Harvesting Twitter data requires that you have a Twitter account. So, if you do not already have one, begin by setting up an account. Then, when you first attempt to import Twitter data, select:

> I have a Twitter account, but I have not yet authorized NodeXL to use my account to import Twitter networks. Take me to Twitter's authorization Web page.

NodeXL will walk you through the authorization process, opening up Twitter in your web browser, and prompting you to supply the resulting Twitter authorization PIN, as below.

You can revoke access to any application at any time from the Applications tab (http://www.twitter.com/settings/applications) of your Settings page, where you will see

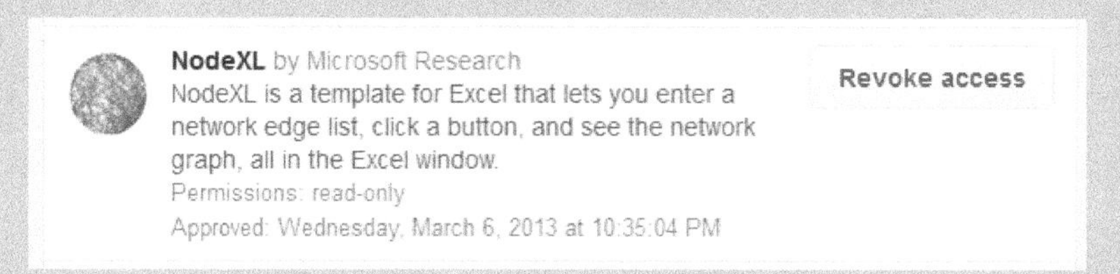

By authorizing an application, you continue to operate under Twitter's Terms of Service (http://www.twitter.com/tos). In particular, some usage information will be shared back with Twitter. For more, see http://www.twitter.com/privacy.

Answers to questions of how to select nodes and ties are driven by what the analyst hopes to accomplish. For example, the researchers who wished to study the effects of assortative mating (homophily in marriage/partnership ties) on furthering societal income disparities [8] clearly needed to focus on married couples. As such, both the node (an individual who got married) and the tie (marriage) were dictated by the research question.

How do we know a tie exists? Sometimes we can use archival data such as marriage records or e-mails. At other times, we ask. Here, too, we have a couple of decision points. First, how do we frame the question (i.e., the ***network stem***) about the tie? In his research, Moreno preferred stem questions for eliciting relationship preferences be behavioral rather than affective. An example of a behavioral question is: Whom would you prefer to dine/room with? An example of an affective question is: Who do you like? The contextualization of the behavioral question makes it more tangible, easier to respond to, and less susceptible to social desirability response biases on the part of the respondent. Second, how do we ***elicit a tie***? Do we require respondents to engage in free-recall to supply a prefixed number of ties? Or do we provide respondents with a roster of all possible ties and have them indicate members of that roster that fulfill the condition stated in the network stem? Again, each approach has its merits. Free-recall is less time-consuming, especially in case of large networks. However, the roster approach permits a more comprehensive mapping of a network space.

Twitter Search Operators*

Operator	Finds tweets...
twitter search	containing both "twitter" and "search". This is the default operator.
"happy hour"	containing the exact phrase "happy hour".
love OR hate	containing either "love" or "hate" (or both).
beer -root	containing "beer" but not "root".
#haiku	containing the hashtag "haiku".
from:alexiskold	sent from person "alexiskold".
to:techcrunch	sent to person "techcrunch".
@mashable	referencing person "mashable".
"happy hour" near:"san francisco"	containing the exact phrase "happy hour" and sent near "san francisco".
near:NYC within:15mi	sent within 15 miles of "NYC".
superhero since:2010-12-27	containing "superhero" and sent since date "2010-12-27" (year-month-day).
ftw until:2010-12-27	containing "ftw" and sent up to date "2010-12-27".
movie -scary :)	containing "movie", but not "scary", and with a positive attitude.
flight :(	containing "flight" and with a negative attitude.
traffic ?	containing "traffic" and asking a question.
hilarious filter:links	containing "hilarious" and linking to URLs.
news source:twitterfeed	containing "news" and entered via TwitterFeed

*https://twitter.com/search-home#

The social media world changes some of these choices. Here, we have to decide whether we wish to construct networks of standing ties (e.g., friendship or following) or event-based ties (e.g., liking or replying to). We need to decide on which social media platform supplies us with data best suited to our analytic purposes. NodeXL provides easy mechanisms for harvesting data from Facebook, Flickr, Twitter, and YouTube. To import data from one of these platforms, select the Import drop-down menu from the Data group on the **NodeXL Tab**, and then pick the appropriate search method and platform. Below, we look at importing Twitter data through NodeXL.

The first time you attempt to import Twitter data, you will need to follow the authorization process described in the "Authorizing NodeXL to Harvest Twitter Data" insert. Thereafter, importing Twitter data through NodeXL will be a breeze. You can import event-based interaction data or standing relationship data. Both will supply data on ties, the text of communications, and associated data such as date and location.

We can import Twitter interaction data in two ways. First, we can determine interactions around a particular topic or search term. To do so, select the Import drop-down menu on the **NodeXL Tab** Data group, and then *From Twitter Search Network . . .* (Note, NodeXL Basic will permit you to import up to two thousand data points, while NodeXL Pro is constrained to the Twitter limits of eighteen thousand records or a week, whichever occurs sooner.) Then, construct your search string in the *Search for tweets that match this query:* box. Use the Twitter operator guidelines provided in the "Twitter Search Operators" insert to do so.

Second, we can obtain interactions with a particular account. To do so, select the Import drop-down menu on the **NodeXL Tab** Data group, and then *From Twitter Users Network . . .* (Note, this option is available only on NodeXL Pro.) You then request the Twitter user or list of users for whom you wish to download interactions. NodeXL will download up to 3,200 of the users' tweets and tweets directed to or mentioning the user. In the Relationship column on the EDGES sheet, NodeXL designates the relationship basis. Both types of imports also download targeted users' profile data on the VERTICES sheet.

Twitter imposes rate limits—that is, constraints on how much data you can download within a certain amount of time. When Twitter encounters this rate limit as it downloads your requested data, it will pause. So be prepared for your download to be time-consuming and plan accordingly.

Better still, construct your search criteria so you can download your data in smaller bites. If you plan to do so, be sure to let NodeXL know to retain the data it previously downloaded. You can do this by selecting the Import drop-down menu on the **NodeXL Tab** Data group, and then *Import Options*. There, uncheck *Clear the NodeXL workbook before the data is imported.* Now, NodeXL will append the newly-imported data to existing data in your file. This option also is useful if you wish to combine results of Twitter Search and Twitter Users queries into a single file. Save often!

If downloading your data in segments, it is possible that NodeXL will download the same record more than once. This is easily remedied. After you have downloaded all your data, click the Prepare Data drop-down menu on the **NodeXL Tab** Data group, and then *Count and Merge Duplicate Edges*. Set the options as depicted in Figure 5.12. You will see a new column labeled Edge Weight on the EDGES sheet. This will tell you how many times a particular data point was downloaded.

On the VERTICES sheet, you will note that NodeXL downloads the URL for each user's profile picture. Unless you are depicting a very small network, you will not want do display the profile picture for every user. In Figure 5.13, I have displayed only my own profile picture and that of the four most followed individuals in my network. I did this by setting the Shape attribute on the VERTICES sheet to *Image* for myself and the four users with the highest number of followers. Much to my amazement, I discover that I am indirectly tied to Katy Perry, Taylor Swift, and Justin Bieber!

Twitter data is most extensively used in analytics, primarily because it is viewed as a broadcast medium that parallels television or billboards. However, as marketers recognize the value of community-based sales, Facebook is gaining recognition as a viral marketing tool, contributing, for example, to the success of the Instant Pot, a combination of pressure cooker and crockpot [9]. Consequently, analytics of Facebook data is replete with insights about prospective communities that might be receptive to and benefit from different types of products and services. So experiment with downloading Facebook data. Note that Facebook no longer honors NodeXL's Timeline request, though. But have fun downloading data from fan pages and groups.

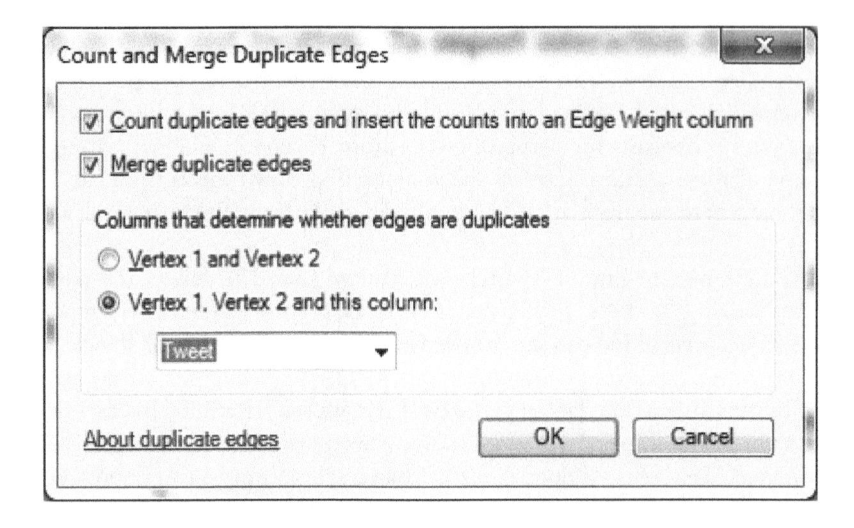

Figure 5.12 Combining Redundant Data in Twitter

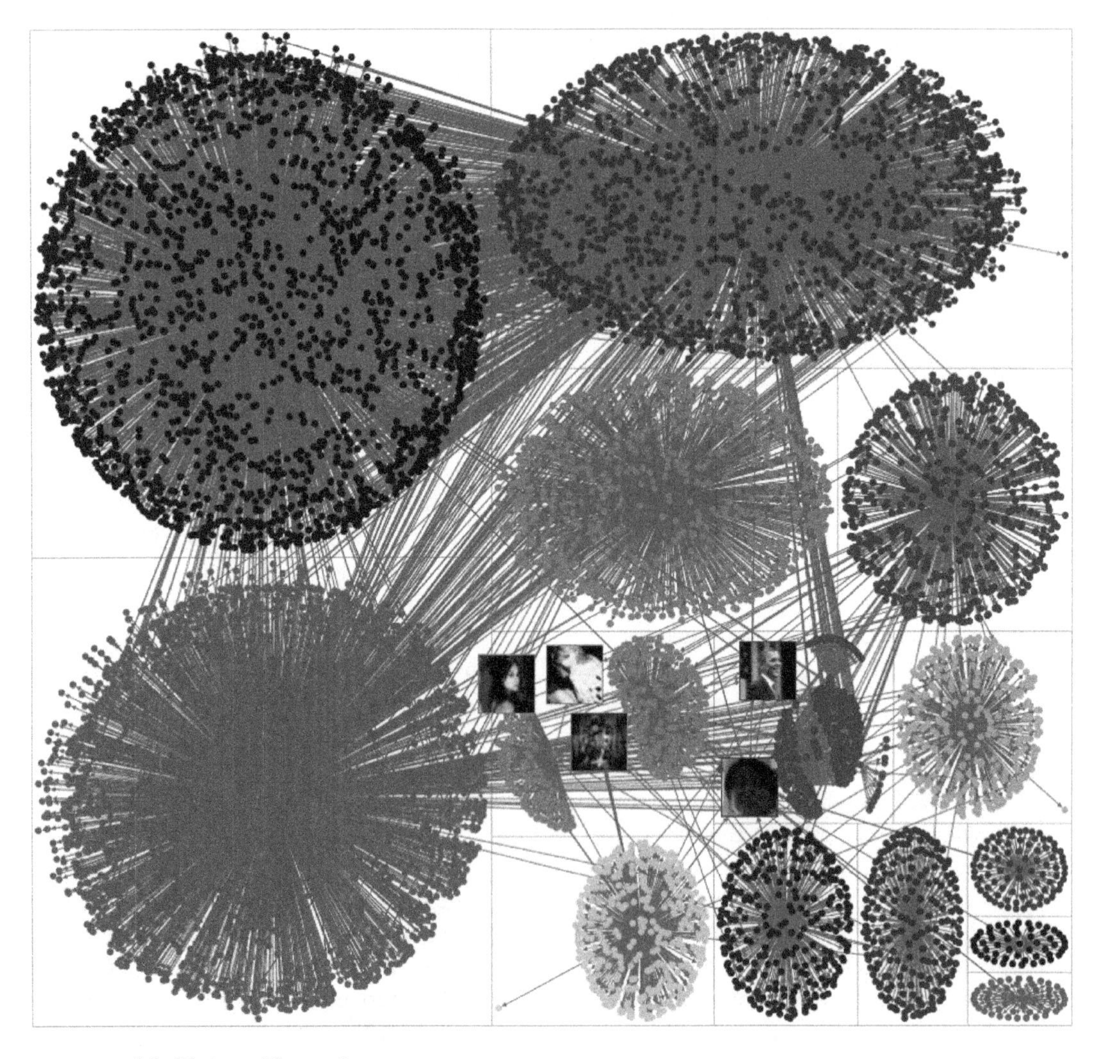

Figure 5.13 My Twitter Network

Tutorial 5.3. Benchmarking BSchool Reciprocity on Twitter

For this tutorial, we will use the ten NodeXL files depicting the long-standing relational networks for the Big XII schools we saw in Chapter 2. Each file contains an edge list representing the school's followers and friends as of July 2017. (See "The BSchool Reciprocity Data" insert for additional information on the data.)

To determine whether an account is reciprocated, we add a Reciprocated column to the VERTICES sheet. In this column, we use the formula

=AND(COUNTIFS(Edges!A:A,[@Vertex])=1,COUNTIFS(Edges!B:B,[@Vertex])=1)

The graphs depicted in Figures 2.2 and 2.3 differentiate between reciprocated and non-reciprocated ties and call out followers with five million or more followers. We reference the Reciprocated and followersCount columns in the Color, Shape, Size, and Label columns of the VERTICES sheet to accomplish this. For example, to specify the vertex color for reciprocated ties for the KStateBusiness account file should be the school's purple, and should be black for non-reciprocated ties, we use the formula *=IF([@Reciprocated],"Purple","Black")* in the Color column. (Purple is a Kansas State color. We can replace "Purple" with the school color for the other BSchools.) To specify that the vertex shape should be a sphere for reciprocated accounts and a square for nonreciprocated accounts, we use the formula *=IF([@Reciprocated]=FALSE,3,5)* in the Shape column. To make the vertex size proportional to an account's number of followers, we use the formula *=[@followersCount]/100000* in the Size column. Finally, to display the account names for accounts with five million or more followers, we use the formula *=IF([@Size]>50,[@Vertex],"")* in the Label column.

The Big XII Summary.xlsx file collates the BSchools' relational information, along with their Twitter activity and responses garnered by their tweets as seen in Table 2.1. We can obtain the rank of each BSchool's reciprocity using *=RANK(F2,$F$2:$F$11)*. This tells us that the Reciprocity rank for Baylor_Business is 1. We can copy this down for the remaining Big XII schools. We can determine the correlation between Reciprocity and Likes is approximately –0.16 using *=CORREL(F2:F11,I2:I11)*. Redoing this for the Inactive Schools and Active Schools on the next two sheets gives us the correlations of 0.97 and –0.34, respectively.

The BSchool Reciprocity Data

Though NodeXL is versatile product, it does have its limits. Obtaining a complete list of an account's followers and friends is one of them. We can, however, obtain these lists via R, Python, or other utilities, and then copy these lists into NodeXL and analyze them. The followers and friends lists for each of the ten BSchool accounts were obtained using the getFollowers() and getFriends() functions from the R twitteR package. Appendix C describes how these lists can be obtained.

The followers and friends lists returned were used to create the edge lists seen on the EDGES sheet of each BSchool's StructuralNetwork NodeXL file. The edges in which the BSchool's account appears as Vertex1 represent its followers list; the edges in which the BSchool's account appears as Vertex2 represent its friends.

The twitteR package also returned the following profile information: statusesCount, followersCount, favoritesCount, and friendsCount. These pieces of information appear on the VERTICES sheet.

Structural network data for all schools are summarized in the BigXIISummary Excel file. This file uses formulas referencing each of the ten BSchool StructuralNetwork NodeXL files to obtain counts of the school's friends, followers, and reciprocated ties. (For these formulas to work, each of the ten StructuralNetwork files needs to be open. Alternatively, use the BigXIISummaryValues Excel file, into which count functions values are pasted.)

Conclusion

In this chapter, we see that SNA can help us understand how and why individuals aggregate in social spaces. Such insights are particularly useful in the context of large, unfamiliar social groups, such as those we experience on social media. Such analyses also can be used to understand organizational affiliations. Later, we also shall use these SNA techniques to analyze large bodies of texts. There, instead of people, we will construct networks of words or concepts. Understanding the disparate groupings of concepts that people use in their discourse will shed light on interpretations of issues of interest to us.

Exercise: SNA Metrics on a Conversation on Twitter

You have a NodeXL file containing data imported from Twitter on a topic of interest to you. The file contains information on relationships among topic participants, participant profile data, and interactions (text of their communications) on the topic.

The EDGES sheet contains the following relational and interaction information:

[A, B] The Vertex1 and Vertex2 columns indicate who is communicating with whom. For tweets directed at someone, these columns will contain two different values; for undirected tweets, the values will be the same—representing self-ties.

[O] The Relationship column indicates the basis of the type of interaction forging the relationship between Vertex1 and Vertex2. These can be replies to, mentions, or a tweet. Tweets always will be a self-tie.

[P] The Relationship Date column provides a date/time stamp for the interaction.

[Q] The Tweet column provides the text of the interaction.

[R, S] URLs in Tweet and Domains in Tweet extract any URLs and domains that the tweet contained.

[T] Hashtags in Tweet extracts all hashtags that the tweet contained.

[W, X] The Latitude and Longitude columns supply the location from which the tweet was posted.

The VERTICES sheet contains the following user profile information:

[A] The Vertex column provides a list of participants in the topic conversation.

[F] The Image File column provides the URL for the Twitter user's profile picture thumbnail.

[AD] The Name column provides the name of the Twitter user.

[AE] The Followed column supplies the number of users following the Twitter user.

[AF] The Followers column supplies the number of users being followed by the Twitter user.

[AG] The Tweets column provides the number of tweets posted by the user.

[AH] The Favorites column provides the number of tweets favorited by the user.

[AI] The Time Zone UTC Offset column provides the numeric equivalent of column AM.

[AJ] The Description column provides the user's Twitter profile description.

[AK] The Location column provides the location, as specified on the user's Twitter profile.

[AL] The Web column provides the user's website URL.

[AM] The Time Zone column provides the time zone from the user's profile.

[AN] The Joined Twitter Date column provides the account creation date from the user's profile.

[AS] The Language column provides the language code associated with the user's profile. See http://dev.datasift.com/docs/sources/public-sources/twitter/twitter-user-languages for the meaning of the codes.

[AV] The Verified column indicates whether or not Twitter has verified the user account.

[AY] The Tweeted Search Term? column indicates whether or not the user tweeted the search term.

Team Assignment Part 1

Choose a data set with your team.

Individual Assignment

Using the data set chosen by your team, complete the following tasks:

1. Obtain in-degree, out-degree, betweenness, closeness, and eigenvector centrality, and clustering coefficient for every Twitter user that participated in the conversation.
2. Obtain metrics for the complete graph.
3. Use two forms of graph partitioning, display the partitioned graphs, and obtain subgraph metrics.

Submit two NodeXL files—one for each partitions—and a Word document. The Word document should provide visuals of your graph partitions and document the partitioning forms used.

Team Assignment Part 2

Put together your team's analyses into a PowerPoint that tells a story about the relationships forged around the conversation topic. Your first slide should name all team members. Your story should reveal at least five insights that explain or predict and lead you to tangible recommendations.

Works Cited

1. Lau, D.C., and J.K. Murnighan, "Demographic Diversity and Faultlines: The Compositional Dynamics of Organizational Groups." *Academy of Management Review*, 23(2; 1998): 325–40.
2. Gettell, O., "Star Wars Monopoly Game to Add Rey Character after Fan Outcry," *Entertainment Weekly*, January 5, 2016, http://ew.com/article/2016/01/05/star-wars-monopoly-game-adding-rey/.
3. McPherson, M., L. Smith-Lovin, and J.M. Cook, "Birds of a Feather: Homophily in Social Networks." *Annual Review of Sociology*, 27(2001): 415–44.
4. Watts, D.J., and S.H. Strogatz, "Collective Dynamics Of 'Small-World' Networks." *Nature*, 393(6684; 1998): 440–42.
5. Barabási, A.-L., and R. Albert, "Emergence of Scaling in Random Networks." *Science*, 286(5439; 1999): 509–12.
6. Johnson, S.L., S. Faraj, and S. Kudaravalli, "Emergence of Power Laws in Online Communities: The Role of Social Mechanisms and Preferential Attachment." *MIS Quarterly*, 38(3; 2014): 795–808.
7. Borgatti, S.P., and D.S. Halgin, "On Network Theory." *Organization Science*, 22(5; 2011): 1168–81.
8. Cowen, T., "The Marriages of Power Couples Reinforce Income Inequality," *New York Times*, December 24, 2015, https://www.nytimes.com/2015/12/27/upshot/marriages-of-power-couples-reinforce-income-inequality.html.
9. Lynch, G.H., "Not Just A Crock: The Viral Word-of-Mouth Success of Instant Pot," *The Salt*, NPR, January 18, 2017, https://www.npr.org/sections/thesalt/2017/01/18/509675621/not-just-a-crock-the-viral-word-of-mouth-success-of-instant-pot.

CHAPTER 6

Subgroup Analysis with R

> **Learning Objectives**
>
> The purpose of this chapter is to introduce you to community detection with R. It covers R commands required to:
>
> 1. identifying subgroups;
> 2. visualize subgroups; and
> 3. develop subgroup metrics.

In Chapter 3, we learned about SNA concepts pertaining to subgroup analysis. This chapter focuses on subgroup analysis (a.k.a. community detection) with R. We review three different approaches to subgroup analyses. We then examine techniques for visualizing the subgroups. Lastly, we look at the metrics available to us that shed further light on membership and distinctness of the subgroups.

Subgroup Analysis Packages

In addition to the R **igraph** package, we will need the **cluster** package in this chapter. The igraph package permits us to identify communities and visualize them. The cluster package is not specific to SNA, but provides the algorithms necessary for discovering communities. Install the two packages and load them.

Identifying Subgroups

The first type of subgroup igraph permits us to examine is the clique. Cliques are fully connected subgroups. We can determine the number of cliques (fully connected vertices) and clique membership, the size of the largest clique, and the vertices in the largest clique. The ***cliques(GraphFrame)*** command obtains the number and membership of every clique in the graph. We can restrict the minimum clique size with the "min=" argument and the maximum clique size with the "max=" argument. The ***clique.number(GraphFrame)*** function tells us the size of the largest clique. The ***largest.cliques(GraphFrame)*** function gives us the vertex numbers of vertices in the largest clique.

A second subgraph characteristic of interest is homophily or assortativity. Unlike NodeXL, where we first partition the graph based on a specified attribute and examine the resulting modularity coefficient to determine the extent to which that attribute contributes to fault lines in the graph, igraph provides a direct metric of network homophily. We have three versions of the assortativity functionality. The first is to ascertain whether a numeric vertex attribute (e.g., age) contributes to homophily. This is the ***assortativity(GraphFrame, TypeColumn)*** function. Assortativity indices close to +1 suggest the tendency for individuals to associate with similar others; indices close to −1 suggest a tendency for individuals to avoid similar others. Indices close to 0 suggest an absence of systematic biases in association choices. The second version permits us to determine whether a categorical variable, (e.g., gender) contributes to homophily. This is the ***assortativity_nominal(GraphFrame, TypeColumn)*** function. Note, assortativity_nominal() expects the second argument to be a factor variable. If you are unsure whether your column is a factor variable, use the ***as.factor(TypeColumn)*** to ensure that the column is being read as a factor variable. Third, R also permits us to determine the extent to which egos within our network tend to affiliate with alters of similar degree centrality. We do this using ***assortativity_degree(GraphFrame)***.

Community Detection Algorithms

edge_betweenness	Operationalizes the Girvan-Newman community detection algorithm
fast_greedy	Directly optimizes modularity score
infomap	Minimizes expected description length of a random walk trajectory
label_prop	Fast algorithm that iteratively labels vertices using a neighborhood majority vote
leading_eigen	Calculates the leading nonnegative eigenvector of the modularity matrix
louvain	Applies a multilevel modularity optimization algorithm
optimal	Obtains optimal community structure by maximizing modularity over all possible partitions
spinglass	Applies a spin-glass model and simulated annealing
walktrap	Uses a random walk algorithm, based on the premise that random walks tend to stay within the same community

Finally, cluster—or community—detection is the process of discovering subgroups that are densely interconnected, with weak connections across the subgroups. The **igraph** package provides several algorithms for detecting communities [2]. (Note that these algorithms also require the **cluster** package.) We use ***cluster_ALGORITHM(GRAPHNAME)***, replacing "ALGORITHM" with one of the clustering algorithms described in the "Community Detection Algorithms" insert, to detect subgroups or communities. For example, using ***cluster_infomap(GRAPHNAME)*** will invoke the infomap algorithm.

Visualizing Communities

Once we have ascertained our graph fault lines using a community detection algorithm, we can embed our preferred clustering algorithm within a plot() function: ***plot(cluster_ALGORITHM(GRAPHNAME), GRAPHFRAME)***. Alternatively, we can assign the output of the clustering algorithm to a list data object, which stores the cluster membership, and then invoke this in our plot() function using ***plot(CLUSTERMEMBERSHIP, GRAPHFRAME)***. Several plot arguments give us control over the resulting visualization. See the "Compendium on Plot Arguments" insert for ways to manipulate some key plot attributes.

Community Metrics

We can apply several metrics to our saved partitions: ***modularity(PARTITION)*** returns the modularity coefficient, ***membership(PARTITION)*** indicates the clusters to which each node has been assigned, ***length(PARTITION)*** indicates the number of clusters, ***sizes(PARTITION)*** reports the number of nodes assigned to each cluster, and ***algorithm(PARTITION)*** recalls the partitioning algorithm used. Additionally, ***crossing(PARTITION, GRAPHFRAME)*** tells us whether each node bridges different clusters.

Viewing Clique Membership

Because of combinatorics, the size of the list of cliques can get very large, precluding R from displaying all cliques. In fact, in response to **`cliques(CSG, min=5, max=5)`**, R listed the first ten thousand cliques and noted that it was unable to list the rest of these cliques unless *max.print* was increased. Simply increasing max.print is insufficient, though, because earlier portions of the list will scroll of the console. We overcome this problem in four steps: increasing max.print, routing our output to a file, requesting the clique list, and closing the file after we are done. The following commands accomplish this:

```
options(max.print=5.5E5) #set max.print
sink(file='output5.txt') #route to file
cliques(CSG, min=5, max=5)
sink(NULL)               #close file
```

Compendium on Plot Arguments

Attribute	Argument	Values
Node Attributes		
Color	vertex.color	RGB format or named color
Border color	vertex.frame.color	RGB format or named color
Shape	vertex.shape	circle; square; csquare; rectangle; crectangle; vrectangle; pie; raster; sphere; none
Size	vertex.size	Number (default is 15)
Node Label Attributes		
Labels	vertex.label	Character vector
Colors	vertex.label.color	RGB format or named color
Font family	vertex.label.family	Times or Helvetica
Font	vertex.label.font	1=plain, 2=bold, 3=italic, 4=bold italic, 5=symbol
Font size	vertex.label.cex	Numeric multiplier: less than 1 (smaller font); 1 (default); more than 1 (larger font)
Edge Attributes		
Color	edge.color	RGB format or named color
Width	edge.width	Number from 1 (default)
Arrow size	edge.arrow.size	Number from 1 (default)
Arrow width	edge.arrow.width	Number from 1 (default)
Line type	edge.lty	0=blank; 1=solid (default); 2=dashed; 3=dotted; 4=dotdash; 5=longdash; 6=twodash
Curvature	edge.curved	Number between 0 (default) and 1
Custom Subgroups		
Membership	mark.groups	Vertex attribute that defines subgroups
Subgroup Polygon Attributes		
Color	mark.col	RGB format or named color
Border color	mark.border	RGB format or named color
Shape	mark.shape	-1 (hooked corners); 0 (sharp corners); 1 (rounded corners - default)
Size	mark.expand	Number

Tutorial 6.1. Understanding Communities in the Legislative Bills

Let's begin by loading the **igraph** package and our CoSponsors.csv edges and Legislators.csv vertices files. Then, we'll recreate a simplified (i.e., without loops or self-ties) graph data frame named *CSG*. Now we are ready to dissect our legislator network, looking for fault lines based on legislator attributes and discovering the underlying mechanism that structures the legislators into communities.

Recall that a clique is a fully connected component. We can obtain lists of all cliques of a specified size within the legislators' network. **(This requires a lot of computing time, so I don't recommend doing this unless you have a fair amount of wait and computing time available.)** For example,

```
cliques(CSG, min=5, max=5)
```

tell us that there are 142,507 cliques of 5 legislators and lists all these cliques. (See the "Viewing Clique Membership" insert for issues with this command and how to resolve them.)

To determine the largest clique of legislators, we use

```
clique.number(CSG)
```

This tells us that the largest clique in our graph contains 30 members. Requesting

```
largest.cliques(CSG)
```

produces the following list of the 30 fully connected vertices:

```
## + 30/35 vertices, named:
##  [1] SP2 BF1 BF2 BG  BL  CC  CH  CM  DJ  EC  JB  JC1 JC2 JK  JR  KB  KG
## [18] LB  MC  MM1 MM2 PK  PO  PS  RB  RN  RW  SP1 TP  WH
```

Next, we want to investigate homophily among our legislators. First, we would like to determine whether tenure in Congress is a basis for homophily. To do so, we use

```
assortativity(CSG, Legislators$Tenure, directed=F)
```

This produces an assortativity coefficient of ~–0.012, suggesting that there is no tenure-based homophily. The usual suspect for homophily, of course, is gender. We can determine the extent to which gender plays a role in representatives' legislative ties using

```
assortativity_nominal(CSG,Legislators$Gender,directed=F)
```

We find no evidence of gender-based homophily, with an index of ~–0.03. The other most obvious categorical basis for homophily is party membership. We can ascertain the extent to which party engenders homophily using

```
assortativity_nominal(CSG,Legislators$Party,directed=F)
```

Based on this, we determine the homophily index to be ~0.24 for party membership, which, given we have only two Democrats in the data set, we should interpret with some caution. Finally, we wish to determine the extent to which degree centrality engenders homophily. Using

```
assortativity_degree(CSG, directed=F)
```

we find the predilection for egos within our network to affiliate with alters of similar degree to be relatively high, at ~0.58.

Next we would like to detect natural fault lines or communities within our legislator network. The statement

```
cluster_walktrap(CSG)
```

produces the output:

```
## IGRAPH clustering walktrap, groups: 4, mod: 0.031
## + groups:
##   $`1`
##    [1] "BF1" "BF2" "BG"  "BL"  "CC"  "CH"  "CM"  "DJ"  "EC"  "JB"  "JC1"
##   [12] "JC2" "JK"  "JR"  "KB"  "KG"  "LB"  "MC"  "MM1" "MM2" "PK"  "PO"
##   [23] "PS"  "RB"  "RN"  "RW"  "SP1" "TP"  "WH"
##
##   $`2`
##   [1] "DE"  "EJ"  "LS"  "MB"
##
##   $`3`
##   [1] "SP2"
##   + ... omitted several groups/vertices
```

This output tells us that the Walktrap algorithm discovered four clusters. It then tells us which legislator is a member of each of the first three clusters, having assigned twenty-nine legislators to cluster 1, four to cluster 2, and one to clusters 3. It does not, however, provide the cluster membership for the fourth cluster or any subsequent clusters that occur. To grab the membership roster for the fourth cluster, or any cluster after the third, we can save the cluster memberships to a list data object, and then obtain the membership roster for the specific cluster we wish—for example, the fourth cluster, using

```
wc=cluster_walktrap(CSG)
wc[4]
```

This tells us that only PG is located in the fourth cluster. This clustering algorithm revealed a modularity coefficient of ~0.031. Recall that modularity is the proportion of within-cluster ties to cross-cluster ties. Since highly separated clusters would have dense within-cluster ties and sparse cross-cluster ties, higher modularity indicates the extent to which the graph contains communities. As modularity coefficients go, ~0.031 is quite low. Since the walktrap algorithm is a random walk algorithm, perhaps increasing the number of steps in the random walk would produce a better solution. We can accomplish this with the "steps=" argument. The default number of steps equals four. We increase the number of steps to 200 using

```
wc=cluster_walktrap(CSG, steps=200)
wc
```

This produces the following output, which tells us that now two clusters were discovered, with an optimal modularity coefficient of ~0.039. Thirty of the legislators are assigned to the first cluster; five to the second. If we send our cluster output to a named graph object, we can plot it. We can accomplish this by directing our cluster output to a partition data frame and plotting the graph data frame using the partition information.

```
## IGRAPH clustering walktrap, groups: 2, mod: 0.039
## + groups:
##   $`1`
##   [1] "DE"   "EJ"   "LS"   "SP2" "MB"
##
##   $`2`
##    [1] "BF1" "BF2" "BG"   "BL"   "CC"   "CH"   "CM"   "DJ"   "EC"   "JB"   "JC1"
##   [12] "JC2" "JK"   "JR"   "KB"   "KG"   "LB"   "MC"   "MM1" "MM2" "PK"   "PO"
##   [23] "PS"   "RB"   "RN"   "RW"   "SP1" "TP"   "WH"   "PG"
```

To plot this cluster solution, we use the statement below to produce the graph in Figure 6.1:

```
plot(wc, CSG)
```

Experimenting with edge_betweenness, fast_greedy, leading_eigen, optimal, and other algorithms, I find they also yield a modularity of ~0.039 with three clusters; however, label_prop and infomap yield a modularity of ~0.026 and two clusters. With strong indication of a three-cluster solution, we can graph one of them using the commands below to produce Figure 6.2. In order to display the legislators' names, rather than initials, we precede our plot command by letting R know where to obtain node labels from before requesting the plot:

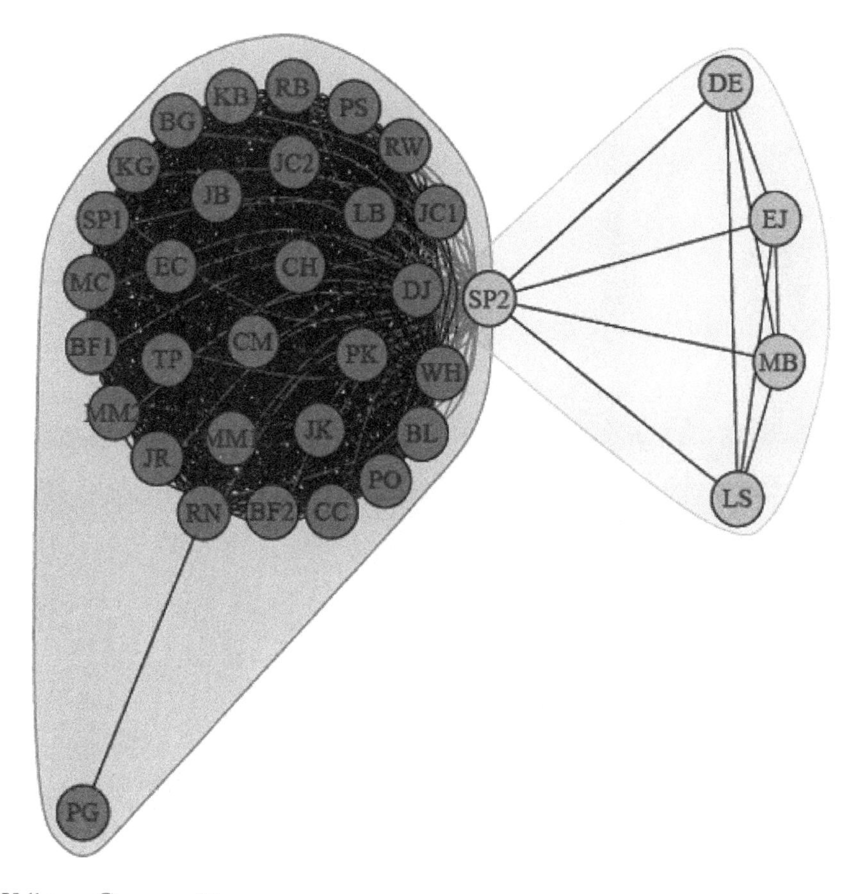

Figure 6.1 Walktrap Communities

```
oc=cluster_optimal(CSG)
plot(oc, CSG, margin=-.275,
    edge.color='darkred',vertex.label=V(CSG)$Legislator,
    vertex.size=evcent(CSG)$vector*5,
    vertex.shape='sphere',
    vertex.label.family='sans',vertex.label.font=2,
    vertex.label.cex=.7,vertex.label.dist=.25)
```

Whereas the Walktrap algorithm treated PG/Paul Gosar as a member of the large, red group, the remaining algorithms producing the three-cluster solutions assign him to his own cluster. The overwhelming evidence of a three-cluster solution is consistent with our data because the three groups identified in Figure 6.2 are each associated with a different piece of draft legislation:

1. **The top group**—PG and RN (Randy Neugebauer)—with H.R. 26 (Terrorism Risk Insurance Program Reauthorization Act of 2015)
2. **The middle group**—including RN—with H.R. 399 (Secure Our Borders First Act of 2015)
3. **The right group**—including SP2 (Steven Palazzo)—with H.R. 810 (National Aeronautics and Space Administration Authorization Act of 2015)

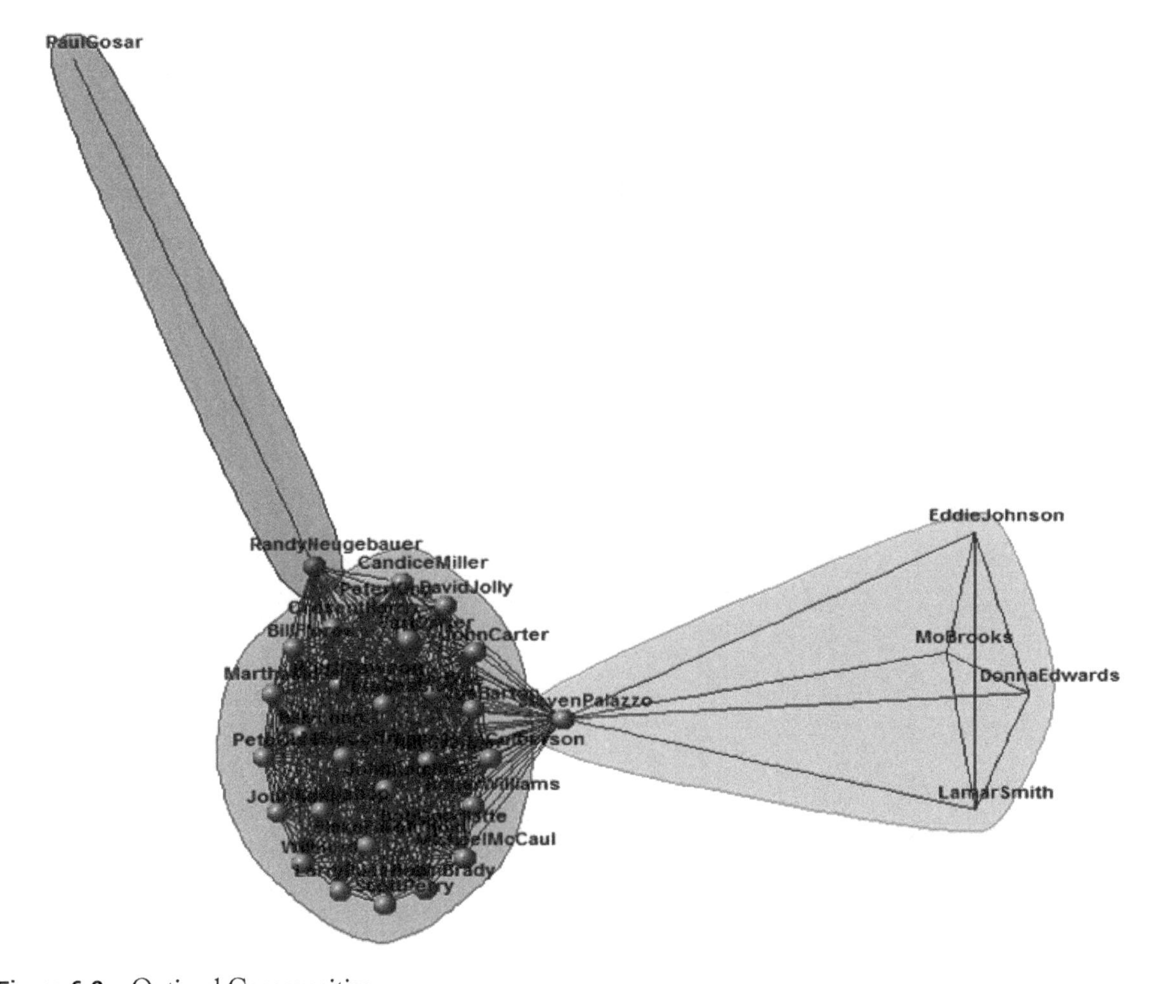

Figure 6.2 Optimal Communities

We can output partitions to a data frame/file for further analyses. For example,

```
CSGPartitions=data.frame(cbind(oc$names, oc$membership))
colnames(CSGPartitions)=c('Legislator','Group')
```

outputs the cluster membership surfaced by the Walktrap algorithm to CSGPartitions, which we can save to a file or otherwise leverage for subgroup analyses.

Conclusion

In this chapter, we looked at subgroup/community detection in R. These techniques are useful for understanding how relationships are structured in a social space, one key social analytics task. We will revisit these techniques in Chapter 11, where we will see their power in text mining, the other core task in social analytics.

Exercise: Analyzing the Structure of a Twitter Conversation with R

The purpose of this assignment is to revisit the network properties of our Twitter conversation from the Exercise in Chapter 5 to see what additional insights we might glean using the functionality R provides. We will be copying the data from the NodeXL EDGES and VERTICES sheets to two CSV files. As we saw in Chapter 4, it is important that the order of the vertices matches the order of their appearance in edges. NodeXL does this automatically, so unless you resorted your VERTICES sheet, you should be fine. **If you resorted your VERTICES sheet, please revert to the original NodeXL file provided before beginning this assignment.**

Individual Assignment

From the NodeXL file you used for the Chapter 5 Exercise, create two CSV files—Edges.csv and Vertices.csv. Copy the following columns from the EDGES sheet to the Edges.csv file:

- Vertex1
- Vertex2

From the VERTICES sheet of your Chapter 5 Exercise file, copy the following columns to the Vertices.csv file:

- Vertex
- Name
- At least any two other attributes—one that is text/categorical and one that is continuous/numeric—that describe vertices from the Vertices sheet that are of interest to you (avoid attributes with a lot of missing data)

Set up your graph data frame. As you set up your data frame and proceed through the rest of this exercise, be mindful that your Twitter data set represents a directed graph (unlike the undirected legislator network) and set your "directed=" arguments accordingly. Then, complete the following tasks:

1. Using two different layout algorithms, provide two visualizations of your network, varying node color based on some vertex attribute.
2. Obtain graph density and reciprocity metrics.
3. Obtain degree, closeness, betweenness, and eigenvector centrality for each graph ego.
4. Provide a "key actor" analysis:
   - Develop a scatterplot of actors' betweenness and eigenvector centrality.
   - Develop a scatterplot matrix of actors' degree, closeness, betweenness, and eigenvector centrality.
5. Is there a demographic basis for homophily in your network? Investigate homophily based on at least one categorical attribute, one continuous attribute, and participants' degree centrality.

6. Do the committee communications reflect distinct communities? Apply at least two different community detection algorithms to answer this question.

Comment on the results of your analysis. Be sure to use appropriate titles for your graphical displays. Copy all your code and output into a Word file named with your first and last name, and submit it.

Team Assignment

Put together your team's analyses into a PowerPoint that tells a story about your Twitter conversation. Your first slide should name all team members. Your story should reveal at least five insights that explain or predict and lead you to tangible recommendations.

Works Cited

1. Burt, R.S., *Structural Holes: The Social Structure of Competition*. Cambridge, MA: Harvard University Press, 1995.
2. Bommarito II, M.J., "Summary of Community Detection Algorithms in igraph 0.6," R-bloggers, 2012, https://bommaritollc.com/2012/06/17/summary-community-detection-algorithms-igraph-0-6/.
3. Pons, P., and M. Latapy, "Computing Communities in Large Networks Using Random Walks." *J. Graph Algorithms Appl.*, 10(2; 2006): 191–218.
4. Newman, M.E.J., and M. Girvan, "Finding and Evaluating Community Structure in Networks." *Physical Review E*, 69(2; 2004): 1–16.

PART III

Text Analysis and Mining

CHAPTER 7

Introduction to Text Analysis

What are people saying about Star Wars? Are they positively disposed toward the movie? What topics are repeated through the conversation? These are some of the questions for which text analysis can provide answers. With burgeoning access to textual information, decision makers in a variety of spheres are beginning to avail of text analysis to rationalize and expedite decisions. In college or job recruiting, for example, automated text analysis of resumes and cover letters can efficiently short-list a set of applicants [2]. Venture capitalists wishing to assess the entrepreneurial orientation of founders seeking their support can score their text samples—including proposals, resumes, social media posts—to predict the founders' likelihood of success [3].

Learning Objectives

The purpose of this chapter is to acquaint you with:

1. the origins and applications of text analysis and mining;
2. the vocabulary and concepts used in text analysis and mining;
3. word count–based approaches; and
4. dictionary-based approaches.

In this chapter, we will begin by exploring the roots of text analysis and the types of problems to which the techniques can be applied. We will review some of the distinctive vocabulary and concepts underlying text analysis and mining. We then will explore two major approaches to text analysis with the assistance of two different pieces of software—count-based approaches with your favorite word cloud generator and dictionary-based approaches with the Linguistic Inquiry and Word Count (LIWC) software.

Origins and Applications of Text Analysis

In 1962, Philip Stone and his colleagues at Harvard University published an article entitled "The General Inquirer: A Computer System for Content Analysis and Retrieval Based on the Sentence as a Unit of Information" [1]. The manuscript described a new computer-based research tool that Stone had developed to analyze texts such as abstracts of research articles, study protocols, and observer notes. The tool, which until the mid-1990s ran exclusively on an IBM mainframe [4], automated ***content analysis***, which Stone defined as "making inferences by systematically and objectively identifying specified characteristics within text" [5: p. 5]. In its early days, the General Inquirer was used to diagnose psychological disorders [6]. Recently, as noted in Chapter 1, the General Inquirer was used to assess the effects of negative language in news articles about firms on firms' earnings and stock market performance [7]. While available to researchers, the Harvard site notes that the product "is not packaged to be commercially available" and the researchers do not plan to provide "the support services such availability would require" [4].

Alternatives abound, though. One of the more accessible of these alternatives is LIWC. In the mid-1980s, James Pennebaker and colleagues began investigating the effects that writing about the traumatic events experienced had on people's physical and psychological well-being. They found that repeatedly writing about the traumatic experience in a way that revealed both the facts of the experience and their emotional response to the experience improved study participants' short- and long-term well-being across a range of metrics [8]. Pennebaker went on to use LIWC to study a variety of phenomena, including the effects of reflective writing on coping with the stress of being away at college for the first time [9], the linguistic composition of people's writing as they underwent bereavement [10], and using language to predict deception [11].

Many alternatives to the General Inquirer and Pennebaker approach are evolving. A plethora of SaaS tools enable informative and aesthetically appealing visuals of word frequencies. It is important to note that analysts frequently employ more than one approach, technique, or tool to gain insights from their text data. Versatility with a range of approaches and technologies is thus valuable.

Vocabulary and Concepts

Text analysis has its own vocabulary with which we first need to get familiar. A ***corpus***, literally a body, refers to the text to be analyzed. Corpuses can vary from a single speech to the complete set of novels by a particular author. These units within a corpus are called ***documents***. Documents can include social media posts about a particular topic within a specified time frame or all posts by a particular person. So our first text analysis task is to determine what our corpus is (i.e., what documents) it will contain.

Next, we undertake three steps to prepare our text for analysis. The first of these steps is to determine our unit of analysis, also known as a ***token***. A token most typically is a word, but can be a phrase or some other meaningful symbol. Once we have determined the token for our analyses, we need to tokenize. Tokenization is the process of decomposing text into these units of analyses or, in some cases, grouping text to denote a single token. For example, in Figure 7.1A, Tagul automatically tokenized the tweets about Star Wars from February 8–9 into words. In Figure 7.1B, I realized it did not make sense to treat "Star" and "Wars" as two separate words, so I combined them. I did the same for John Williams, Darth Vader, Diana Farrell, Jason Ward, and Rick Rubin.

The second step is ***word normalization***, which entails treating words that differ only in conjugation, singular/plural, or case similarly. There are two parts to word normalization—case conversion and stemming. Converting the entire text to all upper- or all lower-case ensures upper- and lowercase instances of the same word are treated equivalently. Through stemming (i.e., reducing all words to their stem), words with different

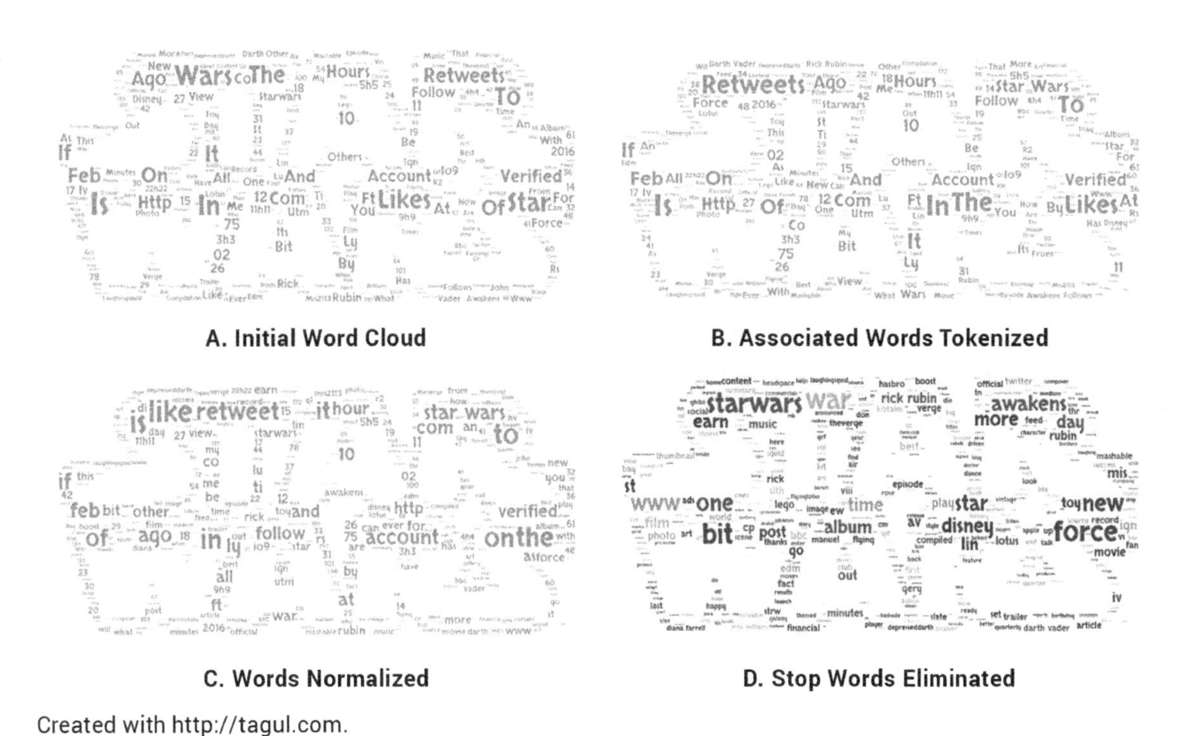

Figure 7.1 Tokenizing, Normalizing, and Applying Stop Words to Star Wars Tweets

inflexions (i.e., suffixes such as resulting from verb conjugations or noun plurals) are treated similarly. For example, in Figure 7.1C, likes/like/liked/liking are treated the same, as are views/view/viewed/viewing, hours/hour, and retweets/retweet/retweeted/retweeting. An alternative to stemming is lemmatization, which we will see in Chapter 10.

The third step is to prevent words not meaningful to our analyses from overwhelming it. Such words, which are not inherently interesting to our analyses, but clutter it, and which we would like to filter out, are known as ***stop words***. Typically stop words are commonly used words such as articles, prepositions, and conjunctions. Predefined stop word lists exist (e.g., Snowball Stemmer) [12]. But the choice of stop words should be context-dependent. In Figure 7.1C, for example, we see words such as "like," "retweet," and "verified," which have to do with the Twitter platform, and words such as "hour" and "Feb," which have to do with the timing of the posts. Since these do not concern the content of the communications, they should be added to our stop word list. Further, "StarWars," while the topic of the conversation we are analyzing, does not illuminate the conversation. Dropping it may reveal more insights on the conversation. In addition to frequently used words and numbers, Figure 7.1D eliminates the following context-specific stop words: like (148 instances), retweet (139), StarWars (134), account (87), verified (86), ago (81), hour (77), feb (61), follow (37), all (24), and view (19). This enables us to see actors such as Disney, topics such as album, and accounts such as @starwars and @depresseddarth, which were the focus of the two-day conversation. As you might imagine, developing an effective context-specific stop word list requires iterative effort. When using standard stop word lists, it always is a good idea to inspect the list. Stop words that are effective in some—or even most—contexts may result in the loss of meaningful information in ours.

Inherent in text analyses are one of two different levels of representation. The lower representation level treats a text as a bag of words. In this ***bag of words*** representation, the words in a text are disassembled prior to analyses, and information about their position in the text is not retained. Consider, for example, the following three sentences:

I really like the new Star Wars movie.

I really do not like the new Star Wars movie.

The movie is like a mashup of the first two Star Wars movies!

With a little stemming (movie/movies), these two sentences get reduced to the bag of words and corresponding sentence-word vectors, also known as a ***term-document matrix***, depicted in Table 7.1.

The bag of words model is used in many text analysis problems, such as the text classification required for spam detection and sentiment analysis. While the most accessible to text analysis, this representational approach has some obvious shortcomings. First, surrounding words that change—even reverse—meaning (e.g., the use of negation) are ignored. Thus "like" would be treated as an expression of positive sentiment in both the first two sentences, even though the sentiment being expressed in Sentence 2 clearly is negative. Second, homonyms lose their contextualized meaning and are subject to misinterpretation. In Sentence 3, the word "like" is not being used to express sentiment, but rather to express a comparison. Nonetheless, it would be treated equivalently to its use in the first two sentences.

The ***string of words*** representational model preserves the contextual information contained in a text. As a result, this representational model provides greater semantic fidelity. Fewer algorithms apply this model, relying instead on the shallower bag of words model [13]. Yet we are seeing incremental evolution of text analysis toolsets. For example, the 2015 version of LIWC permits custom dictionary entries to be phrases, thereby enhancing the validity of the LIWC dictionary [14].

Some text analysis approaches distinguish between content and function words. ***Content words*** reveal the focal points of a story. They usually are nouns and regular verbs, but also include many adjectives and adverbs [15]. For example, in the sentence, "The rain in Spain stays mainly in the plains," "rain," "Spain," "stays," and "plains" are content words. Content words are rich in meaning and reveal the who, what, when, and where of a communication [16]. ***Function words*** are not essential to conveying the main ideas of a story, but glue together the content words [15]. They include articles such as "the," prepositions such as "in," and the adverb "mainly."

Table 7.1 Term-Document Matrix—Bag of Words and Sentence-Word Vectors

Bag of Words	Sentence 1	Sentence 2	Sentence 3
a	0	0	1
do	0	1	0
first	0	0	1
i	1	1	0
is	0	0	1
like	1	1	1
mashup	0	0	1
movie	1	1	2
new	1	1	0
not	0	1	0
of	0	0	1
really	1	1	0
star	1	1	1
the	1	1	2
two	0	0	1
wars	1	1	1

Instead of conveying meaning directly, they play a grammatical role in sentences [16]. Function words reveal author sentiment [15], demographics such as gender and age [17], and even personality traits [18].

Word Count–Based Approaches

Some of the most basic questions we might want answered about a corpus include: Which words occur most frequently? What do authors appear to be emphasizing? These word count–based approaches help the analyst identify the key concepts emphasized in a text or corpus and understand the relative salience of different concepts to an author or community of authors. NodeXL, for example, provides some basic word frequency statistics. Upon request, the WORDS sheet provides a list of words, their frequency counts, and their "salience" or frequency divided by total word count, among other information. Additionally, NodeXL identifies the top ten URLs in tweets, domains in tweets, and hashtags in tweets.

An alternate approach to identifying the most frequently occurring words is to represent word frequency graphically. ***Word clouds***, also known as tag clouds, are images that represent the frequency with which words appear in a text. As we have seen in Figure 7.1, they are an accessible and meaningful way of representing relative word frequency or importance. For example, the word cloud in Figure 7.2 gives me a quick sense that all is copasetic with the customer base of my favorite coffee shop, Crimson & Whipped Cream: the most frequently used words in Yelp reviews are coffee, good, cupcake, place, bake, cookie, cream, and love! Benchmarking its tweets against a competitor's using word clouds, an Oklahoma casino realized that while their social media posts highlighted shows, their competitor's posts celebrated customer wins, thereby increasing customer excitement about gaming—the core business of the casinos.

Figure 7.2 Analyses of Yelp Reviews of My Favorite Coffee Shop
Word cloud created with http://tagul.com.

A more complex count-based approach is to examine ***word concordance***—that is, counts of the co-occurrence of word pairs. Word concordance indicates the semantic proximity of concepts. As such, beyond simply identifying important concepts, it provides some contextualization of the concepts. Consider our Crimson & Whipped Cream reviews again. The ten most frequently occurring word pairs for the coffee shop reviews were whipped cream, baked goods, crimson whipped, coffee shop, chocolate chip, photo booth, whoopie pie, campus corner, whoopie pies, and red velvet. These word pairs identify the coffee shop's popular products and services—beyond the coffee that we saw in Figure 7.2. Later, we will see that such concordance analysis also feeds into more complex, discovery-based approaches, which we will investigate in Chapter 9.

Word count–based approaches operationalize the bag of words representational approach. Depending on our choice of word cloud generator, we may need to perform some of our tokenization, word normalization, and stop word application prior to importing our data into the generator. Through such preprocessing, we can make content more meaningful by indicating that "Star Wars" is a single tag and equivalent to "star wars" or "Star wars" or "@starwars." Outputs of these word clouds—or other tools that count words—then may inform subsequent dictionary- or discovery-based analyses of our corpora.

Tutorial 7.1. What Are the Key Terms in Talks about the Presidency?

For this tutorial, we will use a data set on presidency tweets—see "The Presidency Tweets Data Set" insert for a brief description. Using our favorite word cloud generator, let's begin by getting a sense for the major terms appearing in the tweets across the two time periods. After stripping noise such as "RT"s—"retweet"s—from, we get the output depicted in Figure 7.3. Even without subtitles, it would immediately be apparent that the word cloud on the left represents the preprimaries conversation, and the one on the right the postinauguration content. We also can identify the public's major concerns—Iowa, the Republican Party, television, and competing candidates before the primaries and the immigration ban, independence of the courts, health care, and China after the inauguration.

The Presidency Tweets Data Set

This data set contains two files. The first—the DT1.xlsx file—contains a sample of 1,313 tweets about Presidential Candidate Donald Trump, collected two days before the start of the 2016 primaries. The second—the DT2.xlsx file—contains a sample of 1,745 tweets about President Donald Trump, collected two weeks after his inauguration. What can we learn about the public and about the presidency from analyzing the tweets across these two time periods? As we analyze these tweets, keep in mind that these two sets of tweets represent exceedingly small samples. As such, the results of our investigations should prompt further analyses rather than immediate forays into public disclosure and policy.

Next, we would like to determine what terms co-occur. We can accomplish this via NodeXL. To do so, let's click the Graph Metrics button on the Analysis group on the **NodeXL Tab**. From the Graph Metrics dialog box, check the Words and Word Pairs option; then click the Options button, as depicted in Figure 7.4. The Options button brings up the Word and Word Pair Metrics dialog box. Here, we first select whether our text

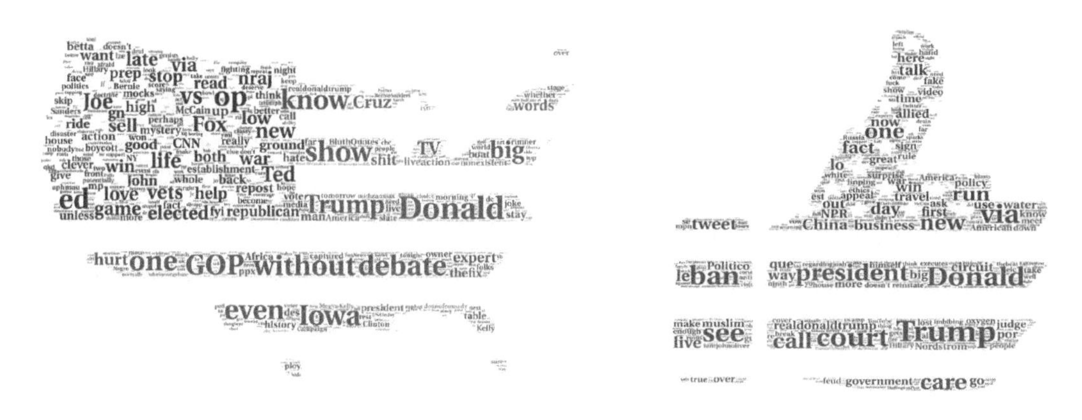

Term Pairs

Donald Trump	Debate Without
Trump Show	GOP Debate
Without Donald	Watch GOP
Show Go	Mystery Iowa

A. Preprimary Tweets

Donald Trump	See Court
Trump See	Travel Ban
Surprised Government	Allies Surprised
Run Business	President Donald

B. Postinauguration Tweets

Figure 7.3 Word Clouds and Term Pairs in the Presidency Tweets Data Set

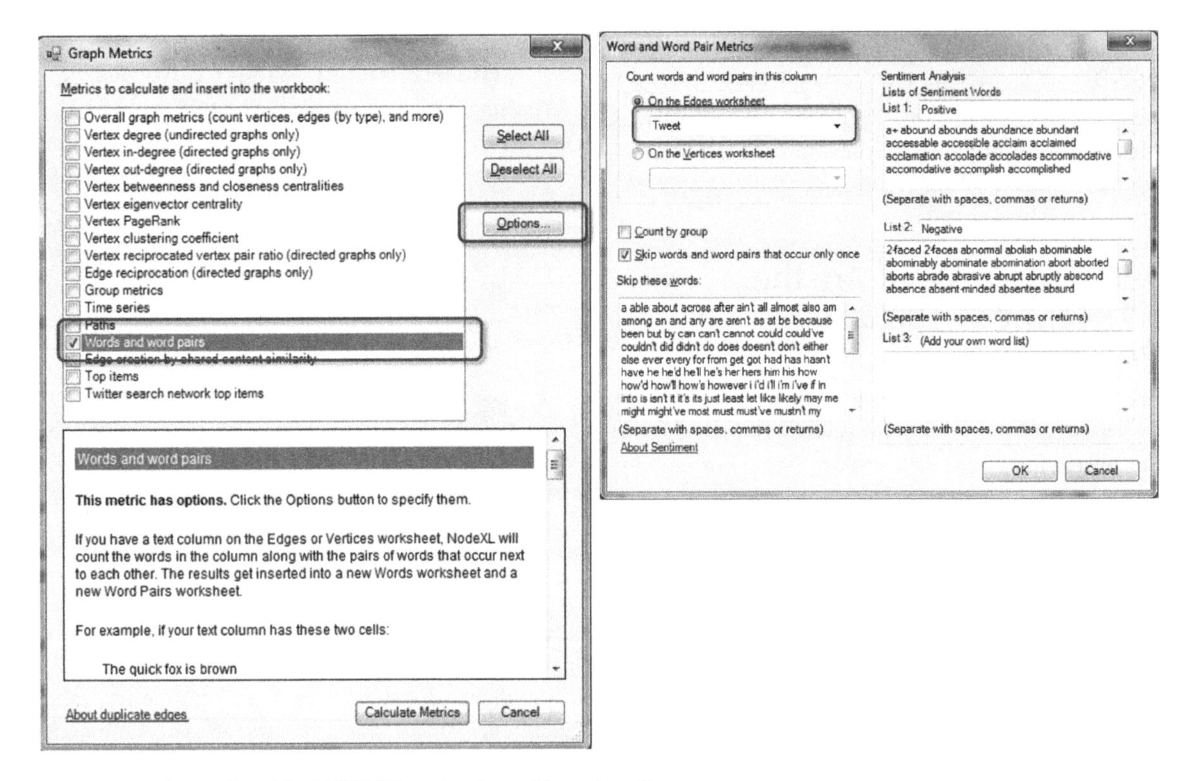

Figure 7.4 Accessing NodeXL's Text Analyses Functionality

to be analyzed is on the EDGES or VERTICES worksheet, and then select the column containing the text—in this case Tweets. Next, click the OK button from the Word and Word Pair Metrics dialog box, and then the Calculate Metrics button from the Graph Metrics box.

Examining the WORD PAIRS sheet, NodeXL created reveals the word pairs depicted in Figure 7.3. Once again, these most frequently occurring word pairs have some commonalities and differences before the primaries and after the inauguration. The word pair count reveals public concern surrounding the party, debate, and the upcoming primaries before the primaries and about the travel ban, chagrined governments and allies, and business issues after the inauguration.

Dictionary-Based Approaches

The General Inquirer and LIWC, along with commercially available DICTION [19], exemplify the dictionary-based approach to text analysis. Even NodeXL now provides rudimentary dictionary-based functionality, visible to the right of Figure 7.4. The main feature of such software is a ***dictionary***—a set of concepts or categories and the specific words, or tag words, that map to that concept. In fact, these and other dictionary-based approaches to text analysis provide multiple dictionaries and/or enable users to construct custom dictionaries. Dictionaries sometimes are called ***lexicons***. As you might imagine, these dictionary-based approaches to analyzing text also use the bag of words approach. Counts are aggregated by dictionary concepts though and/or may be presented also as proportion data to reflect the ratio of words from the text matching each dictionary category to the total number of words.

Many predefined dictionaries that accompany software that does dictionary-based text analysis focus on function words. Pennebaker, in particular, has extensively studied the information specific function word categories or concepts reveal about social dynamics. Along with coauthors, he has considered the extent to which function words provide clues to authors' identity—specifically about their gender, personality traits, and mood states [18]. He found that males tend to use more large words, articles, and propositions, while females use more social words and pronouns. Texts from extraverted individuals had a higher word count and used fewer large words, causal words, and negations. Depression coincided with individuals' higher use of "I" words and more negative emotion words. Complex thinkers use longer sentences and more causal language.

In relationships, Pennebaker found using "we," enhanced audience identification with speakers, establishing common ground between them. Using "we" and "they" can promote the development of group identity: using "they" sets up a counterpoint or antithesis against which the established or assumed "we" is expected to be united [20: p. 21, 148]. Other researchers have found the use of "we" in CEOs' letters to shareholders reflected CEOs' identification with their organizations [22], and that charismatic presidents used "we" more often during periods of change [23].

Use of function words also provides cues into status and social hierarchy. Using "we" was associated with higher rank in military, higher status in laboratory experiments, and higher status in politics. Function words also are useful in engineering change. In this regard, use of words associated with negation has been found useful in breaking with past and calling for change [23]. Speaking to what a collective is not, negation, is an "anti-identity" device [24: p. 151]. Charismatic presidents have been found to use negation more often during periods of change [23].

General Inquirer Dictionary Entries for "Dirty"

In their first description of the General Inquirer, Stone and colleagues provided the following tag words or dictionary entries for the concept "dirty" [1].

ash	damage	herd	pick	spot
awful	darkness	hole	pig	tobacco
bitter	decay	horror	pigeon	train
black	deceive	incest	poison	trick
bothersome	devil	industrial	politic	ugliness
bottom	dig	industry	powder	ugly
cellar	dirty	labor	rat	vice
chimney	discharge	mass	rear	war
cities	disgust	mill	scheme	waste
city	dull	mine	shame	worker
clay	dust	mouse	slave	worm
coal	evil	mud	slop	worse
commercial	floor	murder	smoke	worst
cruel	fly	murderer	soil	wound
curse	hell	naked	spit	

Of course, dictionary-based approaches are very appropriate for ***sentiment analysis*** (i.e., the process of categorizing the opinions and affect expressed in a text). Some dictionaries capture just positive and negative emotion; others capture more nuanced emotional responses. LIWC provides three different directories. LIWC offers six nested categories of emotion concepts. The largest concept is affective processes, which includes positive and negative emotion. Negative emotion further is broken out into anxiety, anger, and sadness.

The built-in LIWC dictionaries also permit evaluation of ***author motives***, drives, or needs. The premise of this portion of the dictionary is that human behavior is motivated by one of five key motives. Dictionary entries assessing the ***affiliation*** motive capture the extent to which authors express a preference for social relationships and a desire for acceptance. Words assessing the ***achievement*** motive capture expressions of a desire for challenge and accomplishment. Those assessing the ***power*** motive reflect the author's desire for and attentiveness to dominance, status, and position in social hierarchy. Words assessing the ***reward*** motive reflect concern for incentives and goals. Finally, those assessing the ***risk*** motive concern danger and uncertainty.

Software using dictionary-based approaches permit users to develop and use custom dictionaries (i.e., dictionaries that they construct). For example, a recruiter wishing to screen job candidates can create a custom dictionary of keywords associated with the skill sets relevant to the job description. Candidate resumes then can be scored automatically against that dictionary, helping short-list and prioritize job applicants [2].

Text Analysis with LIWC

LIWC is menu-driven and user-friendly. The following are valid input files: text files, Word documents, PDFs, and Excel and CSV files. Running LIWC is simple. Open up the program and select the appropriate input option off the **File menu** (see Figure 7.5). For a single .txt/.docx/.pdf, select the first option—Analyze Text. For multiple files, select the second—Analyze Text in Folder. For .xlsx/.csv files, select the third—Analyze Excel/CSV File.

Once provided with the input, LIWC analyzes the text and develops a table of approximately ninety-five output variables, as depicted in Figure 7.6. Selecting Save Results will permit us to send the output to a .txt, .csv, or .xlsx file. Choosing the .xlsx output option permits us to combine the LIWC output with NodeXL data.

By combining our LIWC outputs with the NodeXL data, we are able to produce outputs such as the one depicted in Figure 7.7. This graph is based on a week's slice of the conversation about the Keystone Pipeline in October 2014. The conversation surrounded the controversial proposal to pipe oil from Canada through US states like Montana and Nebraska down to the Gulf of Mexico. In the graph, we depict nodes as triangles if, on average, tweets from the associated account were more negatively than positively toned (i.e., used more negative than positive words); as disks if they were more positively toned; and as squares if they depicted no emotion or the same amount of positive and negative affect. Imposition of a clustering algorithm then sheds light on the extent to which individuals with shared affect tend to cluster together. In fact, the visual does suggest the presence of affectively homogenous clusters.

LIWC also permits us to develop and apply custom dictionaries. This feature is particularly useful in investigating the prevalence of concepts for which we have tag words. Custom LIWC dictionaries are text (*.txt*) files. The text file contains two segments: ***custom concepts*** or categories and ***tag words*** (i.e., words or word stems associated with the concepts). See Figure 7.8 for a sample custom dictionary to capture different types of positive emotion.

The custom concepts appear between two "%" signs. The first of these will be the first line of your custom dictionary. Each **concept** that follows this first line should be **preceded by a unique number that identifies the concept and a tab**. LIWC permits you to have up to 999 concepts. Each concept should appear on a new line. Concepts on your list need not be alphabetized. Indicate the end of your list of concepts with the second "%".

The tag words / word stems appear in the second segment. This segment should immediately follow the concepts segment, with no intervening blank lines. Each tag should appear on its own line and should appear

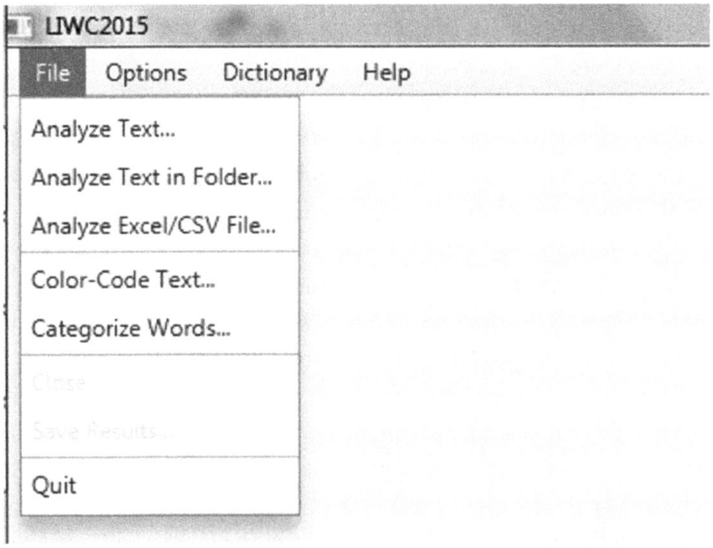

Figure 7.5 LIWC Interface

LIWC2015

File Options Dictionary Help

Analyze Text...
Analyze Text in Folder...
Analyze Excel/CSV File...
Color-Code Text...
Categorize Words...
Close
Save Results...
Quit

		WC	Analytic	Clout	Authentic	Tone	WPS	Sixltr	Dic	function	pronoun	ppron	i	we	you	shehe	they	ipron	article	prep	auxverb	adverb	conj	negate	verb
		19	92.84	70.08	1.00	97.58	19.00	21.05	15.79	0.00	0.00	0.00	0.00	0.00	0.00	0.00	0.00	0.00	0.00	0.00	0.00	0.00	0.00	0.00	0.00
		28	83.00	63.97	4.35	25.77	9.33	10.71	39.29	21.43	0.00	0.00	0.00	0.00	0.00	0.00	0.00	0.00	3.57	7.14	3.57	7.14	7.14	0.00	7.14
		28	83.00	63.97	4.35	25.77	9.33	10.71	39.29	21.43	0.00	0.00	0.00	0.00	0.00	0.00	0.00	0.00	3.57	7.14	3.57	7.14	7.14	0.00	7.14
		14	99.00	50.00	13.15	25.77	14.00	21.43	35.71	14.29	0.00	0.00	0.00	0.00	0.00	0.00	0.00	0.00	0.00	14.29	0.00	0.00	0.00	0.00	0.00
		20	86.59	30.86	3.37	1.00	20.00	35.00	30.00	15.00	0.00	0.00	0.00	0.00	0.00	0.00	0.00	0.00	0.00	5.00	5.00	0.00	0.00	5.00	5.00
10001.txt	1	16	92.84	96.95	1.00	99.00	16.00	25.00	56.25	37.50	6.25	6.25	0.00	0.00	6.25	0.00	0.00	0.00	6.25	12.50	6.25	6.25	0.00	0.00	12.50
10002.txt	1	16	92.84	96.95	1.00	99.00	16.00	25.00	56.25	37.50	6.25	6.25	0.00	0.00	6.25	0.00	0.00	0.00	6.25	12.50	6.25	6.25	0.00	0.00	12.50
10003.txt	1	20	77.33	30.86	3.37	25.77	20.00	40.00	40.00	20.00	0.00	0.00	0.00	0.00	0.00	0.00	0.00	0.00	0.00	5.00	5.00	5.00	5.00	0.00	5.00
10004.txt	1	22	99.00	81.84	11.00	25.77	22.00	36.36	54.55	31.82	4.55	0.00	0.00	0.00	0.00	0.00	0.00	4.55	9.09	13.64	4.55	0.00	0.00	0.00	4.55
10005.txt	1	30	92.84	84.14	3.37	25.77	10.00	6.67	60.00	33.33	10.00	6.67	0.00	0.00	0.00	6.67	0.00	3.33	3.33	13.33	0.00	0.00	6.67	0.00	6.67
10006.txt	1	18	96.85	71.09	23.51	25.77	9.00	11.11	27.78	16.67	0.00	0.00	0.00	0.00	0.00	0.00	0.00	0.00	0.00	11.11	0.00	5.56	0.00	0.00	0.00
10007.txt	1	14	99.00	50.00	52.86	25.77	14.00	28.57	71.43	42.86	0.00	0.00	0.00	0.00	0.00	0.00	0.00	0.00	14.29	14.29	14.29	0.00	0.00	0.00	14.29
10008.txt	1	16	99.00	73.40	35.37	25.77	16.00	31.25	68.75	37.50	0.00	0.00	0.00	0.00	0.00	0.00	0.00	0.00	12.50	12.50	12.50	0.00	0.00	0.00	12.50
10009.txt	1	17	85.18	27.83	6.20	1.00	17.00	35.29	35.29	17.65	0.00	0.00	0.00	0.00	0.00	0.00	0.00	0.00	0.00	5.88	5.88	0.00	0.00	5.88	5.88
1001.txt	1	19	99.00	70.08	4.05	97.58	19.00	21.05	52.63	26.32	0.00	0.00	0.00	0.00	0.00	0.00	0.00	0.00	10.53	10.53	0.00	0.00	5.26	0.00	0.00
10010.txt	1	30	92.84	84.14	3.37	25.77	10.00	6.67	60.00	33.33	10.00	6.67	0.00	0.00	0.00	6.67	0.00	3.33	3.33	13.33	0.00	0.00	6.67	0.00	6.67
10011.txt	1	23	80.03	66.81	27.39	25.77	7.67	21.74	39.13	17.39	0.00	0.00	0.00	0.00	0.00	0.00	0.00	0.00	0.00	4.35	8.70	4.35	0.00	0.00	13.04
10012.txt	1	25	99.00	50.00	1.59	25.77	25.00	24.00	48.00	24.00	0.00	0.00	0.00	0.00	0.00	0.00	0.00	0.00	8.00	12.00	0.00	0.00	0.00	4.00	0.00
10013.txt	1	24	96.08	50.00	1.79	25.77	24.00	29.17	58.33	20.83	0.00	0.00	0.00	0.00	0.00	0.00	0.00	0.00	4.17	8.33	4.17	0.00	0.00	4.17	4.17
10014.txt	1	25	97.89	50.00	1.59	25.77	25.00	24.00	56.00	24.00	0.00	0.00	0.00	0.00	0.00	0.00	0.00	0.00	4.00	12.00	4.00	0.00	0.00	4.00	8.00
10015.txt	1	27	97.65	50.00	1.00	25.77	27.00	18.52	48.15	22.22	0.00	0.00	0.00	0.00	0.00	0.00	0.00	0.00	7.41	7.41	3.70	0.00	0.00	3.70	7.41
10016.txt	1	23	96.18	66.81	1.00	25.77	23.00	26.09	56.52	30.43	4.35	4.35	0.00	0.00	0.00	4.35	0.00	0.00	4.35	13.04	4.35	0.00	0.00	4.35	8.70
10017.txt	1	23	96.18	66.81	1.00	25.77	23.00	26.09	56.52	30.43	4.35	4.35	0.00	0.00	0.00	4.35	0.00	0.00	4.35	13.04	4.35	0.00	0.00	4.35	8.70
10018.txt	1	24	99.00	79.76	7.84	25.77	24.00	29.17	54.17	16.67	0.00	0.00	0.00	0.00	0.00	0.00	0.00	0.00	4.17	12.50	0.00	0.00	0.00	0.00	4.17

Figure 7.6 LIWC Output

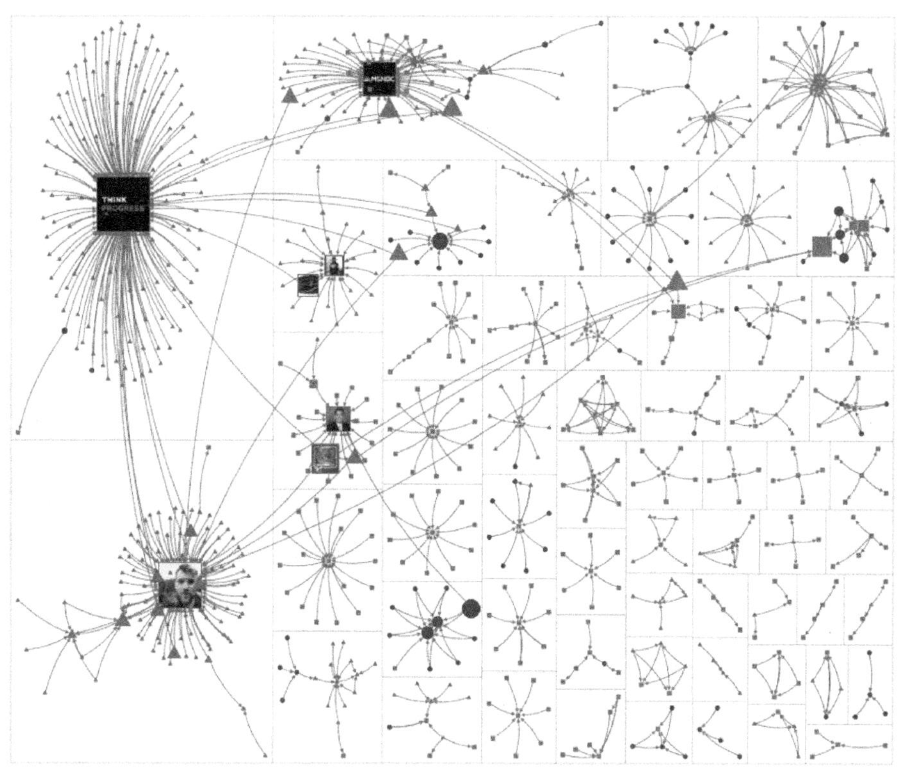

Legend:
Triangular vertices: expressed more negative than positive sentiment
Round vertices: expressed more positive than negative
Square vertices: were neutral or expressed no emotion

Figure 7.7 Depicting Sentiment about the Keystone Pipeline in a Network Graph

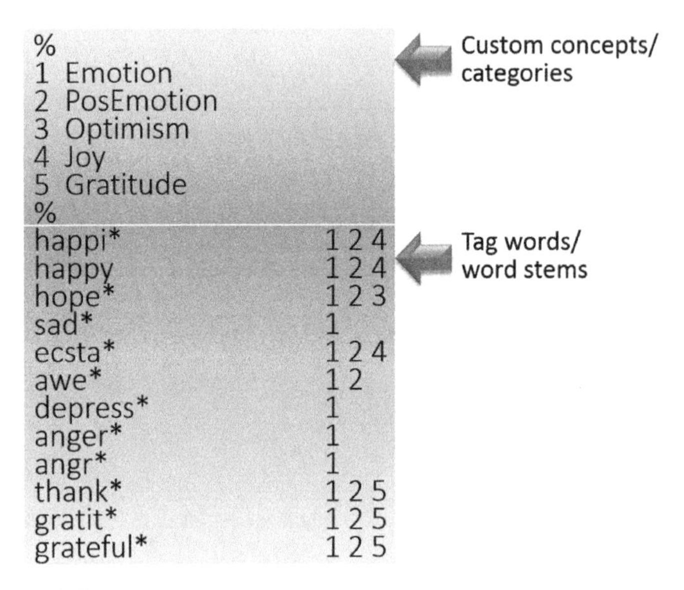

Figure 7.8 Custom LIWC Dictionary

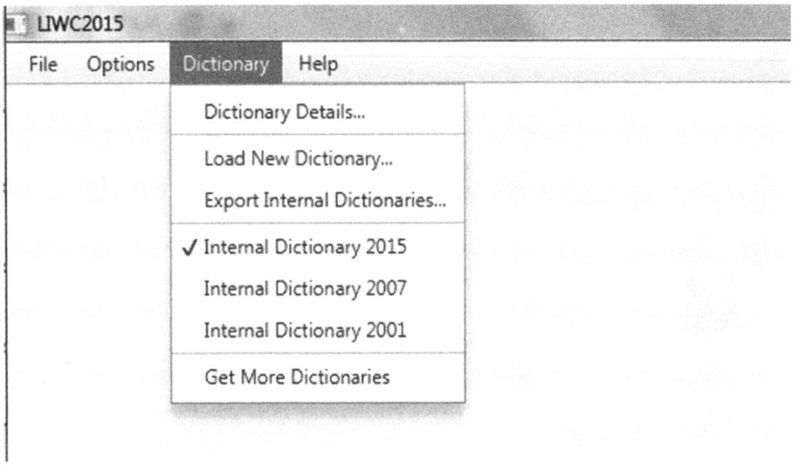

Figure 7.9 LIWC Dictionary Menu

only once in the dictionary. We associate a tag with a concept, by **following the tag with the associated concept number, separated by a tab**. It is permissible to associate a tag word with multiple concepts. This happens often with nested concepts such as emotion, negative emotion, sadness. To associate a tag with multiple concepts, we enter the concept numbers sequentially on the tag line, separating concept numbers with tabs. LIWC 2015 also permits tags to be phrases. Phrases are indicated by words separated by spaces.

We indicate stemming in the tag segment with an asterisk. For example, a dictionary entry for "thank*" will result in words that begin with "thank," including thank, thanked, thanking, thankfully, thankless, and Thanksgiving, being counted. If we include another entry for "Thanksgiving" in the dictionary, all instances of Thanksgiving will be counted twice—once for the stemmed "thank*" tag word and once for the unstemmed "Thanksgiving." LIWC permits an unlimited number of tag words.

Once we have created a custom dictionary, we need to rename the .txt file with a ***.dic*** extension. We then can load that dictionary prior to loading our text to be analyzed. We can do so from the **Dictionary menu** in LIWC as depicted in Figure 7.9, then select Load New Dictionary… and through the browser select the

.dic dictionary file we just created. From this menu, we also can revert to the LIWC 2007 or LIWC 2001 dictionaries if we so wish.

Though easy to use, dictionary-based approaches are not without their limitations. A key limitation—as with other bag-of-word approaches—is their inability to discern context. Thus "like" as an expression of sentiment, and "like" used to construct a simile are indistinguishable, and "like" preceded by negation such as "not" is indistinguishable from "like" without such negation. A second limitation is that, though technically easy to construct, creating useful custom dictionaries requires substantial domain knowledge and iterative efforts of developing, testing, and refining the dictionary.

Tutorial 7.2. Talking about Delta Flight Delays

The DeltaPosts.csv file contains 1,769 posts by the public to Delta Airline's Facebook page in December 2015. The PublicPosts.csv file contains 256 posts mentioning Delta Airlines on other publicly accessible Facebook pages in the same month.

To determine whether posts are about flight delays, we create a custom dictionary. Let's create a text file named Delta.dic. For the moment, we will have a single concept—Delay—associated with three tags, as depicted in Table 7.2.

Open LIWC. Close the Welcome to LIWC dialog. Then let's change the dictionary from the default Internal Dictionary 2015 to the custom Airlines.dic (Dictionary, Load New Dictionary, then select the path containing Airlines.dic and select the file). Using the main LIWC menu, we tell LIWC we wish to Analyze Excel/CSV File. Select the DeltaPosts.csv file; then select the message column (column C). Save the resulting analyses to an Excel file in the folder. Open the file—if we accepted the LIWC default, it should be named LIWC2015 Results (DeltaPosts).xlsx. Notice that LIWC analyzed the header row of our CSV file. Let's move the second row for columns A through J (the original column headers) to row 1. Then let's delete the second row to ensure that subsequent analyses are not contaminated by these numbers. We also see that the numeric data from our original DeltaPosts.csv file has been converted to text. To change it back to numbers, we can select the cells; then click and choose Convert to Number. Repeat this process for the PublicPosts.csv file. We now will use these files to answer the questions below.

Question 1: Where Do Delta Customers Post Messages about Flight Delays?

Let's open a new Excel file, which we call DeltaAirlinesAnalysis.xlsx. In this file, we create a table as shown in Table 7.3. Here we count the **Total Posts** in the DeltaPosts.csv and PublicPosts.csv files in cells B2 and C2 using

```
=COUNT('[LIWC2015 Results (DeltaPosts).xlsx]Sheet0'!$A:$A)
```

and

```
=COUNT('[LIWC2015 Results (PublicPosts).xlsx]Sheet0'!$A:$A)
```

Next we count the **Posts about Delays** in B3 and C3 using

Table 7.2 Custom Dictionary for Identifying Posts Discussing Delays

Concept	% 100 %	 Delay
Tags	delay* late wait*	100 100 100

Table 7.3 Posts about Delays at Delta's versus Other Facebook Pages

	Delta Page	Other Pages
Total Posts	1769	256
Posts about Delays	397	8
% Posts about Delays	22%	3%

=COUNTIFS('[LIWC2015 Results (DeltaPosts).xlsx]Sheet0'!$O:$O,">0")

and

=COUNTIFS('[LIWC2015 Results (PublicPosts).xlsx]Sheet0'!$O:$O,">0")

Finally, we obtain the **% Posts about Delays** in B4 and C4 using *=B3/B2* and *=C3/C2*.

Thus we see that 22% of the public's posts to Delta's page concern flight delays, but only 3% of posts about Delta on other Facebook pages mention flight delays. We can determine whether this difference is statistically significant by first obtaining the combined σ in cell B6 using *=SQRT((B4*(1-B4)/B2)+(C4*(1-C4)/C2))*. We then obtain the z-score in B7 using *=(ABS(B4-C4))/B6*. Finally, we compute the probability of a z-score as high as or higher than the one obtained using *=1-NORMSDIST(B7)*. With a z-score greater than 13, we find the probability of the observed difference of 19% in the rate at which the public discusses flight delays on Delta Airlines' Facebook page versus other pages is negligible. This suggests that Delta Airlines would do well to focus exclusively on their own Facebook page to monitor issues and customer sentiment concomitant with flight delays.

Question 2: How Do Delta Customers Feel about Flight Delays at Different Airports?

We answer this question, focusing on five of the busiest Delta Airline hub cities: Atlanta, Detroit, Minneapolis/St. Paul, New York City, and Los Angeles. Collectively these five hub cities account for over 2,500 daily departures and serve almost 700 destinations [25]. To identify posts mentioning these hub cities, we begin by augmenting Delta.dic with the airport codes and other possible descriptions for these hub cities, as noted in Table 7.4, structuring the entries as seen in Figure 7.8 and Table 7.2.

To obtain LIWC scores for mentions of these city hubs and for customer sentiment, we run the Facebook posts from our DeltaPosts.csv file through LIWC twice. (We ignore the PublicPosts.csv file since the total number of posts is relatively small and the proportion of posts discussing delays is negligible.) The first time, we run the analysis on the DeltaPosts.csv file, selecting the standard 2015 LIWC dictionary. The second time, we run the analyses on the resulting output file, LIWC2015 Results (DeltaPosts).xlsx, selecting our custom Delta.dic dictionary. Both times, we point to the message in column C, keeping in mind that row 1 contains an additional row of headers, specifying the original column letters, the second time. If we accepted the default file names, our final results file is named LIWC2015 Results (LIWC2015 Results (DeltaPosts)).xlsx.

To clean up this results file for analysis, let's move the row 3 headers for columns A through J to row 1 and the row 2 headers for columns K through CY to row 1. We then can delete rows 2 and 3. We then select columns H through CY and convert them from text format to numbers as described earlier. Inspecting the worksheet, we notice that the initial WC, WPS, Sixltr, and Dic columns as well as the final punctuation columns have been duplicated across the two analyses. To eliminate these duplicates, let's delete columns CN through DC. Let's also rename Sheet0 LIWCScores and add another sheet called SentimentSummary. For Atlanta, we obtain the average PosEmo and NegEmo for messages not discussing flight delays and messages discussing delays using the formulas:

Table 7.4 Custom Dictionary Entries to Identify Airport Mentions in Posts

Concept (Hub City)	Tags (City Names and Airport Codes)		
1. Atlanta	atlanta	atl	
2. Detroit	detroit	dtw	
3. NYC	new york city new york nyc	la guardia laguardia lga	jfk kennedy
4. Minneapolis	minneapolis	st. paul	msp
5. Los Angeles	los angeles	lax	

Not Delayed, PosEmo:

=AVERAGEIFS(LIWCScores!AO:AO,LIWCScores!CN:CN,">0",LIWCScores!CS:CS,"0")

Not Delayed, NegEmo:

=AVERAGEIFS(LIWCScores!AP:AP,LIWCScores!CN:CN,">0",LIWCScores!CS:CS,"0")

Delayed, PosEmo:

=AVERAGEIFS(LIWCScores!AO:AO,LIWCScores!CN:CN,">0",LIWCScores!CS:CS,">0")

Delayed, NegEmo:

=AVERAGEIFS(LIWCScores!AP:AP,LIWCScores!CN:CN,">0",LIWCScores!CS:CS,">0")

Change the column referenced in the second argument of the AVERAGEIFS formula (i.e., CN:CN) to reflect the columns for Detroit, NYC, Minneapolis, and Los Angeles (i.e., to CO:CO, CP:CP, CQ:CQ, and CR:CR, respectively) to obtain the average sentiment scores for the other cities. We then compute the difference between the amount of positive and negative sentiment expressed when not discussing delays and discussing delays. Graphing the resulting differences in sentiment scores produces the visual in Figure 7.10.

When people post messages not dealing with flight delays, we see expressions of positive sentiment unfailingly exceed expressions of negative sentiment. When discussing flight delays, expressions of positive sentiment usually decrease and expressions of negative sentiment usually increase. However, expressions of positive sentiment with regard to flights to/from Detroit increase when discussing delays and expressions of negative sentiment with regard to flights to/from Minneapolis decrease when discussing delays. The most negative reaction to delays we see is for Los Angeles. Oddly we see a favorable reaction to delays for Detroit, where the relative amount of positive to negative sentiment expressed increased when discussing delays.

What is the nature of the negative sentiment most affected across the different city hubs? To determine the average of anxiety, anger, and sadness across posts without and with mentions of delays, we once again modify the AVERAGEIFS formulas above, this time replacing the first argument—AO:AO and AP:AP—with AQ:AQ for anxiety, AR:AR for anger, and AS:AS for sadness. Figure 7.11 depicts differences in three negative sentiments between posts discussing delays and not discussing delays. We find that delays result in an increase in anxiety for flights to/from the Detroit and Minneapolis airports, a steep rise in anger for flights to/from Los Angeles, and an increase in sadness for flights to/from Atlanta. Such information on how individuals express themselves when flight delays occur could prove useful in Delta's training of their gate agents.

Tutorial 7.3. What Drives the Presidency Tweets?

In this portion of our investigation of the presidency tweets, we dig further into the conversation about the presidency and how it changed between the 2016 presidential primaries and the 2017 presidential inauguration.

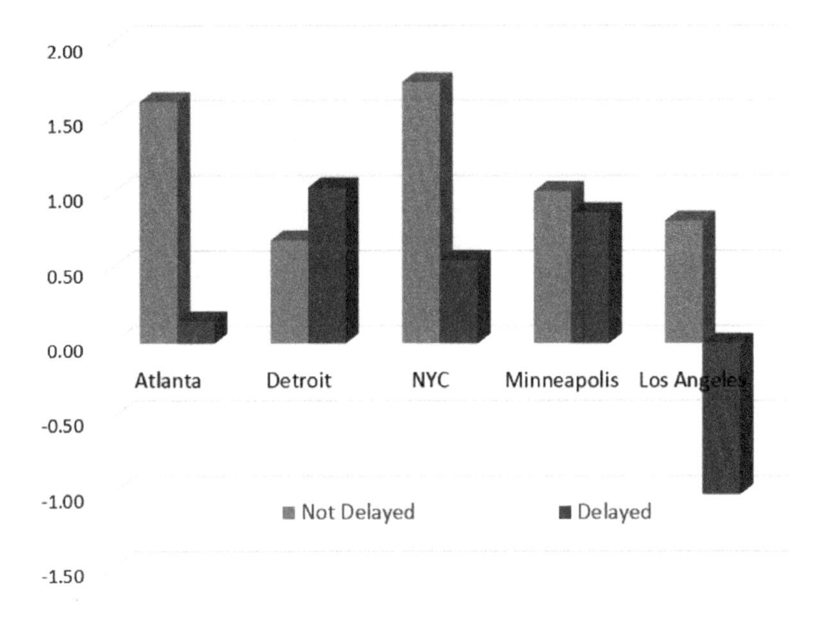

Figure 7.10 Difference in Positive and Negative Sentiment across Five Airports

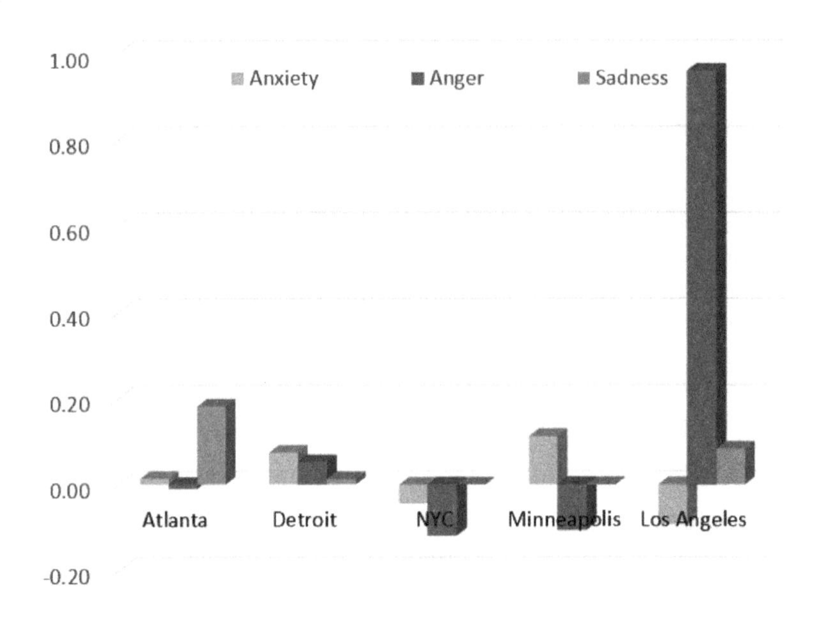

Figure 7.11 Difference in Negative Sentiments across Five Airports

We begin by analyzing the two corpora of tweets using LIWC. Then, we address a series of questions based on the LIWC output.

Open LIWC. Using the main LIWC menu after closing the Welcome to LIWC dialog, we tell LIWC we wish to Analyze Excel/CSV File. Select the DT1.xlsx file; then select the Tweet column (column Q). Save the resulting analyses to an Excel file in the folder. Then repeat for the DT2.xlsx file. If we accepted the defaults, we should have two CSV files, each named with "LIWC 2015 Results" and the name of the file analyzed in parentheses. Let's inspect these two files. We will notice that LIWC scores have been assigned for the two header rows from our NodeXL workbooks. Let's delete these two rows from each of our LIWC results files so they do not contaminate any subsequent analyses and save the files. We now will use these files to answer the questions below.

Question 1. Have Public Sentiment and Motives Changed between the Two Periods?

To address this question, we create a new Excel file. Let's call it DTAnalysis.xlsx. In it, we create a table as depicted in Table 7.5. We create a row for each of the two major LIWC affect concepts (posemo and negemo in columns BE and BF) and for each of the five LIWC drives concepts (affiliation . . . risk). In the next two columns, we obtain the column averages for each of these concepts from our LIWC2015 Results (DT1).xlsx and LIWC2015 Results (DT1).xlsx LIWC output file. Finally, working across sheets, we use the following Excel statistical analysis function to determine whether the mean differences are statistically significant:

T.TEST(Array1, Array2, Tails, Type)

where ARRAY1 and ARRAY2 are our data columns corresponding to each row from Table 7.5, TAILS indicates whether we are conducting a 1-tail (expecting one mean to be higher than the other) or 2-tail (expecting means to be different, but don't know the direction), and TYPE indicates whether not our variances are (1) paired, (2) homoscedastic, or (3) heteroscedastic.

To interpret our findings in Table 7.10, we first need to pick an α-level or acceptable chance of committing a Type I error (i.e., a probability of rejecting the null hypothesis when it is true). Given our large sample size, 1,313 + 1,745 = 3,058 observations, the chances of committing a Type II error, against which we balance the chances of committing a Type I error, are relatively slim. So we adopt a more conservative α-level of 0.01—that is, we expect to be accurately rejecting the null hypothesis at least 99% of the time. In other words, we are 99% confident in our conclusions. Now, looking at Table 7.5, we can conclude that there were significant changes in the amount of affect shown and in manifestation of the achievement motive. Looking at the means we find, on average, expression of the positive and negative emotion and the achievement motive increased after the inauguration.

Now we would like to visualize this on our graph. To do so, we first must combine our network and text analysis data. To do so, let's open up our NodeXL files and the LIWC output files. Notice that the LIWC output corresponds to the tweet data we have on the EDGES sheet in our NodeXL file. We can copy all or portions of our LIWC output to the EDGES sheet. Doing so permits us to set edge attributes based on our LIWC output.

Let's begin by filtering **Self-ties** in column AA to reduce visual clutter, using

=[@[Vertex 1]]=[@[Vertex 2]]

Table 7.5 Comparing Sentiment and Motives across the Two Periods

LIWC Concept	Preprimary	Postinauguration	p(t)
posemo	1.34	1.86	0.0000*
negemo	1.49	1.77	0.0090*
affiliation	1.45	1.28	0.0650
achieve	0.70	1.05	0.0000*
power	2.95	3.23	0.0533
reward	0.57	0.74	0.0131
risk	0.29	0.39	0.0361

*Significant changes between periods

Next, we copy the **posemo, negemo, affiliation, achieve, power, reward**, and **risk** columns from our LIWC files to columns AB:AH of the EDGES sheet of our NodeXL files. Now I can set my edge color, shape, and width relative to the data in these columns. We can do so using regular Excel cell addressing (e.g., *A3*) or NodeXL's structured cell references (e.g., *[@[Vertex 1]]*). To visualize the amount of sentiment in the tweets, we want edge colors to be blue if the tweet expressed more positive than negative sentiment; red if it expressed more negative than positive sentiment; and gray if it were neutral or lacking in sentiment. To do so, we use the following formula for **Color** on the EDGES sheet:

=IF([@posemo]>[@negemo],"Blue",IF([@negemo]>[@posemo],"Red","Gray"))

We can also set the **Style** of the edge lines to dashed for predominantly positive sentiment, solid for negative sentiment, and dotted for neutral tweets:

=IF([@posemo]>[@negemo],"Dash",IF([@negemo]>[@posemo],"Solid","Dot"))

Next, given the differences in manifestation of the achievement motive across the two periods, we want to highlight the tweets in which the dominant motive was achievement. Specifically, we want the width of edges representing these tweets to be thicker. To accomplish this, we set the following formula for the **Width** column on the EDGES sheet:

=IF(AND(AE3=MAX(AD3:AH3),AE3>0),2,1)

Let's also filter self-ties. Then on the VERTICES sheet, we can set the color, shape, and size attributes similarly. First, we obtain the average positive and negative (NegEmo) sentiment expressed by each account in PosEmo and NegEmo columns, respectively. To do so, we use the following formulae:

=IFERROR(AVERAGEIFS(Edges!AB:AB,Edges!$A:$A,[@Vertex]),0)
=IFERROR(AVERAGEIFS(Edges!AC:AC,Edges!$A:$A,[@Vertex]),0)

Note: Using *=IFERROR()* takes care of accounts that have not tweeted, but simply have had tweets directed at them. To set the **Color** to red for vertices that expressed more negative than positive sentiment, to blue for those that expressed more positive than negative sentiment, and to gray for those that expressed no sentiment or equal amounts of positive and negative sentiment, we use the following formula:

=IF([@PosEmo]=[@NegEmo],"Gray",IF([@PosEmo]>[@NegEmo],"Blue","Red"))

To set the Shape to solid triangles for accounts that expressed more negative sentiment, to disks for those that expressed more positive sentiment, and to solid squares for those that expressed no sentiment or equal amounts of positive and negative sentiment, we use the following formula:

=IF([@PosEmo]=[@NegEmo],"Solid Square",IF([@PosEmo]>[@NegEmo],"Disk","Solid Triangle"))

Finally, after running Graph Metrics, and requesting Vertex eigenvector centrality, we set node Size proportional to eigenvector centrality using

*=[@[Eigenvector Centrality]]*1000*

Now, using the Fruchterman-Reingold layout algorithm (followed by clicking Lay Out Again a judicious number of times), we can produce the visualizations depicted in Figure 7.12. The visuals tend to confirm the observations from the statistical analyses summarized in Table 7.5: we see more of the solid and dashed lines and more thick edges in the preprimaries than in the postinauguration graph. The visuals also provide some interesting information that the statistics alone did not.

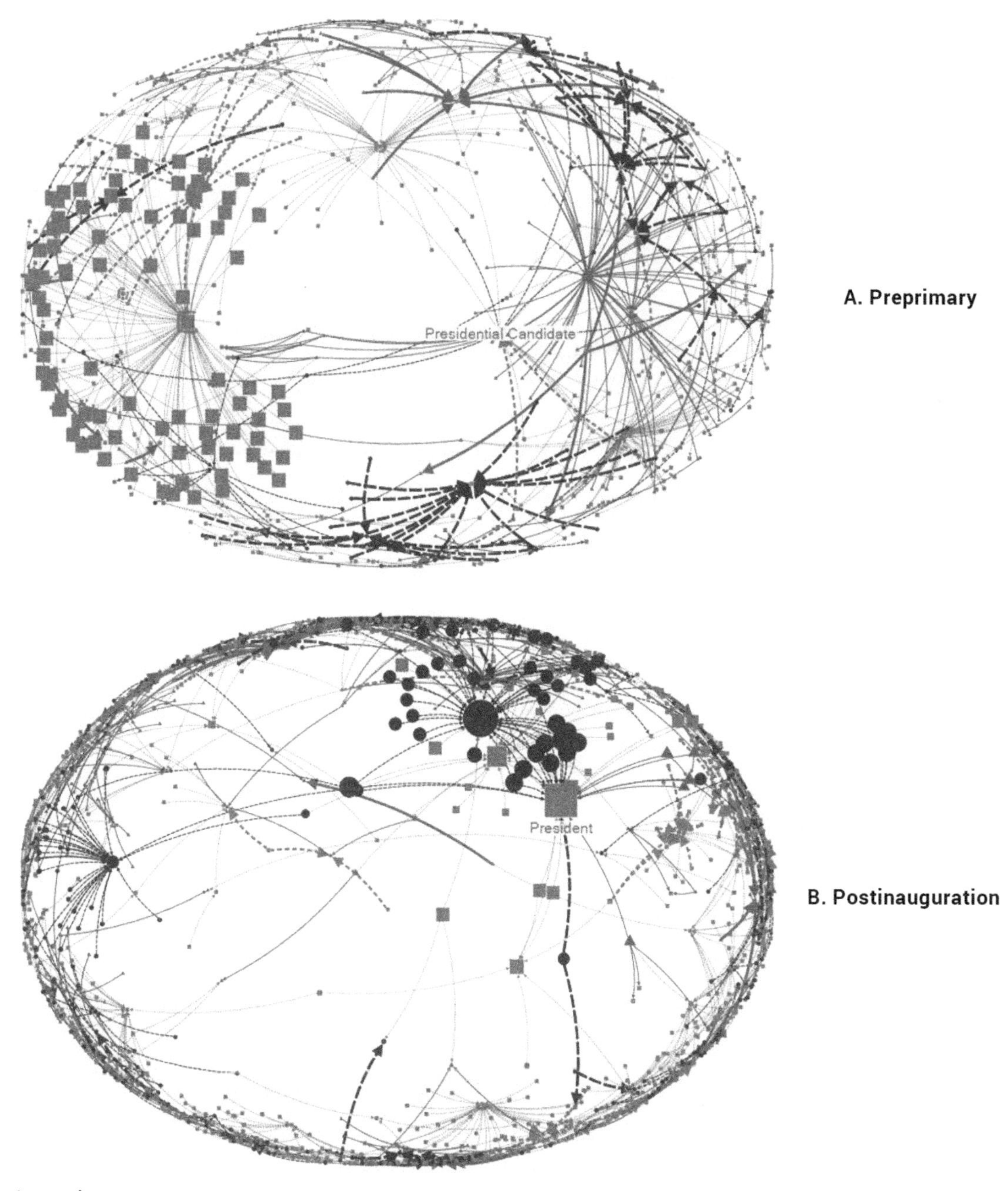

Figure 7.12 Visualizing Sentiment and the Achievement Motive

From Figure 7.12, we see more of the thicker edges in the preprimaries graph tend to be solid or dashed than in the postinauguration graph, suggesting a higher level of emotionality associated with expressions of the achievement motive before the primaries. In fact, while 71% of the tweets in which achievement was the dominant motive in the preprimaries period were emotional (nonneutral), only 58% of the tweets in which achievement dominated in the postinauguration period were emotional.

Note that figuring this out is a conditional probability problem (i.e., the probability that a tweet is emotional, given that it is driven primarily by the achievement motive). Can you do it? *Hint:* We can get the marginal probability of a tweet being driven primarily by the achievement motive from column D and the joint probability of a tweet being both emotional and driven primarily by the achievement motive from columns C and D.

Question 2. Does Expression of Emotion and Motives Coincide with Network Centrality?

To answer this question, we need to do two things. First, we need to obtain network centrality metrics for the accounts in our data set. Let's go ahead and generate these metrics—be sure to request eigenvector centrality. Second, we need to develop a profile of sentiment and motive expression for each account in our data set. We do so by creating seven new columns on the VERTICES sheet, beginning in column AZ, into which we aggregate the sentiment and motives scores across tweets by each account in our data set. Below are the seven column headers and the formulas we need:

PosEmo (column AZ):

=IFERROR(AVERAGEIFS(Edges!AB:AB,Edges!$A:$A,[@Vertex]),0)

NegEmo (column BA):

=IFERROR(AVERAGEIFS(Edges!AC:AC,Edges!$A:$A,[@Vertex]),0)

Affiliation (column BB):

=IFERROR(AVERAGEIFS(Edges!AD:AD,Edges!$A:$A,Vertices[@Vertex]),0)

Achieve (column BC):

=IFERROR(AVERAGEIFS(Edges!AE:AE,Edges!$A:$A,Vertices[@Vertex]),0)

Power (column BD):

=IFERROR(AVERAGEIFS(Edges!AF:AF,Edges!$A:$A,Vertices[@Vertex]),0)

Reward (column BE):

=IFERROR(AVERAGEIFS(Edges!AG:AG,Edges!$A:$A,Vertices[@Vertex]),0)

Risk (column BF):

=IFERROR(AVERAGEIFS(Edges!AH:AH,Edges!$A:$A,Vertices[@Vertex]),0)

We now can ascertain the correlation between social influence, for which we use eigenvector centrality, and each of our sentiments and motives. As we see in Table 7.6, while vibrant affective or motivational expression correlates negatively with actors' influence prior to the primaries, influence correlates positively with expressions of positive emotion, and motivation based on affiliation and power.[1]

1 With the preprimary correlations in column B, postprimary correlations in column C, and sample sizes in row 10, we can determine the probability of the two correlations being different purely by chance using the formula: *=2*(1-NORMSDIST(ABS((FISHER(B2)-FISHER(C2))/SQRT(1/($B$10-3)+1/($C$10-3))))).*

Table 7.6 Correlations between Influence† and Sentiment/Motives

LIWC Concept	Preprimary	Postinauguration	p(Z)
posemo	-0.09	0.09	0.0000*
negemo	-0.11	-0.07	0.2924
affiliation	-0.12	0.10	0.0000*
achieve	-0.07	-0.04	0.5123
power	-0.15	0.11	0.0000*
reward	-0.07	-0.04	0.5030
risk	-0.04	-0.03	0.8073

†Eigenvector centrality; *significant changes between periods

Question 3. Do Ideological Birds-of-a-Feather Flock Together?

To determine whether we have ideological or motive-based homophily (i.e., whether individuals driven by the same motives tend to talk mainly to each other), we begin by determining the dominant motive for each Twitter account in a **Drive** column on our VERTICES sheet using the formula below:

```
=IF(COUNTIFS(BB3:BF3,MAX(BB3:BF3))>1,"Mixed",CHOOSE(MATCH(MAX(BB3:BF3),BB3:BF3,0),BB$2,BC$2,BD$2,BE$2,BF$2))
```

This formula (1) determines whether we have ties for a maximum motives score, in which case Drive is set to "Mixed," and (2) identifies the cell with the highest non-tie maximum value and finds it matching motive. Now, we can use this column as our Vertex attribute in subgroup analyses. Next, we generate Group and Overall graph metrics. This gives us the density of each of our motive-based groups and graph modularity, which we use to determine the extent to which motive-based homophily prevails. To label our subgroups with the motive and the motive's subgroup density, we use the following formula in the **Labels** column on the GROUPS sheet:

```
=[@Group]&" ("&TEXT([@[Graph Density]],"0.000")&")"
```

Partitioning our subgroups into separate panes produces the visuals depicted in Figure 7.13. The visuals contain a great deal of information, overlaying affect communication (edge color), affective disposition (vertex color), communication of achievement motive (edge thickness), and influence (vertex size) over the motive-based subgroups.

First, the proportion of actors in the "Mixed" motive category, who presumably could serve as ideological integrators, dropped from 68% in the preprimaries conversation to 53% in the postinauguration conversation. The most prominent pure motive in both conversations was power, dominating for 19% of participants in the preprimaries conversation and increasing to 28% of participants in the postinauguration conversation. The second-most prominent pure motive in both conversations was affiliation, initially dominating among 11% of participants and later dropping off to 6% of participants. Second, we see that in the conversation occurring prior to the primaries, expressions of power tend to be affectively negative, affiliation mainly positive, and risk affectively neutral. The association between sentiment and motives breaks down in the postinauguration conversation, though, with thickets of positive, negative, and neutral communication across all motives. Third, we notice the conversational tone is less neutral postinauguration. Other than the RealDonaldTrump account, which did not tweet at all but acquires centrality because it is the focus of others' tweets, centrality and ebullience seem to go hand-in-hand during this period.

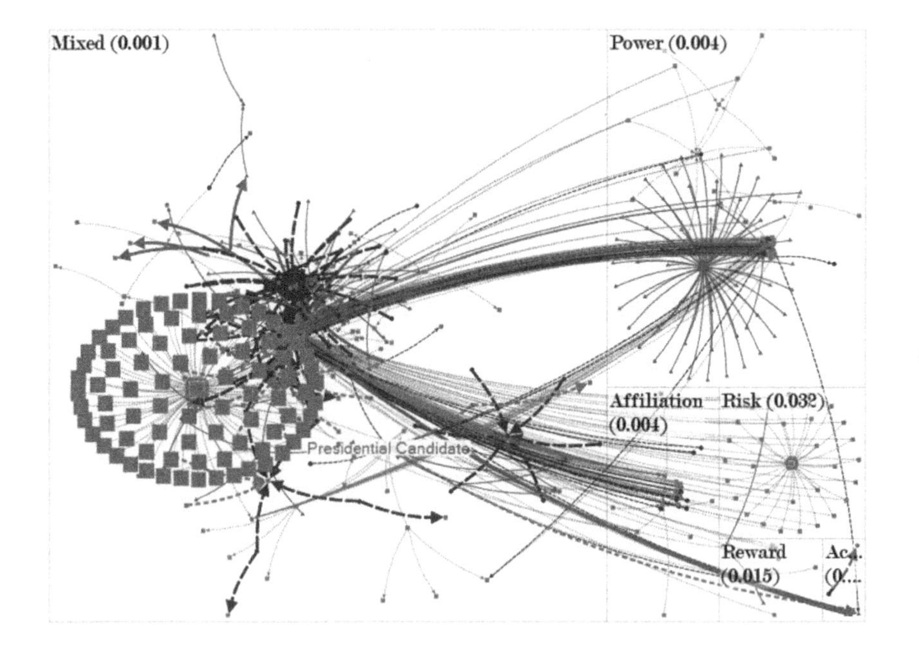

A. Preprimary (modularity = 0.19)

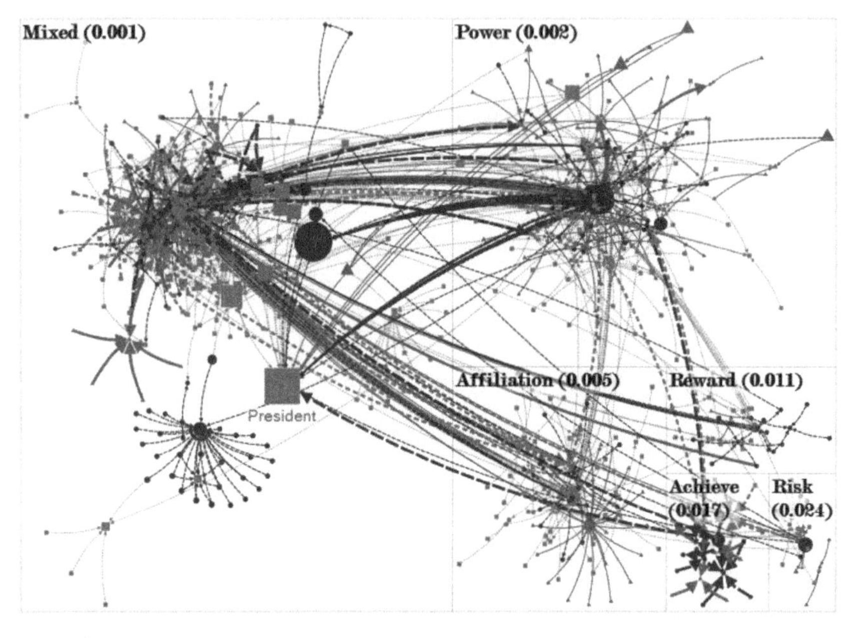

B. Postinauguration (modularity = 0.40)

Legend:
Solid edges/triangular vertices: expressed more negative than positive sentiment
Dashed edges/round vertices: expressed more positive than negative
Dotted edges/square vertices: were neutral or expressed no emotion
Vertex size: influence (eigenvector centrality)
Edge thickness: emphasis of achievement motive

Figure 7.13 Visualizing Motive-Based Homophily

The visuals, along with the modularity coefficients, also provide compelling evidence of changes in motivational homophily between the two time periods. Between the preprimaries and the postinauguration, graph modularity more than doubled—from 0.19 to 0.40. Interestingly, though, average within-subgroup density decreased from 0.018 to 0.010, suggesting that people generally were speaking less to each other postinauguration, even within their motive-based islands. However, these analyses are based on only 3,058 tweets. So let's not get too depressed!

Conclusion

In this chapter, we examined three text analyses tools—word cloud generators, NodeXL's fledgling text analysis capabilities, and LIWC. While individually easy-to-use, our ability to deploy these tools effectively toward developing insight depends on our creativity in how we approach our data, the questions we ask, and our facility for cobbling together multiple tools. Keeping in mind their linguistically simple algorithm, we also need to exercise caution in how we interpret and use text-analysis results from dictionary-based tools as we develop our insights. The best reality check, ultimately, always is the raw data, to which we should return repeatedly.

Exercise: Text Analysis of a Twitter Conversation

Use the data provided by your professor for this exercise. The purpose of this exercise is to surface the words that are important to your specific corpus, to understand the sentiment expressed, to determine what appear to be key concepts that emerge in the conversation, and to see how the words, sentiments, and concepts relate to the network properties of the data.

Individual Assignment

1. Using your favorite word cloud generator, investigate your entire corpus of tweets. Tokenize, normalize, and apply conventional and domain-appropriate stop words. What seem to be the important residual words in your corpus?
2. What word pairs surface to the top?
3. Run LIWC.
4. Comment on the sentiment and/or motives scores you see. On average, are people positively or negatively disposed to the topic of the conversation? What tends to be their dominant motive? Identify at least one other LIWC concept that grabs your attention within the context of your data.
5. Copy at least two columns of LIWC scores you wish to visualize into your NodeXL file. Use the LIWC output to add information to the vertices or edges of your NodeXL graph. What does the visual convey?

Copy salient output into a Word file and annotate it with your observations and comments. Upload your LIWC file, your NodeXL file, and your Word file to D2L.

Team Assignment

Put together your team's analyses into a PowerPoint that tells a story about the qualities of the conversation and the relationships forged around those conversation qualities. Your first slide should name all team-members. Your story should reveal at least five insights that explain or predict and lead you to tangible recommendations.

Works Cited

1. Stone, P.J., et al., "The General Inquirer: A Computer System for Content Analysis and Retrieval Based On the Sentence as a Unit of Information." *Behavioral Science*, 7(4; 1962): 484–98.
2. Robinson, R.L., R. Navea, and W. Ickes, "Predicting Final Course Performance from Students' Written Self-Introductions: A LIWC Analysis." *Journal of Language and Social Psychology*, 32(4; 2013): 469–79.
3. Short, J.C., et al., "Construct Validation Using Computer-Aided Text Analysis (CATA): An Illustration Using Entrepreneurial Orientation." *Organizational Research Methods*, 13(2; 2009): 320–47.
4. Hurwitz, R., "The General Inquirer Home Page," 2003, http://www.wjh.harvard.edu/~inquirer/.
5. Stone, P.J., D.C. Dunphy, and M.S. Smith, *The General Inquirer: A Computer Approach to Content Analysis*. Cambridge, MA: MIT Press, 1966.
6. Maher, B., K.O. McKean, and B. McLaughlin, "Studies in Psychotic Language," in *The General Inquirer: A Computer Approach to Content Analysis*, edited by P.J. Stone, D.C. Dunphy, and M.S. Smith. MIT Press: Cambridge, MA: MIT Press, 1966.
7. Tetlock, P.C., M. Saar-Tsechansky, and S. Macskassy, "More than Words: Quantifying Language to Measure Firms' Fundamentals." *The Journal of Finance*, 63(3; 2008): 1437–67.
8. Pennebaker, J.W., and S.K. Beall, "Confronting a Traumatic Event: Toward an Understanding of Inhibition and Disease." *Journal of Abnormal Psychology*, 95(3; 1986): 274.
9. Pennebaker, J.W., M. Colder, and L.K. Sharp, "Accelerating the Coping Process." *Journal of Personality and Social Psychology*, 58(3; 1990): 528.
10. Pennebaker, J.W., *Opening Up: The Healing Power of Expressing Emotions*. New York: Guilford Press, 1990.
11. Newman, M.L., et al., "Lying Words: Predicting Deception from Linguistic Styles." *Personality and Social Psychology Bulletin*, 29(5; 2003): 665–75.
12. Boulton, R., "Snowball. Tartarus," 2014, http://snowball.tartarus.org/algorithms/english/stop.txt.
13. Aggarwal, C.C., and C. Zhai, *Mining Text Data*. New York: Springer Science & Business Media, 2012.
14. Pennebaker, J.W., et al., "The Development and Psychometric Properties of LIWC2015." Austin: University of Texas at Austin, 2015.
15. Tausczik, Y.R., and J.W. Pennebaker, "The Psychological Meaning of Words: LIWC and Computerized Text Analysis Methods." *Journal of Language and Social Psychology*, 29(1; 2010): 24–54.
16. Bell, A., et al., "Predictability Effects on Durations of Content and Function Words in Conversational English." *Journal of Memory and Language*, 60(1; 2009): 92–111.
17. Pennebaker, J.W., and L.A. King, "Linguistic Styles: Language Use as an Individual Difference." *Journal of Personality and Social Psychology*, 77(6; 1999): 1296.
18. Pennebaker, J.W., *The Secret Life of Pronouns: What Our Words Say about Us*. New York: Bloomsbury Press, 2011.
19. Hart, R.P., *Diction 5.0: The Text-Analysis Program: User's Manual*. Austin, TX: Digitext, 2000.
20. Cheney, G., "The Rhetoric of Identification and the Study of Organizational Communication." *Quarterly Journal of Speech*, 69(2; 1983): 143–58.
21. Fiol, C.M., "Capitalizing on Paradox: The Role of Language in Transforming Organizational Identities." *Organization Science*, 13(6; 2002): 653–66.
22. Fiol, C.M., "A Semiotic Analysis of Corporate Language: Organizational Boundaries and Joint Venturing." *Administrative Science Quarterly*, 34(2; 1989): 277–303.
23. Fiol, C.M., D. Harris, and R. House, "Charismatic Leadership: Strategies for Effecting Social Change." *The Leadership Quarterly*, 10(3; 1999): 449–82.

24. Barney, J.B., et al., "A Strategy Conversation on the Topic of Organization Identity," in *Identity in Organizations: Building Theory through Conversations*, edited by D.A. Whetten and P.C. Godfrey, 99–165. Thousand Oaks, CA: Sage, 1998.

25. Wikipedia, "Delta Air Lines," July 17, 2017, https://en.wikipedia.org/wiki/Delta_Air_Lines.

CHAPTER 8

Basic Text Analytics with R

In this chapter, we will begin by exploring R's text data objects, which we will need to use for our text analytics. We then will look at conducting preprocessing—that is, text normalization and application of stop words—in R. Next, we will look at applying the two text analytics approaches discussed in Chapter 7 using R. Illustrating the count-based approach, we will obtain word frequencies and develop different types of word clouds. Illustrating the dictionary-based approach, we will conduct sentiment analysis using an R package and applying a non-R dictionary.

> **Learning Objectives**
>
> In this chapter, you will become familiar with R text analytics tools related to the two approaches introduced in Chapter 7. You will develop skills required to:
>
> 1. work with text data objects;
> 2. conduct preprocessing of texts;
> 3. use count-based approaches to
>   a. obtain simple and weighted word frequencies and understand the significance of tf-idf scores,
>   b. develop simple and pictorial word clouds,
>   c. develop comparative and comparison word clouds,
>   d. surface word co-occurrences; and
> 4. use dictionary-based approaches to
>   a. perform sentiment analysis,
>   b. apply custom dictionaries.

Text Analysis Packages

For our foray into text analytics with R, we will need several R packages. We will use the **tm** and **SnowballC** packages to prepare our documents for text analysis. We will work with **wordcloud** and **wordcloud2** to produce word clouds, augmenting our control over the color palette with the **RColorBrewer** package. Lastly, we will use the **syuzhet** package for sentiment analysis. (Alternate sentiment analysis packages for R include the recently released **RSentiment** and **sentimentr** packages and the legacy **sentiment** package.) We also will use the **ggplot2** and **reshape2** packages in our visualizations.

Text Data Objects in R

Before we embark on our voyage through text analytics with R, it will be useful to familiarize ourselves with the data objects with which we will be working. The first of such objects is a corpus. The tm ***Corpus(SOURCE)*** function converts imported text data into a document format that is accessible to text processing. The Corpus() function accepts several different data sources, including ***DataframeSource(DATAFRAME)***, ***DirSource(DIRECTORY)***, and ***VectorSource(VECTOR)***. Specifying these source types ensures that each value within the data frame, directory, or vector is treated as a document. **DataframeSource()** is useful if our data are contained in an R data frame. **DirSource()** is useful if we wish to import multiple text files from a specified directory. The most

Table 8.1 Illustrating Corpus Creation

Data Source	Sample Code
DataframeSource	`MyDF=data.frame(doc_id=c('Doc1', 'Doc2', 'Doc3'), text=c('This is a text.', 'This is another one.', 'And this is a third.'))` `MyCorp=Corpus(DataframeSource(MyDF))`
DirSource	`SpeechCorp=Corpus(DirSource('Speeches'))`
VectorSource	`MobyDickCorp = Corpus(VectorSource( scan('http://www.gutenberg.org/files/2701/2701-0.txt', what='character', sep='\n')))`

versatile of the data source controls, **VectorSource()**, enables us to work with a single row or a column of text from a data frame or list. Table 8.1 illustrates use of these three data source controls to create a corpus.

The second text data object is the term-document matrix (or the document-term matrix). Recall that terms are the different words occurring in our corpus (e.g., "able," "add," "advanced," "again," and "ago"), and documents are the individual texts in the corpus (e.g., Dream.txt, for Martin Luther King's "I Have a Dream" speech, and Gettysburg.txt, for Abraham Lincoln's Gettysburg address). We do so using the ***TermDocumentMatrix(Corpus)*** or the ***DocumentTermMatrix(Corpus)*** function. The results of TermDocumentMatrix() and DocumentTermMatrix() contain the same information—counts of each word across documents in the corpus. But the two functions differ in the orientation of the matrix produced, with the former producing a matrix in which rows are terms and columns are documents and the latter producing a matrix where documents are rows and columns are terms. The term-document matrix is a matrix with a row for every word and a column for every document or category of document, for which word frequencies are to be compared. The document-term matrix is a matrix with a row for every document and a column for every word. In other words, the term-document matrix and the document-term matrix are the transpose of each other. See Figure 8.1A for a view of the `DocumentTermMatrix(SpeechCorp)` and Figure 8.1B for a view of the `TermDocumentMatrix(SpeechCorp)`. **As we will see, different text processing packages require a specific orientation of this matrix.**

Once created, we can use ***inspect(TextObject)*** to scan the contents of the text object—corpus, term-document matrix, or document-term matrix. Inspecting a corpus produces metadata on the corpus (i.e., the number of documents and the number of characters per document). For example, `inspect(SpeechCorp)` tells us that we have two documents in the corpus and displays the document contents; `inspect (TermDocumentMatrix(SpeechCorp))` produces the following output.

	Dream.txt	Gettysburg.txt
able	8	0
again	2	0
ago	1	1
ahead	1	0
alabama	3	0

A. Vertically Oriented Term-Document Matrix

	able	again	ago	ahead	alabama
Dream.txt	8	2	1	1	3
Gettysburg.txt	0	0	1	0	0

B. Horizontally Oriented Document-Term Matrix

Figure 8.1 Matrices of Terms and Documents in the Speech Corpus

```
<<DocumentTermMatrix (documents: 2, terms: 580)>>
Non-/sparse entries: 635/525
Sparsity           : 45%
Maximal term length: 14
Weighting          : term frequency (tf)
Sample             :
                Terms
Docs              and freedom from have not our that the this will
  Dream.txt        54      20   18   17  13  17   24 103   20   27
  Gettysburg.txt    6       0    2    5   5   2   13  11    4    1
```

This tells us that our document-term matrix consists of 580 terms. Across our two documents, this means we have 1160 cells. The inspect() output informs us that 525 of these—or ~45%—are empty (or sparse), indicating terms that have not occurred in both documents. Next, the output shows us a portion of the matrix. Even for our relatively small speech corpus, inspect() does not permit us to view the entire matrix. We can overcome this by coercing the inspected content into a matrix data object using the ***as.matrix(DTMorTDM)*** function, and then viewing it using ***View(Matrix)***. For example, to produce Figure 8.1, we use `View(as.matrix(DocumentTermMatrix(SpeechCorp)))` and `View(as.matrix(TermDocumentMatrix(SpeechCorp)))`.

We can remove from the term-document matrix words that appear only rarely in the documents using ***removeSparseTerms(DTMorTDM, Sparsity)***, where SPARSITY is the permissible proportion of documents that may not contain the term (i.e., the threshold for retaining terms in the matrix). The larger the threshold, the more the terms that will be retained; the smaller the threshold, the fewer the terms retained. For example, `removeSparseTerms(SpeechTDM, 0.5)` will remove terms that occur in 50% (or less than 50%) of the documents, thereby retaining only terms that occur in both speeches and eliminating the terms 1, 2, 3, and 5 in Figure 8.1.

Text Preprocessing in R

Preprocessing is a key step in text analysis. Without preprocessing, we are unlikely to detect anything interesting in our corpus. We can preprocess in one of two ways—preprocess the corpus or preprocess as we are creating the document-term (or term-document) matrix from the corpus. While the syntax for performing the two methods varies slightly, the underlying concepts are the same. Regardless of the method, we need to plan the order in which we will complete the various preprocessing tasks before beginning to preprocess. For example, if we attempt to eliminate "StarWars" as a stop word after normalizing, we will be unsuccessful because stemming would have eliminated the "s" and converting the text to lowercase would result in "starwar," which does not match the term "StarWars," which we wish to eliminate.

We subject a corpus to preprocessing using the ***tm_map(Corpus, PreProcessingTask)*** function. This function transforms a corpus in accordance with the specific arguments used. Different arguments perform different the preprocessing tasks—normalizing case, stemming, and eliminating stop words. See the "Preprocessing Tasks and How to Perform Them" insert for arguments to be used to perform the different preprocessing tasks. Thus, to remove punctuation and numeric characters, we use `SpeechCorp=tm_map(SpeechCorp, removePunctuation)` and `SpeechCorp=tm_map(SpeechCorp, removeNumbers)` to strip the corpus of the characters or we use `SpeechDTM=DocumentTermMatrix(SpeechCorp, control=list(removePunctuation=T, removeNumbers=T))` to strip the document-term matrix of the characters. In addition to the built-in functionality available, the tm package also provides a ***content_transformer(FUN)*** wrapper that enables us to perform custom preprocessing tasks or invoke functions from packages other than tm. We use this, for example, to invoke the ***tolower*** function to change all text to lowercase—for example, `SpeechCorp=tm_map(SpeechCorp, content_transformer(tolower))`.

Preprocessing Tasks and How to Perform Them with R's tm Package

Below are the preprocessing tasks we may wish to do and the syntax for executing them directly on the corpus or while creating the term-document (or document-term) matrix.

Task	Specific Function	Directly Transform Corpus	Transform When Creating DTM/TDM (within control= list() argument)
Tokenize	Specify analysis unit	MC_tokenizer(CORPUS) *or* scan_tokenizer(CORPUS)	tokenize='MC' | 'scan' | 'words' | CUSTOMTOKENIZER
Normalize	Convert to lower case	tm_map(CORPUS, content_transformer(tolower))	tolower
	Stem	tm_map(CORPUS, stemDocument)	stemming=TRUE
	Control for word count	*Perform after we create the term-document matrix with* weightTfIdf(TDM, normalize=T | F) *function*	weighting=weightTf | weightTfIdf | weightBin | weightSmart
Eliminate clutter	Punctuation	tm_map(CORPUS, removePunctuation)	removePunctuation=TRUE
	Numbers	tm_map(CORPUS, removeNumbers)	removeNumbers=TRUE
	Stop words	tm_map(CORPUS, removeWords) *to remove standard stop words;* tm_map(CORPUS, content_transformer(FUN)) *to perform custom transformations*	stopwords=TRUE *to remove standard stop words;* dictionary=CHARACTERVECTOR *to retain only words appearing in specified dictionary/ character vector;* bounds=list(local=c(LOWERBOUND, UPPERBOUND) *to retain only words occurring at least as frequently as the LowerBound (lower limit=0) and less frequently than the UpperBound (upper limit=Inf);* wordLengths=NUMBEROFCHARACTERS *to retain only words of specified length*
	Extra spaces	tm_map(CORPUS, stripWhitespace)	

The **tm** package uses the dictionaries supplied by the **SnowballC** package for eliminating stop words and for stemming. Both these preprocessing tasks may be performed on the corpus or document-term or term-document matrix. To determine the languages for which the SnowballC provides a stop word dictionary, run ***getStemLanguages()***. Currently, in addition to SnowballC's Danish, Dutch, English, Finnish, French, German, Norwegian, Portuguese, Spanish, Swedish, and Russian language dictionaries, stopwords() also supports Catalan and Romanian, with the default language being English. Invoking ***stopwords('LANGUAGE')*** permits us to inspect the standard stop words for that language dictionary. The following are the 174 stop words for the English language.

```
  [1] "i"          "me"         "my"          "myself"     "we"         "our"         "ours"
  [8] "ourselves"  "you"        "your"        "yours"      "yourself"   "yourselves"  "he"
 [15] "him"        "his"        "himself"     "she"        "her"        "hers"        "herself"
 [22] "it"         "its"        "itself"      "they"       "them"       "their"       "theirs"
 [29] "themselves" "what"       "which"       "who"        "whom"       "this"        "that"
 [36] "these"      "those"      "am"          "is"         "are"        "was"         "were"
 [43] "be"         "been"       "being"       "have"       "has"        "had"         "having"
 [50] "do"         "does"       "did"         "doing"      "would"      "should"      "could"
 [57] "ought"      "i'm"        "you're"      "he's"       "she's"      "it's"        "we're"
 [64] "they're"    "i've"       "you've"      "we've"      "they've"    "i'd"         "you'd"
 [71] "he'd"       "she'd"      "we'd"        "they'd"     "i'll"       "you'll"      "he'll"
 [78] "she'll"     "we'll"      "they'll"     "isn't"      "aren't"     "wasn't"      "weren't"
 [85] "hasn't"     "haven't"    "hadn't"      "doesn't"    "don't"      "didn't"      "won't"
 [92] "wouldn't"   "shan't"     "shouldn't"   "can't"      "cannot"     "couldn't"    "mustn't"
 [99] "let's"      "that's"     "who's"       "what's"     "here's"     "there's"     "when's"
[106] "where's"    "why's"      "how's"       "a"          "an"         "the"         "and"
[113] "but"        "if"         "or"          "because"    "as"         "until"       "while"
[120] "of"         "at"         "by"          "for"        "with"       "about"       "against"
[127] "between"    "into"       "through"     "during"     "before"     "after"       "above"
[134] "below"      "to"         "from"        "up"         "down"       "in"          "out"
[141] "on"         "off"        "over"        "under"      "again"      "further"     "then"
[148] "once"       "here"       "there"       "when"       "where"      "why"         "how"
[155] "all"        "any"        "both"        "each"       "few"        "more"        "most"
[162] "other"      "some"       "such"        "no"         "nor"        "not"         "only"
[169] "own"        "same"       "so"          "than"       "too"        "very"
```

In addition to standard stop words for a specified language, we can remove corpus-specific stop words by enclosing the set of stop words in the concatenate—c()—function, following the removeWords argument. For example, to remove the words "ago," "all," "and," "civil," and "come" from our speeches corpus, we use `SpeechCorp=tm_map(SpeechCorp, removeWords, c('ago','all','and','civil','come'))`. Alternatively, we could enumerate the list of terms to *retain* when creating our term-document matrix using the "dictionary=" option within the "control=list()" argument of the TermDocumentMatrix() function. But this is far more cumbersome, since we first would need to obtain the list of all terms in the corpus.

Word Frequency and Weighted Word Frequency

Once we have created the document-term or term-document matrix, we can request the most frequently occurring terms with ***findFreqTerms(DTMorTDM, ThresholdFrequency)***. For example, we can request a list of all terms from our Speeches corpus that occur at least five times using `findFreqTerms(SpeechDTM, 5)`.

We also can display total word counts across our corpus for each term. In order to do so, we first need to convert the term-document matrix or document-term matrix data object to a regular matrix data object using ***as.matrix(DTMorTDM)***. To obtain word counts from a term-document matrix, we use the ***colSums(Matrix)*** function. For example, `SpeechTerms = colSums(as.matrix(SpeechDTM))` gives us a data object containing word counts for each term in *SpeechDTM*. To obtain word counts from a document-term matrix, we use the ***rowSums(Matrix)*** function.

To facilitate viewing of the most frequently occurring terms, we can sort the matrix based on the word frequency with ***sort(DataFrame)***, using the "decreasing=T/F" argument to set the sort order. For example, using `SpeechTerms = sort(SpeechTerms, decreasing=T)` sorts the list of terms in descending order of word frequency. With no preprocessing of our speeches corpus, we find that the most frequently occurring term is "the." Eliminating standard stop words and after stemming, we find the most frequently occurring terms are "will" and "freedom." Applying the tf-idf weighting to the original corpus instead, using `SpeechDTM = DocumentTermMatrix(SpeechCorp, control=list(removePunctuation=T, removeNumbers=T, weighting=weightTfIdf))`, we find the most frequently occurring terms are "dedicated" and "freedom."

Tutorial 8.1. Surfacing the Content of the WhereIsRey Tweets

We will use the data set of the WhereIsRey tweets that we saw in Chapter 1. This file contains a total of 2,096 tweets over a ten-week period. We will load the *WheresRey.csv* file into a dataframe called *ReyPosts* using

```
ReyPosts=read.csv('WheresRey.csv',header=T)
```

To ready our ReyPosts for text analysis, let us convert it to a corpus using the Corpus() function, with the nested VectorSource():

```
ReyCorp=Corpus(VectorSource(ReyPosts$Posts))
```

Next, we want to preprocess our corpus. From the English language standard stop words we saw above, we know it would be a mistake to eliminate punctuation before removing stop words. We also saw that all stop words in the stop word dictionary were lowercase. We begin by converting our corpus to lower case text, eliminating stop words, and then the unwanted characters—punctuation, numbers, whitespace, and any stray Unicode characters—from our corpus.

What Is Term Frequency–Inverse Document Frequency?

In the text mining arena, we often will encounter "tf" and "tf-idf." As seen in the "Preprocessing Tasks and How to Perform Them" insert, these are weighting factors applied to a term-document (or document-term) matrix for the purpose of normalizing the word count. What do these acronyms mean? Term frequency—"tf"—refers to the number of times a term occurs in a document. Because some words such as "the," "be," and "to" naturally occur more frequently, using a simple word count can divert our attention to the uninteresting—unless we have eliminated stop words. Using an inverse document frequency—"idf"—weighting provides an alternative to stop word elimination by down-weighting such frequently-occurring words, but permitting them to participate in our visual or other analyses.

The inverse document frequency of a term—i—is the logarithmic function of the total number of documents divided by the number of documents in which term i occurs:

$$idf_i = log_2 \left(\frac{Number\ of\ documents}{Number\ of\ documents\ where\ term\ i\ occurs} \right)$$

Term frequency-inverse document frequency—"tf-idf"—weights the term frequencies in the term-document matrix by the inverse document frequency.

```
ReyCorp=tm_map(ReyCorp,content_
   transformer(tolower))
ReyCorp=tm_map(ReyCorp, removeWords, stopwords('english'))
ReyCorp=tm_map(ReyCorp, removePunctuation)
ReyCorp=tm_map(ReyCorp, removeNumbers)
ReyCorp=tm_map(ReyCorp, stripWhitespace)
```

By varying the order in which we execute the commands, and then viewing the resulting term-document matrix using

```
View(as.matrix(TermDocumentMatrix(ReyCorp)))
```

we confirm that removing stop words before removing punctuation, numbers, and whitespace yields fewer terms than removing stop words last. We can similarly investigate consequences of not converting our corpus to lower case text before removing stop words. **Note that viewing a term-document matrix is memory intensive and may crash R if your computer lacks sufficient memory.**

Our corpus includes URLs and hard returns that we would like to eliminate, but cannot using the "removeWords" argument. Instead, we will need to do a wildcard search-and-replace. In order to do so, we create a custom *StripString* function (see the "Custom Functions in R" insert) and wrap it in the content_transformer() function using

```
StripString=content_transformer(function(x,pattern) gsub(pattern,'',x))
```

This custom function uses the ***gsub(OriginalString, ReplacementString, InText)*** function to search for a specified original string in a given text and replace it with the specified replacement string. We now can apply

Custom Functions in R

It often is useful to create a custom function to complete repetitive tasks such as doing a wildcard search and replace. A function is a piece of code that accepts certain input and provides some output. For example, SUM(WHATTOSUM) is a built in R function that accepts a set of numbers and returns their sum. Corpus(SOURCE) is a function supplied by the tm package to convert source data into a corpus.

To write a custom function in R, we begin the block of code with ***function(InputParameters)***. We follow that with the code that instructs R on what the function should do with the INPUTPARAMETERS. If the function contains more than one line of code, these lines should be enclosed in { }. We can call R base or package functions from within our custom function and/or call a custom function from an R base or package function. Thus our custom *StripString* function nests a custom search-replace (gsub()) function, available with base R, within the **tm** package's content_transformer() function. Assigning any such combination of custom and R functions, a name (e.g., *StripString*) enables us to call that combination of functions from elsewhere in our code for the duration of a session. In fact, once executed, this function will appear in our Global Environment.

the custom function to a variety of different wildcard search-and-replace tasks. We designate specific character classes between square brackets [ ] and nonspecific wildcards with an asterisk. For example, using

```
ReyCorp=tm_map(ReyCorp, StripString,
   'http[[:alnum:]]*')
```

strips any text beginning with "http" and followed by any alphanumeric string—that is, any alphanumeric character from the set of 0-9, A-Z, or a-z, in any arrangement, from our corpus. Terminating the search string with an asterisk tells R that we are searching for anything that begins with the text preceding the asterisk. (If, for some reason, we wanted to replace only the first instance of a string, we would use the ***sub(ORIGINALSTRING, REPLACEMENTSTRING, INTEXT)*** function.) We also can use our custom *StripString* function to remove new lines (hard returns) from posts using

```
ReyCorp=tm_map(ReyCorp,StripString,'[\r\n]')
```

To eliminate tabs, we use

```
ReyCorp=tm_map(ReyCorp,StripString,'[\t]')
```

Another useful custom function permits us to search for a specified string and, rather than simply deleting it, replace it with another string. This is useful for text cleansing tasks such as fixing spelling errors or other variations (e.g., organising versus organizing) and retokenizing (e.g., "star wars" to starwars). We create this function using

```
SearchReplace=content_transformer (function(x,pattern1, pattern2) gsub(pattern1,pattern2,x))
```

We can apply this custom function using

```
ReyCorp=tm_map(ReyCorp, SearchReplace, 'star wars','starwars')
```

To eliminate those pesky non-ASCII characters that appear in tweets, we can create another custom function:

```
latin2Ascii=content_transformer (function(x) iconv(x, 'latin1', 'ASCII', sub=' '))
```

We then can apply this function to convert our tweets to ASCII format:

```
ReyCorp=tm_map(ReyCorp, latin2Ascii)
```

We would like to eliminate words related to the movie name and characters from the corpus—specifically, "whereisrey," "rey," and "starwars". We do so with:

Regular Expression Syntax

http://www.endmemo.com/program/R/gsub.php

<table>
<tr><th>Syntax</th><th>Description</th></tr>
<tr><td>\\d</td><td>Digit, 0,1,2 . . . 9</td></tr>
<tr><td>\\D</td><td>Not digit</td></tr>
<tr><td>\\s</td><td>Space</td></tr>
<tr><td>\\S</td><td>Not space</td></tr>
<tr><td>\\w</td><td>Word</td></tr>
<tr><td>\\W</td><td>Not word</td></tr>
<tr><td>\\t</td><td>Tab</td></tr>
<tr><td>\\n</td><td>New line</td></tr>
<tr><td>^</td><td>Beginning of the string</td></tr>
<tr><td>$</td><td>End of the string</td></tr>
<tr><td>\</td><td>Escape special characters; e.g., \\ is "\", \+ is "+"</td></tr>
<tr><td>|</td><td>Alternation match; e.g., /(e|d)n/ matches "en" and "dn"</td></tr>
<tr><td>.</td><td>Any character, except \n or line terminator</td></tr>
<tr><td>[ab]</td><td>a or b</td></tr>
<tr><td>[^ab]</td><td>Any character except a and b</td></tr>
<tr><td>[0-9]</td><td>All digit</td></tr>
<tr><td>[A-Z]</td><td>All uppercase A to Z letters</td></tr>
<tr><td>[a-z]</td><td>All lowercase a to z letters</td></tr>
<tr><td>[A-z]</td><td>All uppercase and lowercase a to z letters</td></tr>
<tr><td>i+</td><td>i at least one time</td></tr>
<tr><td>i*</td><td>i zero or more times</td></tr>
<tr><td>i?</td><td>i zero or 1 time</td></tr>
<tr><td>i{n}</td><td>i occurs n times in sequence</td></tr>
<tr><td>i{n1,n2}</td><td>i occurs n1–n2 times in sequence</td></tr>
<tr><td>i{n1,n2}?</td><td>non greedy match; see above example</td></tr>
<tr><td>i{n,}</td><td>i occurs >= n times</td></tr>
<tr><td>[:alnum:]</td><td>Alphanumeric characters: [:alpha:] and [:digit:]</td></tr>
<tr><td>[:alpha:]</td><td>Alphabetic characters: [:lower:] and [:upper:]</td></tr>
<tr><td>[:blank:]</td><td>Blank characters: e.g., space, tab</td></tr>
<tr><td>[:cntrl:]</td><td>Control characters</td></tr>
<tr><td>[:digit:]</td><td>Digits: 0 1 2 3 4 5 6 7 8 9</td></tr>
<tr><td>[:graph:]</td><td>Graphical characters: [:alnum:] and [:punct:]</td></tr>
<tr><td>[:lower:]</td><td>Lowercase letters in the current locale</td></tr>
<tr><td>[:print:]</td><td>Printable characters: [:alnum:], [:punct:], and space</td></tr>
<tr><td>[:punct:]</td><td>Punctuation character: ! " # $ % & ' ( ) * + , - . / : ; < = > ? @ [\ ] ^ _ ` { | } ~</td></tr>
<tr><td>[:space:]</td><td>Space characters: tab, newline, vertical tab, form feed, carriage return, space</td></tr>
<tr><td>[:upper:]</td><td>Uppercase letters in the current locale</td></tr>
<tr><td>[:xdigit:]</td><td>Hexadecimal digits: 0 1 2 3 4 5 6 7 8 9 A B C D E F a b c d e f</td></tr>
</table>

```
ReyCorp=tm_map(ReyCorp, removeWords, c('whereisrey', 'rey','starwars'))
```

Next, we stem using

```
ReyCorp=tm_map(ReyCorp, stemDocument)
```

Now, we create a document-term matrix and a term-document matrix.

```
ReyTDM=TermDocumentMatrix(ReyCorp)
ReyDTM=DocumentTermMatrix(ReyCorp)
```

If we see the error `inherits(doc, "TextDocument") is not TRUE`, it means that R converted our VCorpus data object to a List data object. We need to recreate the corpus and then create ReyTDM or ReyDTM.

To check the contents of the resulting matrices, we can use

```
inspect(ReyDTM)))
```

or

```
View(data.frame(as.matrix(ReyDTM)))
```

If we call our newly created matrix using `ReyDTM`, we can obtain its metadata, including its estimated sparsity of 100% and that its longest word is 181 characters. Actually sparsity is a little under 100%, as perfect sparsity would imply zero frequency counts for all terms across all documents, which is simply impossible. To retain only terms that occur in at least 1% of the documents (~21 documents), we use

```
ReyDTM=removeSparseTerms(ReyDTM,0.99)
```

This brings the number of terms retained in the term document matrix to 138, sparsity to 97%, and a maximal term length of 23 characters. To see terms left in our matrix, we use

```
ReyDTM$dimnames$Terms
```

To determine which terms occur at least 200 times across our corpus, we use

```
findFreqTerms(ReyDTM, 200)
```

This produces the following list:

```
[1] "charact" "femal"   "set"     "target"  "toy"     "girl"    "hasbro"
[8] "disney"  "main"    "merch"   "action"  "figur"   "get"
```

To obtain a list of all terms in our document-term matrix and their associated frequencies, we create a Reyfreq object containing the column sums of the document-term matrix. After sorting it, we can check the contents of Reyfreq, using

```
Reyfreq=colSums(as.matrix(ReyDTM))
Reyfreq=sort(Reyfreq, decreasing=T)
cbind(Reyfreq)
```

Or if we want to list only terms that show up at least 100 times, we can use

```
cbind(subset(Reyfreq, Reyfreq>=100))
```

This produces the following output:

	[,1]				
toy	693	get	210	like	128
charact	508	convers	199	boy	127
figur	477	want	188	black	125
set	476	one	166	widow	123
hasbro	465	sexism	162	store	122
disney	378	view	159	ask	116
action	367	problem	150	includ	110
femal	358	find	143	buy	110
main	323	theforceawaken	141	hero	104
girl	297	just	139	make	102
target	282	miss	138	gamora	100
merch	227	can	129	forc	100

Tutorial 8.2. What Do the Biggest Five Casinos Tweet?

In Chapter 2, we saw word clouds of tweets by the five largest casinos. Here, we confirm our impression that the casinos tweet mainly about gambling and shows. We set our working directory to the one containing the folder with the five text files for Tutorial 8.2. We then read the files in the directory into the CasinoCorpus.

```
CasinoCorpus=Corpus(DirSource('Tutorial 8.2'))
```

Next, if we haven't already done so within this session, we create two custom functions to manage our corpus.

```
StripString=content_transformer(function(x,pattern) gsub(pattern,'',x))
latin2Ascii=content_transformer(function(x) iconv(x, "latin1", "ASCII", sub=" "))
```

We clean our corpus and create the document term matrix. When we do so, we specify a sparsity of 10% (i.e., that each term may be missing in no more than 10% of the documents).

```
CasinoCorpus=tm_map(CasinoCorpus,content_transformer(tolower))
CasinoCorpus=tm_map(CasinoCorpus, removeWords, stopwords('english'))
CasinoCorpus=tm_map(CasinoCorpus, removePunctuation)
CasinoCorpus=tm_map(CasinoCorpus, removeNumbers)
CasinoCorpus=tm_map(CasinoCorpus,StripString,'[\r\n]') #hard returns
CasinoCorpus=tm_map(CasinoCorpus,StripString,'[\t]')   # tabs
CasinoCorpus=tm_map(CasinoCorpus,StripString,'amp')    # ampersands
CasinoCorpus=tm_map(CasinoCorpus, stemDocument)
CasinoCorpus=tm_map(CasinoCorpus, latin2Ascii)
CasinoCorpus=tm_map(CasinoCorpus,StripString,'gtgt')  #'greater than' characters
CasinoDTM=DocumentTermMatrix(CasinoCorpus)
CasinoDTM=removeSparseTerms(CasinoDTM,0.1)
```

Now we determine which terms occur at least five hundred times in our corpus.

```
findFreqTerms(CasinoDTM, 500)
  [1] "can"     "casino"  "come"    "day"     "free"    "get"     "great"
  [8] "just"    "night"   "now"     "play"    "see"     "show"    "thank"
 [15] "ticket"  "tonight" "win"     "won"
```

To visualize the frequency with which each of these terms occurs in the corpus, we first sum the columns in the document term matrix, and then sort the terms in decreasing order of their frequency. We create the CasinoTermFreq data frame containing the subset of terms that occur at least five hundred times in the corpus, clear the row names in the data frame, and set the column names to "Term" and "Freq," which we then can use in our *ggplot* command.

```
CasinoTermFreq=colSums(as.matrix(CasinoDTM)) #to view term frequencies...
CasinoTermFreq=sort(CasinoTermFreq, decreasing=T)
CasinoTermFreq=cbind(CasinoTermFreq)
CasinoTermFreq=data.frame(row.names(subset(CasinoTermFreq, CasinoTermFreq>=500)),
                          subset(CasinoTermFreq, CasinoTermFreq>=500))
row.names(CasinoTermFreq)=NULL
colnames(CasinoTermFreq)=c('Term','Freq')
ggplot(CasinoTermFreq,aes(x=reorder(Term,Freq),y=Freq)) +
         geom_bar(stat='identity', fill='darkred')  +
         labs(y='Frequencies', x='Term') + theme(text=element_text(size=18)) +
         coord_flip()
```

The two most frequently-occurring term is "see," as in MoheganSun's invitation to "*See @LosLonelyBoys in the #WolfDen*" in or "*Tickets to see @DierksBentley & live music from Whiskey Tango this Wednesday at @SanManuelCasino's #CountryNight!*" The second most-frequently occurring term is "win," as in Riverwind's "*Join us Friday for your chance to win big*" tweet. In fact, most terms depicted in Figure 8.2 relate to shows and gambling. Terms such as "get," "just," "great," "come," "can," "now," and "day," which do not, tend to relate indirectly to shows and gambling. For example, Foxwoods tweeted, "*Get your tix to see @AltonBrown Live . . .*" This confirms our observation in Chapter 2 that casinos tweet mainly about shows and gambling.

What of the differences in focus across casinos? To ascertain this, we begin by transposing our term-document matrix into a document-term matrix and creating a data frame that includes the raw frequencies of each casino's use of each term plus the total frequency with which each term is used across the five casinos using the two statements below.

```
CasinoTDM = t(CasinoDTM)
CasinoIndivFreq = data.frame(as.data.frame(as.matrix(CasinoTDM)),
                  rowSums(as.matrix(CasinoTDM)))
```

Next, we cobble together the terms extracted from the data frame row names with the data frame containing the individual casinos' term frequencies and the total frequencies. We set the row names for the revised data frame to NULL and give the data frame meaningful column names. Finally, we limit the data frame to the subset of terms occurring at least five hundred times across all casinos.

```
CasinoIndivFreq=data.frame(rownames(CasinoIndivFreq),CasinoIndivFreq)
rownames(CasinoIndivFreq)=NULL
colnames(CasinoIndivFreq) = c('Term', 'Foxwoods', 'MoheganSun', 'Riverwind',
                              'SanManuel', 'Winstar', 'Total')
CasinoIndivFreq = subset(CasinoIndivFreq, Total>=500)
```

To compare the frequencies with which the five casinos use these frequently-occurring terms, we must reshape the data frame so that the five different casinos become different rows in the data frame (rather than columns). We do so with the melt() function from the reshape2 package. While we are doing so, we also extract

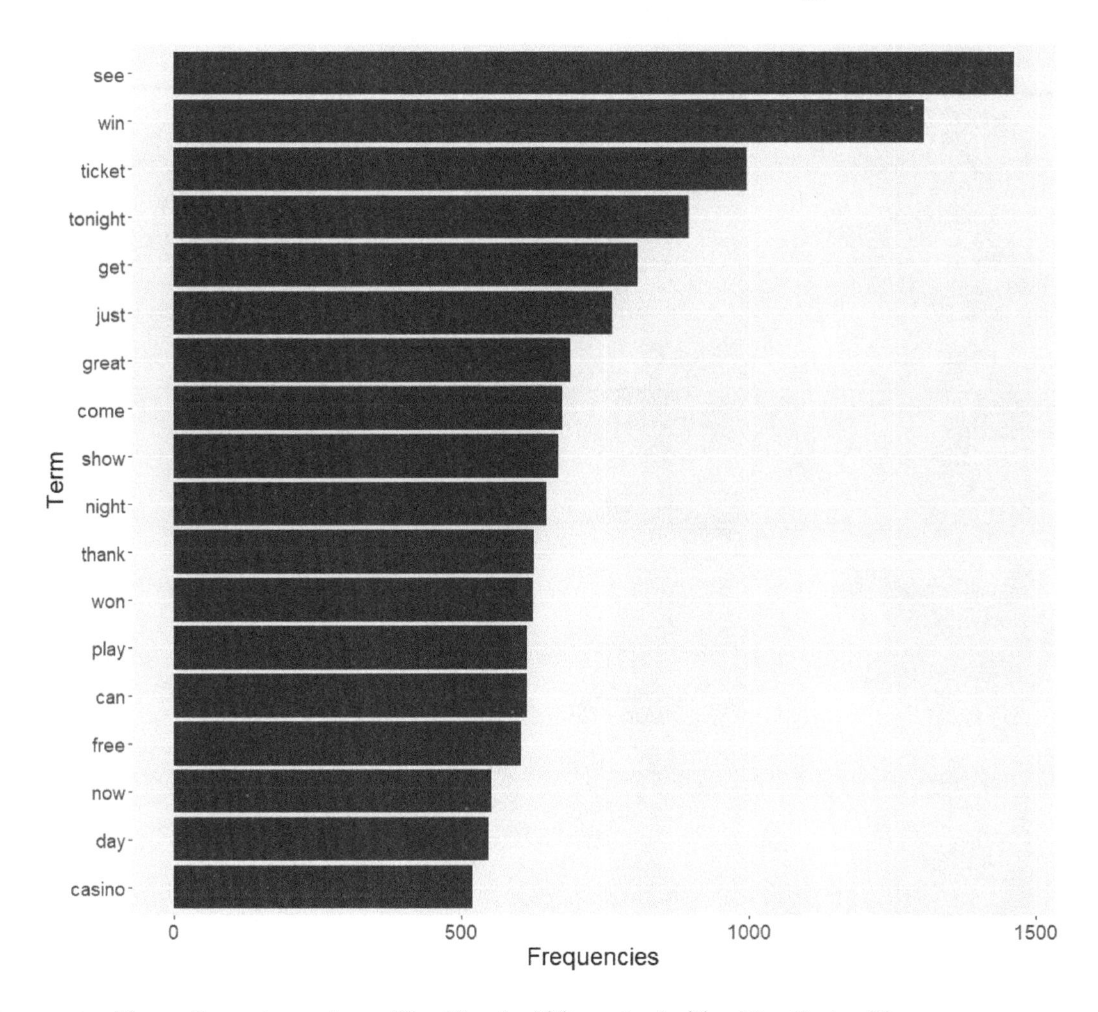

Figure 8.2 Terms Occurring at Least Five Hundred Times in the Top Five Casino Tweets

only the first six columns of the data frame. Now that we have extracted the frequently-occurring terms, we have no further need for the Total column.

```
CasinoIndivFreq = melt(CasinoIndivFreq[1:6], id.var='Term')
```

Finally, the ggplot() statement below produces the graph depicted in Figure 8.3. (If unfamiliar with the ggplot() function from the ggplot2 package, see Appendix E for an introduction.)

```
ggplot(CasinoIndivFreq, aes(fill=variable,x=Term,y=value)) +
                geom_bar(position='stack', stat = "summary", fun.y = "mean") +
                labs(x='Term',y ='Frequency') +
                scale_fill_discrete(name='Casino') + coord_flip() +
                facet_wrap(~variable) + theme(legend.position = c(0.85, 0.2))
```

Again, consistent with our observations in Chapter 2, we see that Foxwoods and Riverwind used the show-related terms, "ticket" and "show," far more frequently than the gambling-related terms, "win" and "won": approximately 650 versus 350 and 430 versus 300 times, respectively. In contrast, Mohegan Sun, San Marcos, and Winstar used the gambling-related terms more frequently than the show-related terms: approximately 330 versus 300, 360 versus 60, and 600 versus 225 times, respectively.

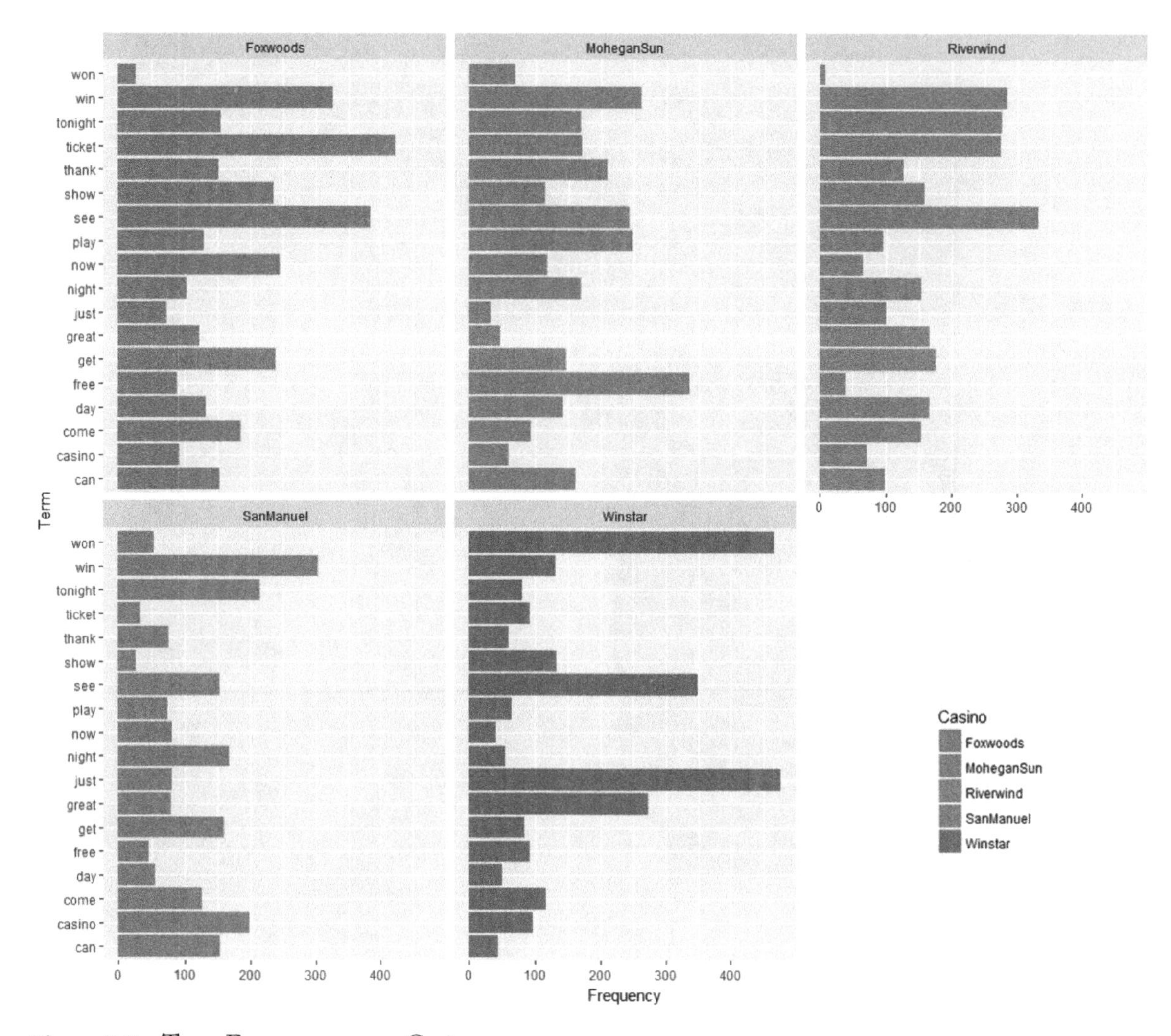

Figure 8.3 Term Frequency across Casinos

Word Clouds: Simple, Pictorial, and Comparison

The barrier to entry in developing a simple word cloud in R is quite low. We can obtain a word cloud with no prep by applying the ***wordcloud(CorpusOrDFColumn)*** function (from the **wordcloud** package) to the text column from our data frame. Because R will be computing word frequency and plotting our word cloud simultaneously, **expect to wait a while though, even on a relatively small corpus**. Also, without preprocessing, we are unlikely to glean much insight from the word cloud. For example, `wordcloud(SpeechCorp)`, executed directly after creating the corpus `(SpeechCorp=Corpus(DirSource('Speeches')))`, produces the word cloud in Figure 8.4.

Two arguments enable us to specify the threshold importance of words and the number of words to be displayed. The "min.freq=" argument permits us to set a threshold word frequency for a word to be included in the cloud. Using "max.words=" further limits the word cloud to the specified number of most-frequently occurring words.

The wordcloud() function also has a few arguments that enable us to control the aesthetics of our output. We can use the "vfont=" argument (for Hershey Vector fonts) to change the word cloud fonts. This argument requires two parameters—the font typeface (serif, sans serif, script, gothic english, gothic german, gothic italian,

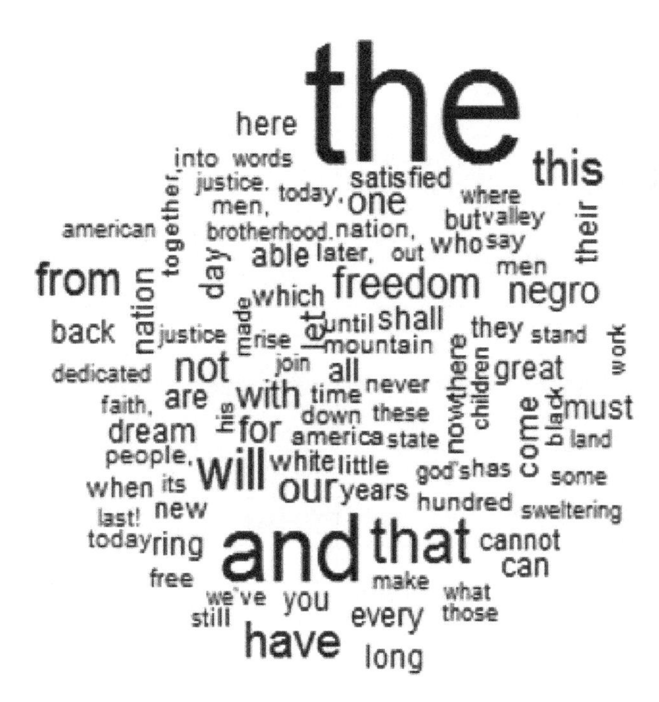

Figure 8.4 Simple Word Cloud of Speeches

serif symbol, sans serif symbol) and the font style (plain, italic, bold, bold italic). **Note that not all combinations of typeface and font styles are available. If you get an error such as "invalid 'vfont' value [typeface = 6, fontindex = 3]", try reverting to a "plain" font style.** (This message tells us that a bold style is not available with the gothic italian typeface.)

By default, words are displayed in a random order within the cloud. Setting the "random.order=" argument to FALSE plots frequently occurring words at the center of the cloud. The "scale=" argument requires a vector containing two numbers—the upper and lower end of the size of words. The "rot.per=" argument specifies the proportion of words that should be rotated 90^0.

The "color=" argument allows us to vary word color. We can use it along with the ***brewer.pal()*** function from the RcolorBrewer package to set the color palette for the word cloud. The Brewer palette provides three types of palettes, each with an upper limit on the number of colors we can use in the word cloud. The qualitative palette arbitrarily assigns different colors to words with different frequencies. The sequential palette assigns lighter colors to lower-frequency words and darker colors to higher frequency words. The function has two arguments: (1) the number of colors to be used (which should be less than the specified number of available colors for the palette selected), and (2) the palette name. Details of these palette options are provided in Table 8.2. From the range of colors provided by each palette, we can specify which of the palette colors should be used in the word cloud by immediately following the palette choice with the index numbers of the desired colors, enclosed in square brackets. Of course, if we are content with a single color, we can specify that color by name or by its RGB hexadecimal code (e.g., 'red' or '#FF0000').

We can apply the brewer.pal() function to our speeches corpus. We remove punctuation and apply the tf-idf weighting to the document-term matrix using `SpeechDTM = DocumentTermMatrix(SpeechCorp, control = list(removePunctuation=T, removeNumbers=T, weighting=weightTfIdf))`. We then construct a matrix of speech terms and their frequencies using `SpeechTerms=colSums(as.matrix(SpeechDTM))`. Since this data object contains two vectors—terms and their frequencies—we save computational time by specifying the source of the terms with a "words=" argument and the source of the frequencies with a "freq=" argument. We obtain the word cloud depicted in Figure 8.5—that is, of

Table 8.2 Brewer Palette Options

Qualitative		Divergent		Sequential			
Palette Name	**Available Colors**	**Palette Name**	**Available Colors**	**Palette Name**	**Available Colors**	**Palette Name**	**Available Colors**
Accent	8	BrBG	11	Blues	9	PuBuGn	9
Dark2	8	PiYG	11	BuGn	9	PuRd	9
Paired	12	PRGn	11	BuPu	9	Purples	9
Pastel1	9	PuOr	11	GnBu	9	RdPu	9
Pastel2	8	RdBu	11	Greens	9	Reds	9
Set1	9	RdGy	11	Greys	9	YlGn	9
Set2	8	RdYlBu	11	Oranges	9	YlGnBu	9
Set3	12	RdYlGn	11	OrRd	9	YlOrBr	9
		Spectral	11	PuBu	9	YlOrRd	9

the 75 most frequently occurring terms with a serif, bold-italicized font and the Dark2 brewer palette using `wordcloud(words=names(SpeechTerms), freq=SpeechTerms, max.words=75, vfont=c('serif','bold italic'), colors=brewer.pal(8, 'Dark2'))`.

The **wordcloud2** package permits to create word clouds that aesthetically are comparable to or better than clouds produced by SaaS products such as Tagul. **Note that if functions from the wordcloud2 package do not perform as described below, run `library(devtools)`, followed by `install_github('lchiffon/wordcloud2')`. This will install a more recent version of the package from the github repository.** Unlike wordcloud(), which requires a document-term matrix, the functions we will use from this package require a term-document matrix. We obtain frequency counts of each term by applying the rowSums() function to the term-document matrix. Thus `SpeechSum = rowSums(as.matrix(TermDocumentMatrix(SpeechCorp, control=list(stopwords=T))))` provides us with the frequency counts for the speech corpus, after eliminating standard stopwords.

The two wordcloud functions we will use from this package require four additional steps. First, because the data object containing results of rowSums (or colSums) is a one-column (or row) data frame containing frequency counts, with row (or column) names being the terms, we need to make the row names a column in the data frame. For example, we use `SpeechSum=as.data.frame(cbind(row.names(as.matrix(SpeechSum)),as.matrix(SpeechSum)))` to bind together the row names and the term frequencies into a single data frame. Second, we need to label the columns so we later can reference them. For example, we name our SpeechSum data frame with `colnames(SpeechSum)=c('word','freq')`. Third, we need to ensure that the freq column is recognized as numbers. We do so using the type conversion functions—for example, `SpeechSum$freq=as.numeric(as.character(SpeechSum$freq))`. Fourth, because the two functions require their input as a list data object, we convert our data frame to a list (e.g., `SpeechSum=as.list(SpeechSum)`).

The wordcloud2() function from the wordcloud2 package produces output similar to that produced by wordcloud() from the wordcloud package. Additionally, the wordcloud2 package allows us to produce word clouds in the shape of words and or pictures. To display a word cloud in the shape of a word, we use the ***lettercloud(ListOfTermsAndFrequencies, DisplayWord)***. For example, to display our speeches corpus within the word "Inspire," we use `letterCloud(SpeechSum, 'Inspire')` to produce the cloud depicted in Figure 8.6. Notice that unlike the wordcloud package, which outputs to the **PLOTS** tab, wordcloud2 functions

Figure 8.5 Controlled Word Cloud of Speeches

Figure 8.6 Lettercloud of Speeches Corpus

output to the **VIEWER** tab, which permits us to interact with the output, depicting frequency counts of words over which we hover.

To display the word cloud as a picture, we first need to specify the path containing the picture we will use to mask the word cloud. We do so with the ***system.file('SubFolder/FileName.Ext', package='PackageFolderContainingFile')***. For example, the following code specifies the LibertyBell.jpg file within a subfolder called "examples" in the wordcloud2 package folder within R: `LBPath = system.file('examples/LibertyBell.jpg', package='wordcloud2')`. We then can generate a pictorial word cloud with the ***wordcloud2(TermFreqList, figPath=PathToGraphicFile)*** function. For example, using `wordcloud2(SpeechSum, figPath=LBPath, color= ifelse`

Figure 8.7 Pictorial Word Cloud (Liberty Bell) of Speeches

`(SpeechSum$freq>10,'red','darkblue'))` produces the output in Figure 8.7. It is worth noting that, unlike Tagul and some other SaaS cloud generators, wordcloud2 does not repeat words across the cloud. This can make for spotty pictorial clouds. For best effect, choose a relatively compact graphic and avoid using pictorial clouds for corpora with high variance in term frequencies.

Using comparison and commonality clouds, R enables us to imbue more information into our word clouds than SaaS products permit. ***Comparison clouds*** depict word frequency distributions across different documents on a single cloud. ***Commonality clouds*** depict words common to the different documents. Document types could be texts about different companies or politicians, from different social media accounts or platforms, or from different geographical locations or time slices.

Developing a comparison cloud requires the ***comparison.cloud(MatrixOfTDM)*** function and ***commonality.cloud(MatrixOfTDM)*** function from the **wordcloud** package. The comparison.cloud() and commonality.cloud() functions require an as.matrix() data conversion of the document term matrix. In plotting the word cloud, the comparison.cloud() function determines the frequency with which every term occurs in every MatrixOfDTM column and across the entire matrix. In the comparison cloud, a term is positioned within the sector representing the document in which it occurred most frequently, and obtains its color from its assigned sector. A term's size indicates the extent to which it is unique to its assigned sector, with more unique

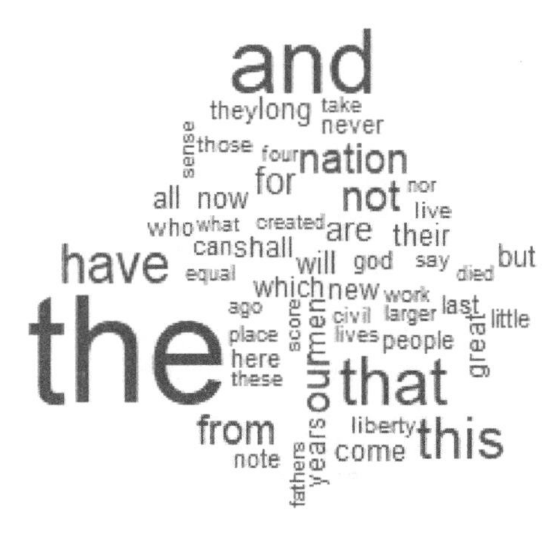

Figure 8.8 Comparison Cloud of Terms in the Two Speeches

terms appearing larger. These larger terms are positioned closer to the center of the cloud. The commonality cloud simply depicts the terms occurring across all documents. For example, to create these clouds in Figure 8.8, we use the statements below. Note that the commonality cloud requires a standard term frequency weighting and does not need the title.size() argument.

```
comparison.cloud(as.matrix(TermDocumentMatrix(SpeechCorp,
        control=list(removePunctuation=T, weighting=weightTfIdf))),
        colors=brewer.pal(9,'Set1'), title.size= 1.5, vfont=c('serif','italic'))

commonality.cloud(as.matrix(TermDocumentMatrix(SpeechCorp,
        control=list(removePunctuation=T))), colors='slateblue3')
```

Sentiment Analysis

In this section, we will examine two ways of conducting sentiment analysis. The first is by using the functionality from the **syuzhet** package. The second examines sentiment analysis via an external, non-R dictionaries such as the General Inquirer (GI) and LIWC dictionaries we saw in Chapter 5. Since the LIWC base dictionaries are proprietary, we will use the GI's sentiment dictionary. Understanding how to use the GI's dictionary also provides insight into how we can work with custom dictionaries in R.

The **syuzhet** package offers several functions for assessing sentiment. Here, we consider two of the most useful functions. The first of these—the ***get_sentiment(DOCUMENT)*** function—computes a polarity measure for a document. Positive values signify a positive tone, negative values a negative tone, and zero a balanced or neutral tone. The get_sentiment() function offers four dictionary-based polarity methods: the default syuzhet [1], bing [2], afinn [3], and nrc [4]. (The get_sentiment() function also offers the stanford method, which employs a parts-of-speech tagger. More on this in Chapter 9.) Metrics generated by the different polarity methods generally are positively correlated, but imperfectly so. It thus is advisable to use a combination of methods, rather than rely on a single metric.

The syuzhet package functions operate on a text vector, not on a corpus, a data frame, or data frame components. So, we first must convert our corpus to a data frame and then extract the text vector from the data frame. We do so using `SpeechDF=data.frame(text = sapply(SpeechCorp, as.character), stringsAsFactors = FALSE)` to create a data frame named *speechDF*. Then, to obtain the polarity score for the two speeches, we use `get_sentiment(SpeechDF$text)`. The polarity scores based on the default syuzhet method are 6.55 for King's "I Have a Dream" speech and 5.05 for Lincoln's "Gettysburg Address," indicating that while both speeches were positive, King's was more positive than Lincoln's. Experimenting with other polarity methods yields inconsistent metrics, though. To extract all four dictionary-based scores to a single data frame, we use the following statement:

```
SpeechPolarity=data.frame(Syuzhet=get_sentiment(SpeechDF$text,method='syuzhet'),
                          Bing=get_sentiment(SpeechDF$text, method='bing'),
                          AFinn=get_sentiment(SpeechDF$text,method='afinn'),
                          NRC=get_sentiment(SpeechDF$text, method='nrc'))
```

The final statement below extracts the row names from the SpeechDF, after dropping the final four characters (i.e., the .txt). The resulting data frame is depicted in Figure 8.9.

```
SpeechPolarity=data.frame(Speech=substr(as.character(row.names(SpeechDF)), 1,
              nchar(as.character(row.names(SpeechDF)))-4), SpeechPolarity)
```

Along with assigning values for positive and negative tone, the second ***get_nrc_sentiment(Document)*** function scores the document for each of eight emotions identified by Plutchik [5]: fear, trust, joy, anticipation, anger, disgust, sadness, and surprise. Emotion scores represent a count of document words corresponding to those in the nrc dictionary of these eight emotions and positive and negative tone. To obtain these scores, we use the statements below to produce the data frame depicted in Figure 8.10.

```
SpeechEmot=get_nrc_sentiment(SpeechDF$text)
SpeechEmot=data.frame(Speech=substr(as.character(row.names(SpeechDF)),1,
    nchar(as.character(row.names(SpeechDF)))-4),SpeechEmot)
```

Tutorial 8.3. Visualizing the #WhereIsRey Conversation

In this tutorial, we examine the nature of the WhereIsRey conversation, considering how its content evolved over the ten-week period.

Question 1. What Is the Content of the WhereIsRey Tweets?

To answer this question, we begin with a simple word cloud. We would like to apply the Brewer palette, selecting specific colors from a palette. For example, [6:8] would select the last three colors from a palette with

	Speech	Syuzhet	Bing	AFinn	NRC
1	Dream	6.55	-4	14	15
2	Gettysburg	5.05	2	3	8

Figure 8.9 Polarity Metrics for the Speeches

	Speech	anger	anticipation	disgust	fear	joy	sadness	surprise	trust	negative	positive
1	Dream	33	32	22	36	35	39	13	40	56	71
2	Gettysburg	1	7	1	6	7	1	3	10	7	15

Figure 8.10 Emotion Word Counts for the Speeches

eight colors; [c(2,4,8)] in the code that follows picks the second, fourth, and eight colors. Below, we pick these colors from the qualitative Dark2 palette to produce Figure 8.11.

```
wordcloud(ReyPosts$Posts, min.freq=50, max.words=100, vfont=c('gothic
    italian','plain'), random.order=FALSE, scale=c(5,0.5), rot.per=.3,
    color=brewer.pal(8,'Dark2')[c(2,4,8)])
```

We can use our Reyfreq data object for a more controlled cloud. Figure 8.12 depicts the results of word clouds produced on our processed WhereIsRey texts. To construct them, we have used custom gray level and rainbow palettes, the code for which appears below the clouds in the figure.

Figure 8.11 A More Controlled Word Cloud

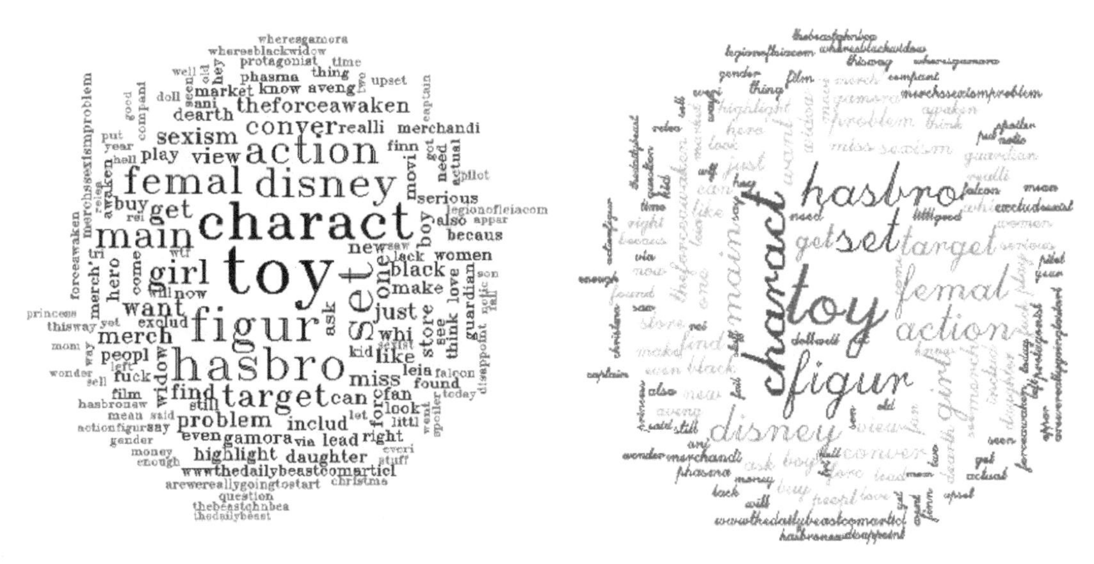


```
grayLevels=gray((Reyfreq+10)/(max(Reyfreq)+10))
wordcloud(words=names(Reyfreq), freq=Reyfreq,
    rot.per=.25, random.order=FALSE,
    vfont=c('serif','bold'), color=grayLevels)
```

```
RBLevels=rainbow(n=10, start=0, end=1)
wordcloud(words=names(Reyfreq), freq=Reyfreq,
    rot.per=.25, random.order=FALSE, vfont=
    c('script','bold'), color=RBLevels)
```

Figure 8.12 Word Clouds Based on Preprocessed Text

Question 2. How Did the WhereIsRey Content Evolve over the Ten Weeks?

To understand whether and how tweets using the WhereIsRey hashtag changed across the ten weeks, we create a comparison and commonality clouds of the terms occurring in posts across the weeks. To do so, we need a data object comprised of ten rows, one for each of the ten weeks. Each row will contain the text of all posts made during that week.

We begin by initializing an empty data frame. This data frame contains a blank row, labeled Week0, which we will need to eliminate later. We then combine the text of posts for each week using the paste() function and repeat for the ten weeks. Then, we eliminate the first element (i.e., the empty Week0) from the WeeklyReyPosts list.

```
WeeklyReyPosts=data.frame(Week0=character())
for(i in 1:10)
{
WeeklyReyPosts=c(WeeklyReyPosts, paste(subset(ReyPosts,Week==i) $Posts, sep='\n', collapse=' '))
}
WeeklyReyPosts=WeeklyReyPosts[2:11]
```

Next, we create a corpus from the texts of the weekly posts, create a term-document matrix from this corpus, and then convert the term-document matrix to a regular matrix. We relabel the document (which are columns in the term-document matrix) with the week numbers. These labels will be displayed in the comparison cloud.

```
WeeklyReyCorp=Corpus(VectorSource(WeeklyReyPosts))
WRTDM=TermDocumentMatrix(WeeklyReyCorp)
WRTDM=as.matrix(WRTDM)
colnames(WRTDM)=c('Week1', 'Week2', 'Week3', 'Week4', 'Week5', 'Week6',
                  'Week7', 'Week8', 'Week9', 'Week10')
```

Now, we can create the comparison cloud. Below, we specify a maximum of a thousand terms are to be displayed and the aesthetics for the different elements of the display. This produces the comparison cloud in Figure 8.13.

```
comparison.cloud(WRTDM,max.words=1000,  vfont=c('serif','italic'),
                 color=c('firebrick','blueviolet','darkgreen','navyblue',
                 'chocolate4', 'darkmagenta', 'darkolivegreen', 'hotpink4',
                 'orangered3','slateblue4'), random.order=F, rot.per=.25,
                 scale=c(2.5,.25), title.size=1)
```

From Figure 8.13, it seems that the majority unique terms occurred in weeks 1 and 5. In interpreting uniqueness, it is useful to keep in mind two things. First, when a term occurs with equal frequency across documents, comparison.cloud() assigns it to the first document. Thus it is very likely that StarWars occurred frequently in subsequent weeks too. Second, comparison.cloud() assesses uniqueness relative to the rate at which a word occurs in a document, relative to its rate of occurrence in other documents. To better understand how frequency plays into the comparison.cloud(), we obtain the counts of some prominent terms from Figure 8.13 and the total word counts for each week using

```
rbind(WRTDM[c('whereisrey','starwars','hasbro', 'disney','rey'),], colSums(WRTDM))
```

The results in Table 8.3A depict the frequency of the five terms across the weeks. Table 8.3B depicts the term rates (calculated in Excel), highlighting the week in which the rate was highest (in bold). This explains the term prominence in Figure 8.13. Interestingly, we see the focus shift away from companies Hasbro and Disney (and Target) after the first two weeks. This may account for the companies' delayed reaction to the merchandising gaffe. In week 5, we see attention to the retailer Kohl's. This attention was positive, as tweets called attention to Rey merchandise that *was* available at Kohl's.

To determine what terms appeared repeatedly across the ten weeks, we create a commonality cloud. Below, we specify a maximum of a thousand terms are to be displayed and the aesthetics for the different elements of the display. This produces the commonality cloud in Figure 8.14. The only two notable commonalities across the weeks are the WhereIsRey hashtag and the StarWars franchise name, confirming the content of the conversation changed substantially across the ten weeks.

Figure 8.13 Weekly Comparison Cloud for WhereIsRey Tweets

```
commonality.cloud(WRTDM,max.words=1000,  vfont=c('serif','italic'),
                  color=c('red','magenta','forestgreen','royalblue'), rot.per=.5)
```

Question 3. How Did Sentiment Change over Time?

To answer this question, we first obtain the polarity measures from the syuzhet package's get_sentiment() function into a ReyPolarity data frame using

```
ReyPolarity=data.frame(Week=ReyPosts$Week,Tweet= ReyPosts$Posts,
         Syuzhet=get_sentiment(as.character(ReyPosts$Posts), method='syuzhet'),
         Bing=get_sentiment(as.character(ReyPosts$Posts), method='bing'),
         Afinn=get_sentiment(as.character(ReyPosts$Posts), method='afinn'),
         NRC=get_sentiment(as.character(ReyPosts$Posts), method='nrc'))
```

This produces the data frame partially pictured in Figure 8.15.

Table 8.3 Frequency and Rate of Select Terms

A. Frequency										
	Week1	**Week2**	**Week3**	**Week4**	**Week5**	**Week6**	**Week7**	**Week8**	**Week9**	**Week10**
whereisrey	4	516	102	6	2	42	85	140	82	2390
starwars	5	217	41	2	3	23	38	48	31	949
hasbro	1	185	27	1	0	0	6	14	4	248
disney	2	25	4	0	0	5	10	25	16	291
rey	0	136	31	1	4	18	43	55	31	971
	60	6373	1376	81	54	604	1345	1564	1215	34544
B. Rate										
whereisrey	7%	8%	7%	7%	4%	7%	6%	**9%**	7%	7%
starwars	**8%**	3%	3%	2%	6%	4%	3%	3%	3%	3%
hasbro	2%	**3%**	2%	1%	0%	0%	0%	1%	0%	1%
disney	**3%**	0%	0%	0%	0%	1%	1%	2%	1%	1%
rey	0%	2%	2%	1%	**7%**	3%	3%	4%	3%	3%

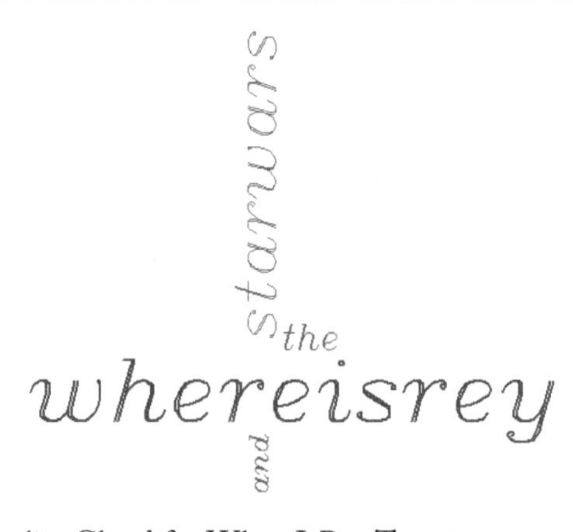

Figure 8.14 Weekly Commonality Cloud for WhereIsRey Tweets

We can visualize any of the metrics. For example, the statement below graphs the syuzhet metric across the weeks.

```
ggplot(ReyPolarity, aes(x=Week,y=Syuzhet)) + geom_point()
```

The more advanced code required to produce Figure 8.16 is provided in Appendix E. From Figure 8.16, we see that sentiment appeared more positive in weeks 4, 5, 6, and 9; in other weeks, sentiment was about as much negative as positive.

	Week	Tweet	Syuzhet	Bing	Afinn	NRC
1	1	Target exclusively released a StarWars toy set with ZERO fema...	0.40	0	0	1
2	1	Hasbro Why do you always leave the girl characters out of yo...	-0.25	0	-1	-1
3	1	Oh look they even included some women IN THE BACKGROU...	1.20	0	2	1
4	1	osakadaioh1 damn serious. Disney sexist marketing alive and ...	-0.45	0	-3	0
5	2	TheMarySue Who is missing from this picture? StarWars TheF...	-0.50	0	-2	-1

Figure 8.15 ReyPolarity Data Frame of get_sentiment() Scores

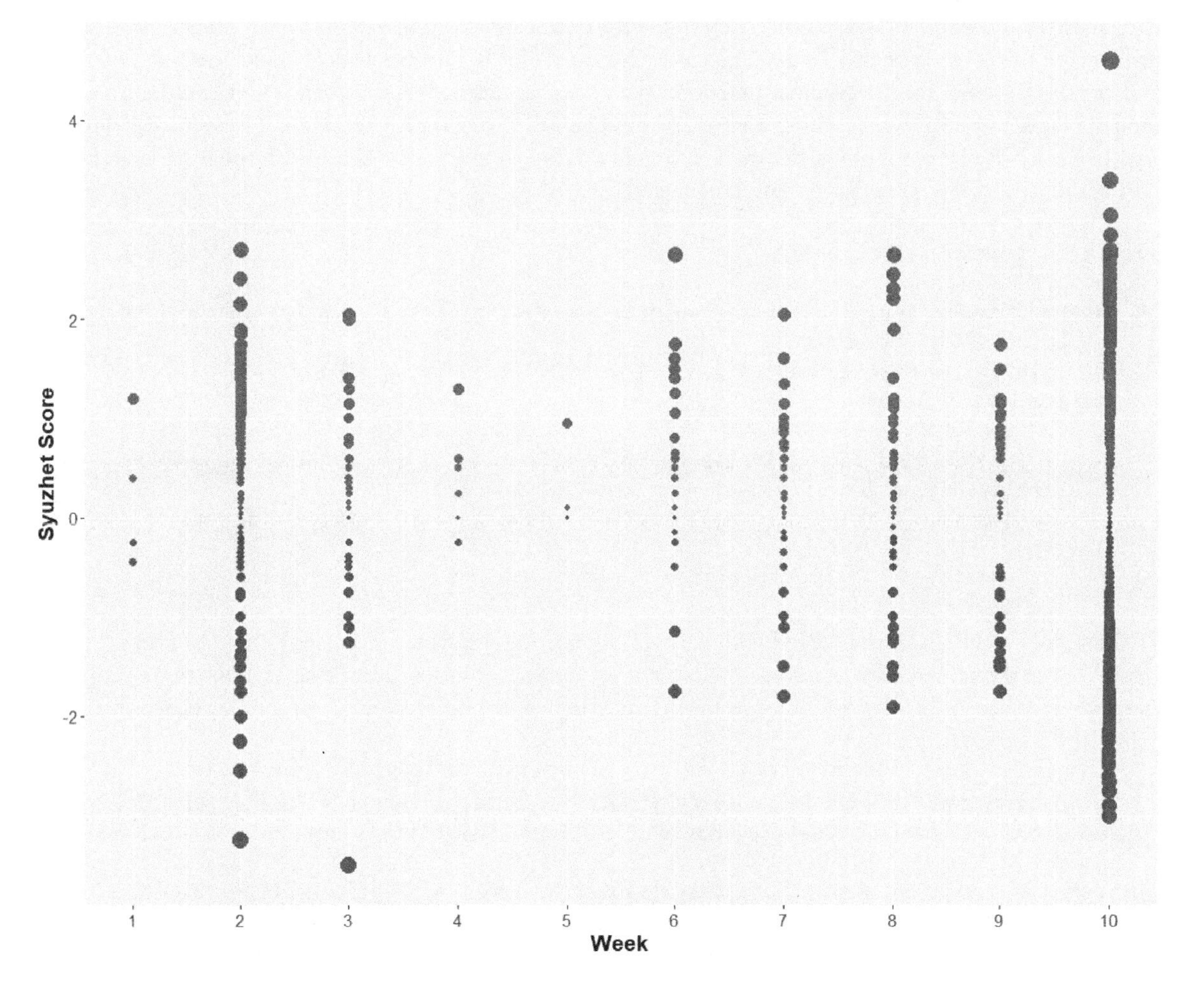

Figure 8.16 Distribution of Syuzhet Scores for Weekly WhereIsRey Tweets

To obtain Plutchik's emotions into a ReyEmotion data frame, we use the following code, first creating our data frame and then labeling its columns.

```
ReyEmotion=data.frame(ReyPosts$Week, ReyPosts$Posts,
                      get_nrc_sentiment(as.character(ReyPosts$Posts)))
colnames(ReyEmotion)=c('Week','Tweet','Anger','Anticipation','Disgust','Fear',
                      'Joy','Sadness','Surprise','Trust','Negative','Positive')
```

This produces the data frame partially depicted in Figure 8.17. Using this, we then can plot any of the emotions over time using the following code:

```
ggplot(ReyEmotion, aes(x=Week,y=Anger)) + geom_bar(stat='summary', fun.y =
      'mean') + scale_x_continuous(breaks=seq(1,10,1))
```

To plot all emotions as depicted in Figure 8.18, see the code provided in Appendix E. Though the overall volume of tweets was low in week 5 (see Figure 1.1), from Figure 8.18, we see that emotions expressed in these tweets peaked in this week, with fear and sadness dominating. This was the week of November 23: Thanksgiving week and a month away from Christmas.

Question 4. What Content Dominated Expressions of Different Emotions?

To answer this question, we first need to determine the dominant emotion expressed in each post. We accomplish this with the code below. To explain, for each row of the ReyEmotion data frame, we first determine whether there are ties for the dominant emotion (i.e., whether more than one of the eight emotions have the same maximum score). If this is false, we leave a "FindEmotion" marker for that row; if it is true, we omit the marker. Then, for rows containing the marker, we obtain the name of the column with the highest score. For rows without the marker, we leave them unchanged (i.e., NULL).

```
for(i in 1:nrow(ReyEmotion))
{
   ReyEmotion$Emotion[i]= ifelse((table(as.numeric(ReyEmotion[i,3:10]))[names(table(as.
      numeric(ReyEmotion
   [i,3:10]))) == max(ReyEmotion[i,3:10])])==1, 'FindEmotion','')
   for(column in 3:10)
   {
       ReyEmotion$Emotion[i]=ifelse(ReyEmotion$Emotion[i] == 'FindEmotion',
       ifelse(ReyEmotion[i,column] == max(ReyEmotion[i,3:10]),
       colnames(ReyEmotion[column]), ReyEmotion$Emotion[i]),ReyEmotion$Emotion[i])
   }
}
```

Next, we collapse all posts tagged with each emotion in the ReyEmotion data frame into a single document. We use the subset() command to obtain the posts for each emotion and the paste() function to combine the posts for each emotion. We then use the c() function to combine the eight emotion documents into a single ReyCompareEmot list.

```
ReyCompareEmot=c(anger=paste(subset(ReyEmotion, Emotion=='Anger')$Tweet, sep='\n',
  collapse=' '), paste(subset(ReyEmotion, Emotion=='Disgust')$Tweet, sep='\n',
  collapse=' '))
ReyCompareEmot=c(ReyCompareEmot, paste(subset(ReyEmotion, Emotion=='Fear')$Tweet,
  sep='\n', collapse=' '))
ReyCompareEmot=c(ReyCompareEmot, paste(subset(ReyEmotion,Emotion=='Sadness')$Tweet,
  sep='\n',collapse=' '))
```

	Week	Tweet	Anger	Anticipation	Disgust	Fear	Joy	Sadness	Surprise	Trust	Negative	Positive
1	1	Target exclusively released a StarWars toy set with ZERO fema...	0	0	0	0	0	0	0	0	0	1
2	1	Hasbro Why do you always leave the girl characters out of yo...	0	0	0	0	0	1	1	0	1	0
3	1	Oh look they even included some women IN THE BACKGROU...	0	0	0	0	0	0	0	1	0	1
4	1	osakadaioh1 damn serious. Disney sexist marketing alive and ...	1	1	1	0	1	0	0	1	1	1
5	2	TheMarySue Who is missing from this picture? StarWars TheF...	0	0	0	1	0	1	0	0	1	0

Figure 8.17 ReyEmotion Data Frame of get_nrc_sentiment Scores

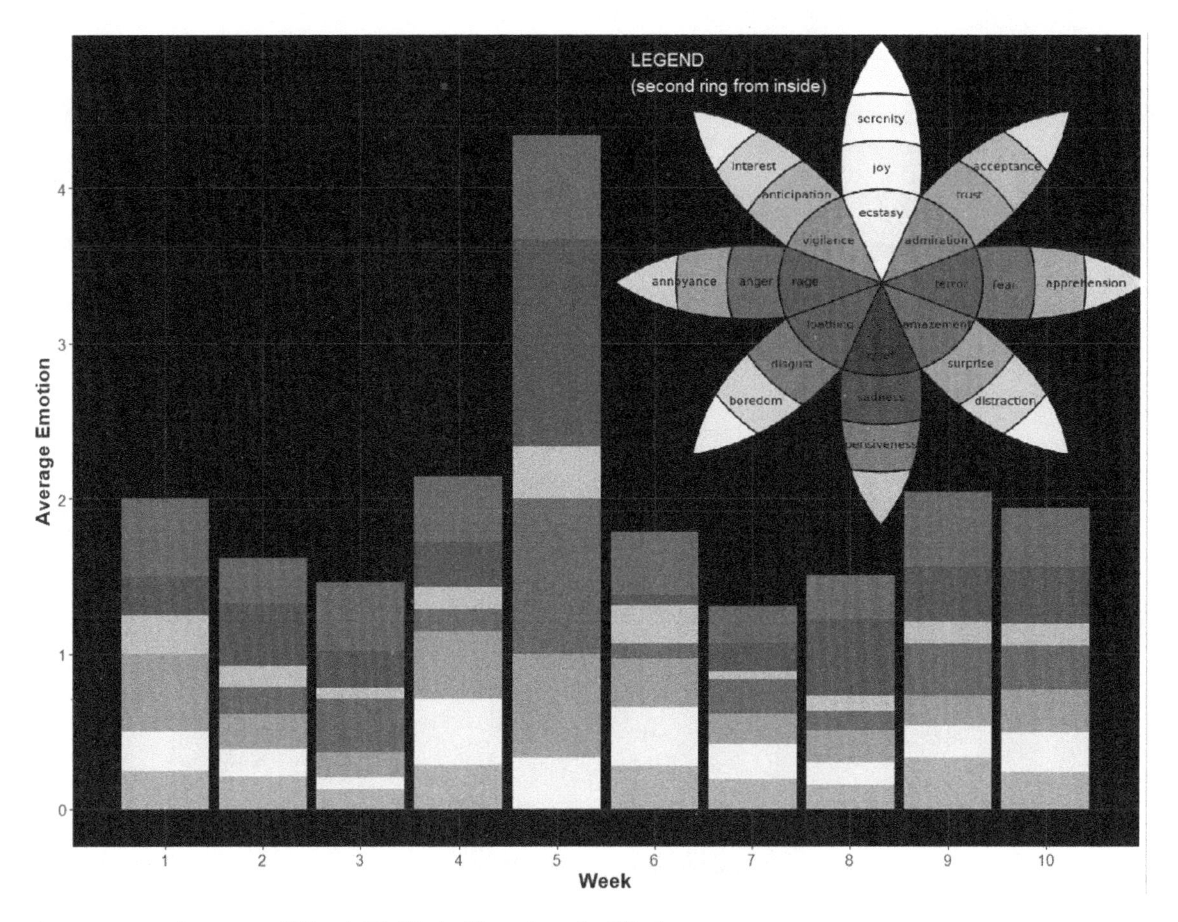

Figure 8.18 Average of Plutchik's Eight Emotions by Week

```
ReyCompareEmot=c(ReyCompareEmot, paste(subset(ReyEmotion,Emotion=='Surprise')$Tweet,
  sep='\n',collapse=' '))
ReyCompareEmot=c(ReyCompareEmot, paste(subset(ReyEmotion,Emotion=='Joy')$Tweet,
  sep='\n', collapse=' '))
ReyCompareEmot=c(ReyCompareEmot, paste(subset(ReyEmotion,Emotion=='Anticipation')$Tweet,
  sep='\n',collapse=' '))
ReyCompareEmot=c(ReyCompareEmot,paste(subset(ReyEmotion,Emotion=='Trust')$Tweet,
  sep='\n',collapse=' '))
```

We convert the list to a corpus; convert the corpus to a term-document matrix; assign column names corresponding to the emotions, which will provide the labels for the comparison cloud sectors; and convert the term-document matrix to a regular matrix. We can then produce the comparison cloud depicted in Figure 8.19.

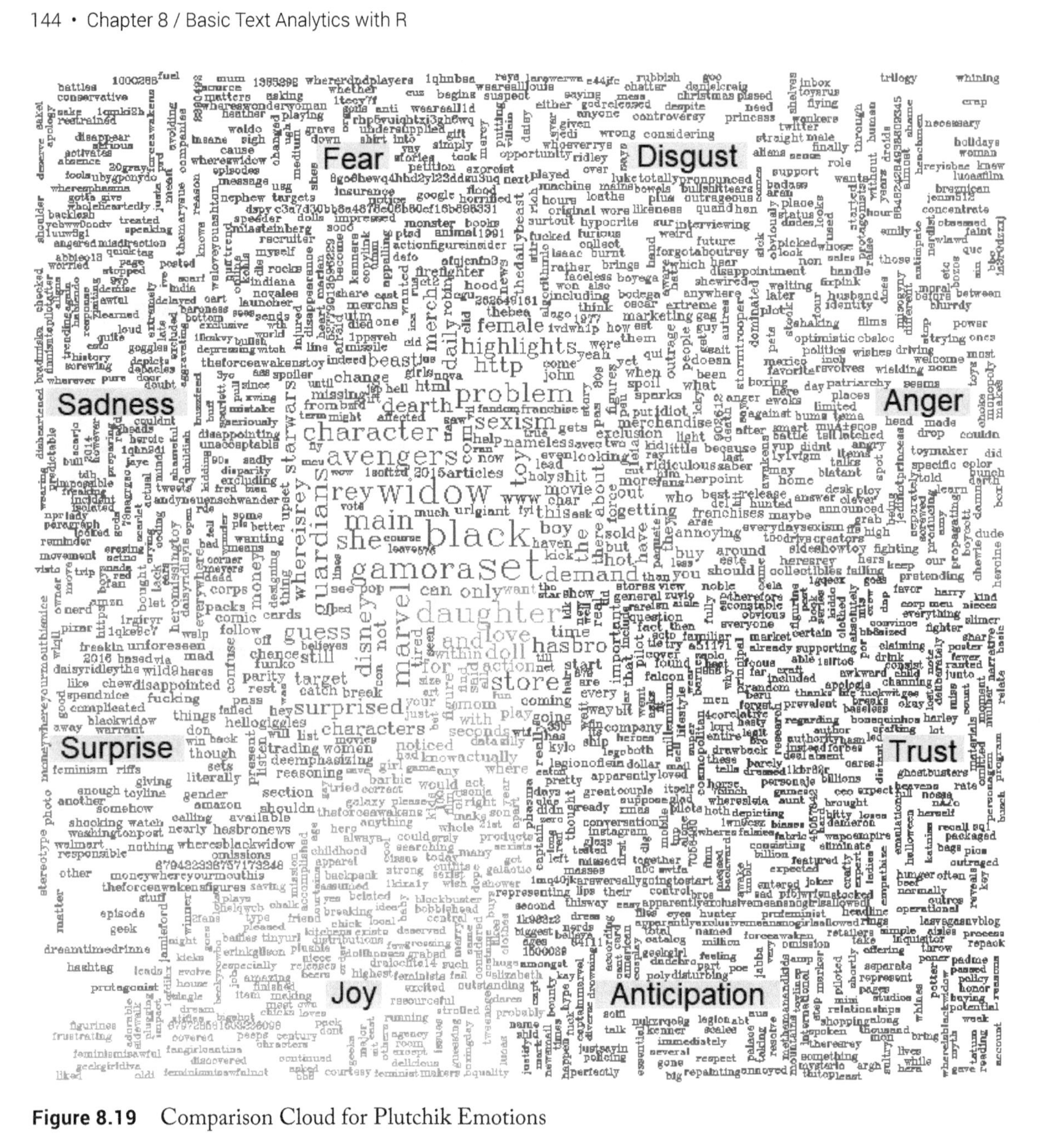

Figure 8.19 Comparison Cloud for Plutchik Emotions

```
ReyCompCorp=Corpus(VectorSource(ReyCompareEmot))
ReyCompTDM=TermDocumentMatrix(ReyCompCorp)
ReyCompTDM=removeSparseTerms(ReyCompTDM,0.99)
colnames(ReyCompTDM)=c('Anger','Disgust','Fear','Sadness','Surprise','Joy',
                      'Anticipation','Trust')
ReyCompTDM=as.matrix(ReyCompTDM)
comparison.cloud(ReyCompTDM, max.words=2000, vfont=c('serif','plain'),
                random.order=F, rot.per=.25, scale=c(2.5,.5), title.size=1.5)
```

From Figure 8.19, we note distinctive terms associated with some emotions. For example, tweets containing the terms "character," "avengers," "black," "widow," "gamora," and "set" tend to reflect *sadness*; those containing "highlights," "problem," "sexism," and "toy" tend to reflect *fear*; those containing "daughter" and "love" tend to reflect *joy*; while those containing "demand" tend to reflect *anger*; those containing "surprised," "guess," "disney," and "target" were associated with *surprise*. (The appearance of "marvel" in this category probably is the result of an incorrect tagging of "marvel" as a verb rather than as an entertainment company.) The term "hasbro" appeared in tweets associated with *anticipation*. Uniqueness was low for terms in posts associated with *disgust* and *trust*.

Conclusion

We have seen a variety of text analytics and visualization techniques in this chapter, but have only scratched the surface of how we can use R for visualizing textual data. Appendix E provides the code for developing more advanced visualizations and for developing comparison and commonality clouds for the ten weeks of WhereIsRey tweets.

Exercise: Text Analysis of a Corpus

The purpose of this exercise is to surface the words that are important to your specific corpus, to understand the sentiment expressed, to determine what appear to be key concepts that emerge in the conversation, and to see how the words, sentiments, and concepts relate to the network properties of the data. Copy the Tweet column from the file used in the Chapter 5 Exercise to a .csv file. Alternatively, use the data provided by your professor. Read your data into R. Load the text mining (tm) package.

Individual Assignment

1. What are the hundred most frequently used terms in your corpus?
2. Classify the tweets in your corpus as positive, negative, or neutral.
3. Identify the ten accounts in your data set that have the most positive tweets and those that have the most negative tweets. Subset or plot these.
4. Produce five different word cloud visualizations. These should not differ only in their aesthetics, but should tell at least three substantially different stories.

Copy salient output into a Word file and annotate it with your observations and comments. Submit your Word file along with your R code file and any other working files.

Team Assignment

Put together your team's analyses into a PowerPoint that tells a story about the qualities of the corpus and the relationships forged around those conversation qualities. Your story should reveal at least five insights that explain or predict and lead you to tangible recommendations.

Works Cited

1. Jockers, M., "*Revealing Sentiment and Plot Arcs with the Syuzhet Package*," February 2, 2015, http://www.matthewjockers.net/2015/02/02/syuzhet/.
2. Wang, Y., Y. Zhang, and B. Liu. "Sentiment Lexicon Expansion Based on Neural PU Learning, Double Dictionary Lookup, and Polarity Association," in *Proceedings of the 2017 Conference on Empirical Methods in Natural Language Processing*. Copenhagen, Denmark: 2017.
3. Nielsen, F.Å., "A New ANEW: Evaluation of a Word List for Sentiment Analysis in Microblogs." *arXiv Preprint*, 1103.2903 (2011).
4. Mohammad, S.M., P. Sobhani, and S. Kiritchenko, "Stance and Sentiment in Tweets." *ACM Transactions on Internet Technology (TOIT)*, 17(3; 2017): 26.
5. Plutchik, R., *The Emotions*. Lanham, MD: University Press of America, 1991.
6. Hurwitz, R., "The General Inquirer Home Page," 2003, http://www.wjh.harvard.edu/~inquirer/.

CHAPTER 9

An Introduction to Text Mining

> **Learning Objectives**
>
> The purpose of this chapter is to acquaint you with:
>
> 1. the origins and applications of text mining;
> 2. the vocabulary and concepts used in text mining;
> 3. the four major text mining tasks; and
> 4. the five major text mining approaches.

One of the tweets in the second presidency data set file we used in the tutorial in Chapter 7 was a retweet of Mikko Hypponen's February 10, 2017 tweet: "This bot watches Donald Trump's tweets for mentions of companies, and automatically executes trades on their stocks." The tweet provided a link to Max Braun's github site, at which he posted the open source code for "a stock trading bot powered by Trump tweets" [1]. The stock trading bot monitored President Trump's tweets about various publicly traded corporations and the market performance of those stocks. For example, on January 3, 2017, President Trump posted the following tweets:

> "General Motors is sending Mexican made model of Chevy Cruze to U.S. car dealers-tax free across border. Make in U.S.A. or pay big border tax!"

and

> "Ford to scrap Mexico plant, invest in Michigan due to Trump policies."

Predictably, the stock market responded negatively to the tweet about General Motors and positively to the tweet about Ford. After observing that stocks generally trended upward when the president's tweets were positive and plummeted when the tweets were negative, Braun proposed and prototyped an open source "machine" to automate buying or shorting of stocks in response to tweets from President Trump. Tongue-in-cheek, he proposed that profits from the "machine" could be used to fund Planned Parenthood.

Returning to our Star Wars scenario, what companies, products, places, and people tend to be discussed in conjunction with Star Wars? What are the themes underlying the conversation? Do groups of people have distinct ways of thinking about the movie? Can we predict weekly box office revenues based on answers to these questions? Can we predict the success of future sequels? These are some more of the questions we can address with text mining techniques. In this chapter, we begin by exploring the roots of text mining and the types of problems to which the techniques can be applied.

As early as 1997, researchers showed that statistical models of a corpus of student essays were just about as revealing of the quality and quantity of student knowledge as were human judges [2]. Text mining algorithms now are the foundation of web search engines that intelligently match web pages containing the word "physician" with a query requesting information on "doctor" [3]. Firms like Admantx use text mining of for contextual advertising (i.e., automated advertisement placement that is personalized to the target's web browsing) [4]. Text mining permits organizations to discover themes underlying online forums [5], policy makers to discover frames in communications from social movement organizations [6], and public health workers to cull information about users' experiences with drugs from websites [7].

In a more lighthearted application of a discovery-based approach, Burr Settles set out to definitively distinguish between a "geek" and a "nerd" [8]. Beginning with a data set of tweets containing search terms "geek" or "nerd," he then examined the words used in conjunction with each search term, producing the graphic in Figure 9.1 and the insight that "geeks are *fans* of their subject, and nerds are *practitioners* of them."

Notably, many of these examples—and most text mining applications—still use a bag of words representations. Below, we begin by considering the different types of text mining tasks. We then explore the range of algorithms used in text mining. We then use the Waikato Environment for Knowledge Analysis (WEKA) for text mining.

Text Mining Tasks

Text mining consists of a set of discovery-based approaches. While count- and dictionary-based approaches are relatively simple, relying exclusively on a bag-of-words representation, discovery-based approaches apply more complex algorithms, based on a string-of-words representation. Table 9.1 summarizes the key tasks of the discovery-based approaches, and the different methods used to address those tasks. We begin by exploring the four key tasks of discovery-based approaches.

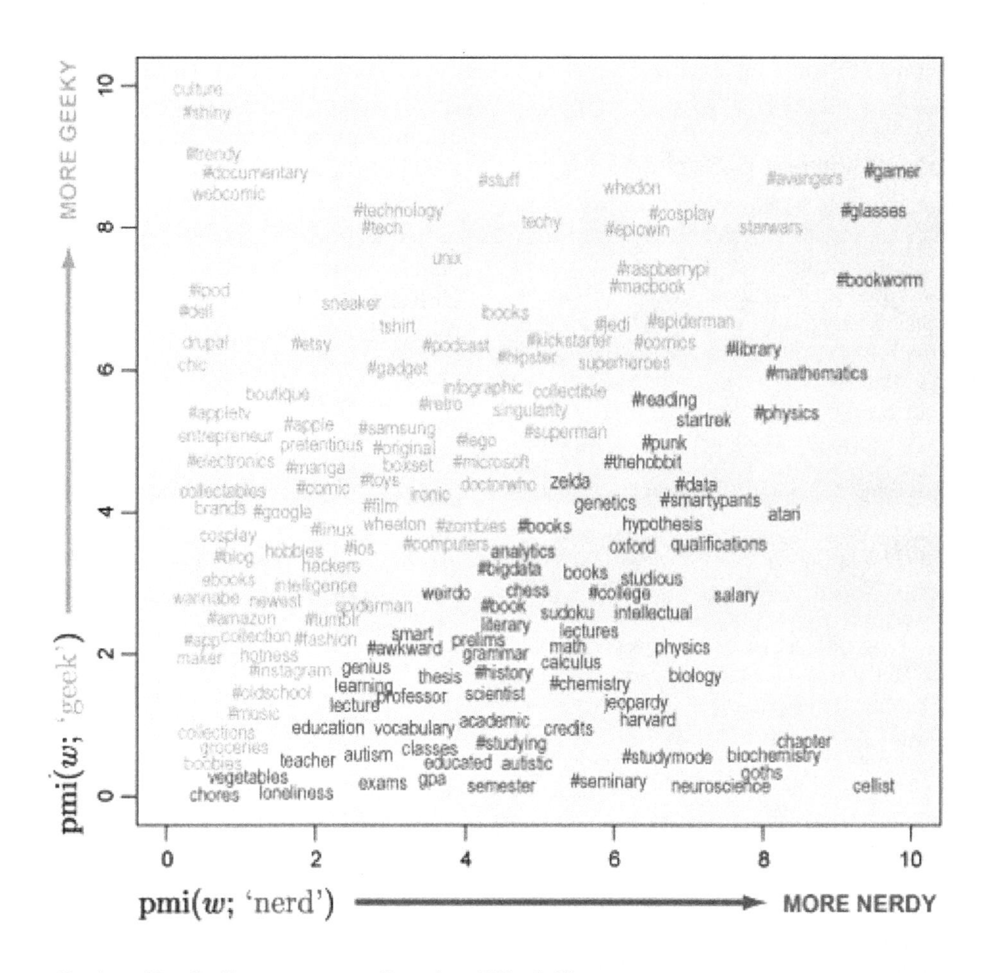

Figure 9.1 Geek or Nerd? Categorization Based on Word Choices
Source: https://slackprop.wordpress.com/2013/06/03/on-geek-versus-nerd/

Table 9.1 Tasks and Methods of the Discovery-Based Approach

Methods	Tasks			
	Information Extraction	**Document Summarization**	**Document Categorization**	**Topic Modeling**
Rule-based algorithms	x		x	
Natural language processing	x	x		
Dimensionality reduction				x
Supervised learning	x		x	
Unsupervised learning	x		x	x
Semisupervised learning	x		x	x

Information extraction deals with surfacing entities and their relationships from unstructured text data [9]. Information extraction is one of the first tasks required for Braun's stock trading bot. Before our bot can decide whether to execute a trade, it needs to flag a tweet as containing information about a publicly traded firm and identify the firm. Two key information extraction tasks are **named entity recognition**, which provides an answer to who (individual or organization), where, and what questions, and **relation recognition**, which addresses how the entities are connected. For example, in the text, "Donald Trump is the president of the United States," "Donald Trump" is a person and "United States" is a location. The relation PresidentOf addresses how the first entity relates to the second. In the text, "Shaila Miranda is employed by the University of Oklahoma," "Shaila Miranda" and "University of Oklahoma" are a person and organization, respectively. EmployedBy captures my relationship with the University of Oklahoma. The "President Trump's Tweets" insert depicts three tweets from the president and identifies the named entities extracted by the Stanford University named entity tagger [10]. Underlying the Ford and Michigan tuple (pair of named entities) in the first tweet is a ExpandIn relationship; underlying the Toyota Motor and Baja tuple in the second tweet is a BuildNewPlantIn relationship. Identifying relationships among entities is easier when the sentence structure is a simple subject-verb-object form and the named entities extracted are subject and object. In the third tweet, the named entities Apple and Cal are interspersed with a lot more information, rendering relation recognition more difficult.

There are three general approaches to named entity extraction [11]. **Dictionary-based approaches** rely on generic or domain-specific lexicons, against which texts are compared. For example, a location lexicon can be constructed from all city, state, and

Corporate Visions of Social Media

Firms target a variety of stakeholders through their press releases. How firms justify their initiatives in their press releases therefore is a good source of information about their strategic vision. To understand the vision underlying Fortune 50 firms' use of social media, we first coded every press release for which of six core values firms invoked to justify their social media use. We counted the number of times firms invoked each of these values across their press releases discussing each of 1,183 social media initiatives. Using RCA, we identified four distinct corporate visions for social media. Within each vision were nested oppositional use cases for social media, i.e., initiatives in which social media was perceived to be relevant in some ways, but not in others.

The first type of vision we identified was *technology-as-efficiency-engineer*, where social media was used simply to make the firm more efficient at what it already was doing. The second was *technology-as-brand-promoter*, where social media was leveraged to bolster public awareness of and loyalty to the companies' brands. The third was *technology-as-good-citizen*, where social media was used to enable firms to engage the public in their social responsibility initiatives or to represent such initiatives to the public. The last was *technology-as-master-of-ceremonies*, where social media was used to enable firms to attract attention by giving attention.

country names, as well as names of topographical features such as rivers, lakes, oceans, and mountains; an organization lexicon can be constructed from the names of all companies listed on various stock exchanges or governed by securities oversight organizations. **Rule-based approaches** to information extraction may be relatively primitive. For example, we might search a text for the occurrence of titles such as "Ms." or "Dr.," and then tag the subsequent word as a person. Obviously this is quite limited because the rule would miss all person names not preceded by a title. More sophisticated rule-based approaches rely on natural language processing. In this approach, terms tagged as proper nouns become candidates for being tagged as person, organization, or location named entities; proximity to prepositions such as "in" or "at" help determine that the candidate named entity is of type location. **Corpus-based approaches** rely on machine learning. Using supervised learning, the analyst trains a model to recognize specific named entities within the corpus.

President Trump's Tweets

Ford said last week that it will expand in Michigan and U.S. instead of building a BILLION dollar plant in Mexico. Thank you Ford and Fiat C!" (January 9, 2017)

"Toyota Motor said will build a new plant in Baja, Mexico, to build Corolla cars for U.S. NO WAY! Build plant in U.S. or pay big border tax." (January 5, 2017)

"Boycott all Apple products until such time as Apple gives cellphone info to authorities regarding radical Islamic terrorist couple from Cal" (February 9, 2016)

Entity	Type
Ford	Organization
Michigan	Location
U.S.	Location
Mexico	Location
Ford	Organization
Fiat	Organization
Toyota Motor	Organization
Baja	Location
Mexico	Location
U.S.	Location
U.S.	Location
Apple	Organization
Apple	Organization
Cal	Location

Document summarization is about accurately condensing or paraphrasing long text passages, permitting the reader to glean salient information without digesting the entire document. We see this in news headlines, tables of content, digests, and abstracts. Document summarization algorithms provide one of two types of summaries: an **extractive summary** condenses the text, culling key words and phrases from the text. We see examples of automated extractive summarization in web search engines, as in depicted in Figure 9.2. An **abstractive summary** paraphrases, synthesizing the text contents, without necessarily using words from the text itself. For example, instead of quoting the initial text from the Rey (Star Wars) Wikipedia page, as contained in the extractive summary, an abstractive summary might read "Daisy Ridley plays Rey, marooned child turned Resistance fighter, in the Star Wars sequel." In fourteen words, this abstractive summary paraphrases the first two sentences from the Wikipedia entry about the Star Wars Rey character, conveying more information than the nineteen-word extractive summary.

Document categorization entails assigning documents to alternate categories. Examples include categorizing incoming e-mail as spam or sentiment analysis. These tasks certainly can be done manually or by using dictionary-based approaches. Manual approaches, of course, are highly labor intensive, requiring a person to read and assign every text to a category. Early e-mail users, for example, made all classification of their e-mail as spam or relevant themselves, by manually screening all incoming e-mail. Today we also conduct some of our screening manually, assigning certain senders or subjects to our Junk folders and moving some messages out of our Junk folders into our Inboxes.

Earlier we saw dictionary-based approaches to text categorization tasks such as sentiment analysis. Because these rely on the bag-of-words representation, the text models applied are context-neutral and therefore are prone to imprecision. While more comprehensive concept dictionaries can alleviate some level of imprecision, developing such dictionaries is labor intensive. Discovery-based text categorization, using a string-of-words representation, reduces the categorization imprecision of dictionary-based approaches and the labor-intensiveness of developing comprehensive concept dictionaries.

Topic modeling surfaces themes or the key issues underlying a corpus and organizes the documents within the corpus according to those themes [12]. These topics—or themes, or issues—are identified from recurrent patterns in the corpus. The topics surfaced may be unrelated, where each is independent of others, or hierarchical, where a higher-order topic reflects multiple subordinate concepts. For example, the procedure we used to model firms' discussion of their social media yielded the topic structure depicted in Figure 9.3. Here, nested in each of the four visions of social media, were one or more ideas of specific problems to which social media could be applied. For example, a vision of social media as an efficiency engineer may play out in generic efficiency-improving initiatives or in enhancing efficiency in innovation processes or in cultural engagements.

Text Mining Methods

We now consider the six major text mining methods used for the four discovery tasks discussed above. ***Rule-based algorithms*** use sets of if-then-else rules to impose structure on and surface meaning from a corpus. As noted in Table 9.1, such methods are useful in information extraction and document categorization tasks. An example of rule-based discovery of named entities is:

if (token-1="Mr." or token-1="Ms." or token-1="Mrs." or token-1="Dr.") and (IsCapital(Left(token,1))) then ENTITY(token)=PersonName

In Figure 9.4, we apply this rule to a *New York Times* article. We find the rule performs relatively well, but not perfectly. Specifically, it misses three instances of person names in the article—Mark Zuckerberg, Orrin

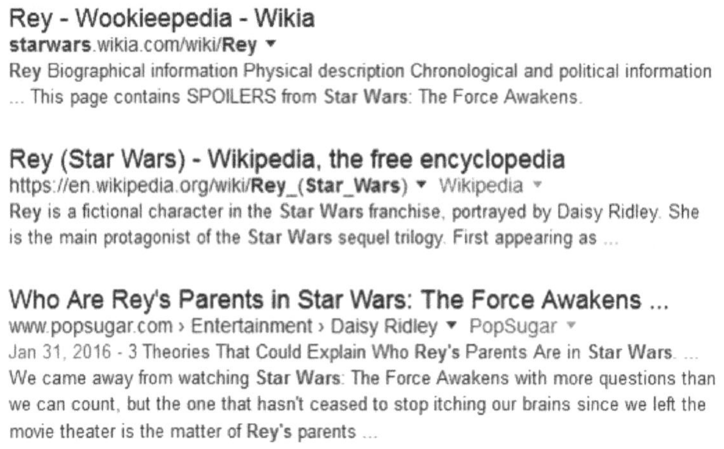

Rey - Wookieepedia - Wikia
starwars.wikia.com/wiki/Rey ▾
Rey Biographical information Physical description Chronological and political information
... This page contains SPOILERS from Star Wars: The Force Awakens.
Rey (Star Wars) - Wikipedia, the free encyclopedia
https://en.wikipedia.org/wiki/Rey_(Star_Wars) ▾ Wikipedia ▾
Rey is a fictional character in the Star Wars franchise, portrayed by Daisy Ridley. She
is the main protagonist of the Star Wars sequel trilogy. First appearing as ...
Who Are Rey's Parents in Star Wars: The Force Awakens ...
www.popsugar.com › Entertainment › Daisy Ridley ▾ PopSugar ▾
Jan 31, 2016 - 3 Theories That Could Explain Who Rey's Parents Are in Star Wars. ...
We came away from watching Star Wars: The Force Awakens with more questions than
we can count, but the one that hasn't ceased to stop itching our brains since we left the
movie theater is the matter of Rey's parents ...

Figure 9.2 Automated Extractive Text Summarization

Social Media Visions
Efficiency-Engineer
Brand-Promoter
Good-Citizen
Master-of-Ceremonies
Generic efficiency
Inspired efficiency
Cultural efficiency
Conventional promotion
Cultural promotion
Social responsibility
Generic distinction
Cultural distinction
Material distinction
Cause-related marketing

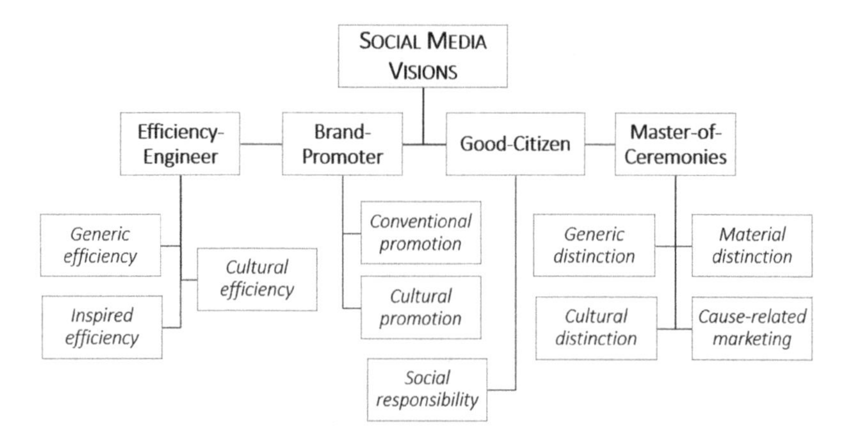

Figure 9.3 Topic Model of Firms' Discussions of Their Social Media Initiatives

G. Hatch, and Bill Gates—because they were not preceded by a Mr., Ms., Mrs., or Dr. The rule also fails to eliminate the possessive "'s" from "Mr. Zuckerberg's." Of course, we could develop a more elaborate rule to handle such possessive cases. But handling the missed persons is difficult, even with rule modifications.

Decision trees are a stochastic variant of rule-based discovery. They are collections of rules that sequentially determine to which of several categories a document should be assigned or classified. With decision trees, rather than a token being definitively classified as a PersonName entity if its first letter is capitalized and the token that precedes it is a conventional salutation, each component of the rule—first letter being capitalized and preceding salutation—would simply increase the likelihood of a token being classified as a PersonName entity.

Figure 9.5 depicts the use of decision trees for a document categorization task. In Figure 9.5A, our tree attempts to distinguish between texts expressing positive sentiment and those not expressing positive

When Mr. Gates Went to Washington

The Mark Zuckerberg show in Washington this past week stirred memories for Senator Orrin G. Hatch... Twenty years ago, the tech titan in the Senate hot seat was another Harvard dropout, Bill Gates, cofounder and chief executive of Microsoft... Mr. Gates was its fearless leader - and made it clear that he wouldn't change his ways for Washington... A few months after Mr. Gates appeared on Capitol Hill, the federal government and 20 states sued Microsoft in a landmark antitrust case... If Mr. Zuckerberg's conciliatory performance in front of multiple congressional committees was any guide, he took the history lesson to heart... When Mr. Gates testified in Congress, there was no tone of compromise or conciliation. Mr. Gates, then 42 and the richest person in America, dressed appropriately if uneasily in a gray suit. He appeared before the Senate Judiciary Committee, chaired by Mr. Hatch, in a four-hour hearing, sharing the day with five other tech executives, including two industry rivals. But Mr. Gates was the day's main event in a hearing called to examine "whether Microsoft is abusing its market power." Mr. Gates used the forum to explain Microsoft's role at the forefront of an "industry that has revolutionized the world in only 25 years." At times, he seemed to be lecturing the less intelligent... It was clear from the start of Mr. Zuckerberg's testimony that he had arrived in Washington with a different message. Shedding his hoodie for a suit, and intensively coached, he appeared humbled and deferential to his congressional interlocutors, even when facing the types of technically unsophisticated questions that easily vexed Mr. Gates during his time in the hot seat [13].

Legend:
Correctly Identified
Missed

Figure 9.4 Simple Rule-Based Named Entity Extraction

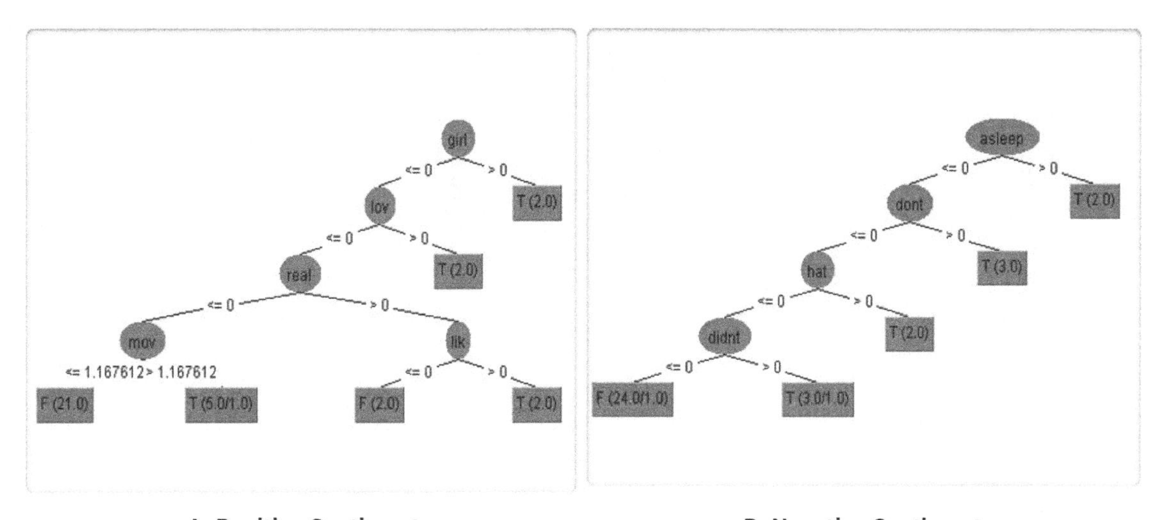

Figure 9.5 Decision Trees for Classifying Positive and Negative Sentiment

sentiment. In Figure 9.5B, our decision tree attempts to discriminate between texts expressing and not expressing negative sentiment. The positive sentiment decision tree in Figure 9.5A uses four text features—girl, lov, real, and mov—to classify texts as reflecting positive sentiment. (Notice the tokenization and stemming in the tree. Only compound features [e.g., "a great"] are quoted in the tree; simple features [e.g., "lov"] are not.) The first rule is whether the text feature—the token "girl"—appears in the document. Its presence is indicative of the presence of the positive sentiment concept. Its absence triggers a search for a second text feature—the stemmed "lov" rule. Its failure triggers the third feature search—the real rule—the failure of which, in turn, triggers the mov rule (reflecting an oddly stemmed "movie" tag). The decision tree for capturing negative sentiment also is based on four features—asleep, dont, hat (reflecting the stemmed "hate" tag), and didnt.

Natural language processing (NLP) is a collection of methods developed at the intersection of computer science, computational linguistics, and artificial intelligence. Natural language refers to spoken language and is distinguished from formal, stylized languages of computer programming, mathematics, or logic. The purpose of NLP is to make the human-computer interface seamless, to facilitate human interaction with computers in a fashion that approximates humans' interaction with each other.

As per Table 9.1, NLP is useful in information extraction and document summarization tasks. Specifically, the intermediate NLP tasks that enable information extraction and document summarization include parts-of-speech tagging, sentence parsing, and coreference resolution. **Parts-of-speech tagging** (POST) entails assigning each word to a part-of-speech category. POST is the second step in text mining, following tokenization. There are nine basic parts of speech in the English language: noun, verb, article, adjective, preposition, pronoun, adverb, conjunction, and interjection. However, each of these basic categories have subcategories. For example, a noun could be singular or plural; it could be proper or common. In fact, English parts-of-speech taggers employ between 50 and 150 parts-of-speech categories. These taggers are based on lexicons or dictionaries that have been tested and refined iteratively. POST lexicons are semantically superior to dictionaries that use a bag of words representation, attributing meaning to a word based on its position in a sentence. Once again, the Stanford NLP group provides a demo of a parts-of-speech tagger (and sentence parser) [14]. To understand how POST works, consider the three problematic sentences we saw earlier:

I really like the new Star Wars movie.
I really do not like the new Star Wars movie.
The movie is like a mashup of the first two Star Wars movies!

Table 9.2 Parts-of-Speech Tags for Star Wars Sentences

I	*really*	*like*	*the*	*new*	*Star*	*Wars*	*movie*	*.*
PRP	RB	VBP	DT	JJ	NNP	NNP	NN	.

I	*really*	*do*	*not*	*like*	*the*	*new*	*Star*	*Wars*	*movie*	*.*
PRP	RB	VBP	RB	VB	DT	JJ	NNP	NNP	NN	.

The	*movie*	*is*	*like*	*a*	*mashup*	*of*	*The*	*first*	*two*	*Star*	*Wars*	*movies*	*!*
DT	NN	VBZ	IN	DT	NN	IN	DT	JJ	CD	NNP	NNP	NNS	.

Legend:

CD	*cardinal number*	NNP	*proper noun*	VB	*bare form verb*
DT	*determiner*	NNS	*plural common noun*	VBP	*present tense general form verb*
IN	*preposition or subordinating conjunction*	PRP	*personal pronoun*	VBZ	*present tense third person singular verb*
JJ	*adjective*	RB	*Adverb*	.	*punctuation*
NN	*common noun*				

The lexical tags for these sentences appear in Table 9.2. As will be apparent, in this method, the word "like" acquires different meanings and is tagged differently in the context of the first and third sentences.

Sentence parsing further contextualizes the tokens, noting their relative position in a sentence. This is done using parse trees, which visually depict the syntactic structure of a sentence. A constituency parse tree depicts the grammatical structure of the sentence. It is useful when the task calls for identifying sub-phrases that constitute the sentence. A dependency parse tree depicts the dependencies of each token on the verb. Figure 9.6 provides examples of the constituency and dependency parse trees of the first and the third of our Star Wars sentences. Note that in the dependency trees, the Stanford parser recognizes Star Wars as a compound word.

Coreference resolution entails identifying words that reference the same entities. For example, in the sentence, "*Star Wars is a great movie; I really liked it!*", "it" and "Star Wars" reference or signify the same entity.

Earlier, we noted three approaches to named entity extraction. Of the three, NLP enables rule-based named entity extraction through parts-of-speech tagging. Sentence parsing then provides information on relationships between named entities thus extracted. In these ways, NLP facilitates information extraction. Coreference resolution permits pronouns to be recognized as interchangeable with specific named entities. As such, it is an essential precursor to document summarization. For example, consider the text "Rey is a scavenger who was left behind on the planet Jakku when she was a child, and later becomes involved with the Resistance's conflict . . . ," together with later references to "Resistance fighters" in the Wikipedia article. Coreference resolution tells us that Rey was a child who was "left behind" or marooned, and that as a person "involved with the Resistance's conflict," she is a Resistance fighter. This produces the following abstractive summary: "Daisy Ridley plays Rey, marooned child turned Resistance fighter, in the Star Wars sequel."

Dimensionality reduction algorithms identify sets of semantically similar or related words. Most text analysis problems begin with exceedingly large numbers of terms. These text features or variables can overwhelm text analysis problems. In smaller corpuses, the large number of variables can engender a statistical power problem (i.e., inability to observe significant relationships even when they exist). Dimensionality reduction decreases the number of variables or features to a more manageable number, rendering the number of observations greater than the number of features analyzed in small data sets. In large data sets too, dimensionality reduction enables subsequently-applied supervised machine learning algorithms to produce more effective models, reducing the overfitting problem (see the "Overfitting Problem in Machine Learning" insert). Through the patterning of terms surfaced by dimensionality reduction, we also elicit the themes or topics underlying a corpus. Dimensionality reduction algorithms include principal component analysis, factor analysis, and latent semantic analysis.

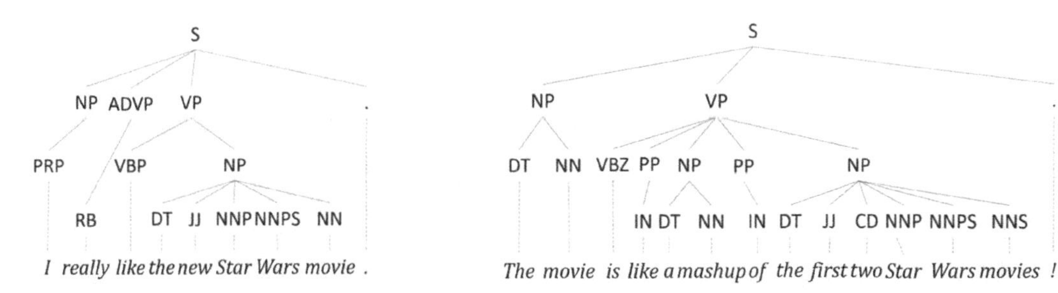

S=sentence; **NP**=noun phrase; **NN**=common noun; **NNP**=proper noun; **NNPS**=plural proper noun; **PRP**=personal pronoun
VP=verb phrase; **VBP**=present tense verb; **VBZ**=third person singular verb; **DT**=determiner; **IN**=preposition or subord. conjunction
ADVP=adverb phrase; **ADJP**=adjective phrase; **RB**=adverb; **JJ**=adjective; .=punctuation

A. Constituency Parse Trees

I really like the new Star Wars movie *The movie is like a mashup of the first two Star Wars movies!*

B. Dependency Parse Trees

Figure 9.6 Sentence Trees

The Overfitting Problem in Machine Learning

Often, our model from training data will appear to perform exceedingly well on all metrics—manifesting a high level of accuracy, validity, precision, and recall. When used against a test data set, though, we may find that it performs exceedingly poorly. This is the result of the overfitting problem (i.e., where our model is too specific to the training data set). Put another way, it is the result of (1) our training data set not being sufficiently representative of the population of observations against which we wish to run the model, and (2) our fitted model being overly complex.

How do we overcome the overfitting problem and ensure that we have a robust predictive model? Our first line of defense is to ensure a sizable and representative training data set. If, for example, we wish to classify news articles of publicly traded firms as good news or bad news, we would want to ensure that our training data set contains articles appearing in a wide range of newspapers and magazines and are about firms in a wide range of industries, of varying sizes and ages, and with varying levels of financial and reputational health. When considering our movie reviews problem, obviously a training data set of reviews of the Star Wars movie has questionable generalizability to reviews of the test data set of reviews of the Kung Fu Panda movie.

The second line of defense, though, is to select as parsimonious a model as possible. The more parameters—numeric variables or linguistic features—we include in the model we construct based on the training data set, the more likely it is that we will optimize model performance across our various metrics. However, as we improve the performance or fit of the model, we also increase the likelihood that the model is selecting variables or features that are specific to classifying the cases in the training data set rather than using variables or features that are generalizable to all data sets. So, a model with five parameters and 90% accuracy is more likely to perform well on test data than a model with 50 parameters and 100% accuracy.

The next three methods entail ***machine learning*** (i.e., system capabilities to automatically improve its performance of a given task based on new information). ***Supervised learning*** algorithms learn to associate inputs and outputs from data on which both inputs and outputs are known; the objective is to be able to predict outputs when inputs are not known. Unlike the dictionary-based approaches, wherein a deterministic association exists between a tag (input) and a concept (output), supervised learning algorithms develop probabilistic associations between tags and concepts. Supervised learning can be used to implement corpus-based named entity extraction in domains where a priori lexicons are unavailable or incomplete and rule-based models might fail. For example, we might wish to extract the names of drugs mentioned in physicians' notes, which might be too linguistically ill-structured to apply NLP-based models. Supervised learning algorithms require extensive training data sets to develop good models and therefore can be laborious.

Unsupervised learning algorithms seek to discover natural groupings of texts within the corpus, without requiring any a priori analyst effort. Texts within groups are similar to each other and dissimilar to texts in other groups. These groups of texts can reveal previously unknown document categories or surface topics underlying the corpus. Unsupervised learning algorithms we will encounter in Chapter 11 include cluster analysis, latent Dirichlet allocation (LDA), and relational class analysis. As with the network clustering algorithms discussed in Chapters 4 and 6 that partition the network, text *clustering* algorithms partition the corpus in groups of texts. These algorithms create groups of texts, where each group has different probabilities/frequencies associated with each word in the text-word vector. LDA identifies the mixture of topics underlying each document and the mixture of terms constituting a topic. Relational class analysis, which produced the model depicted in Figure 9.3, can reveal groups of oppositional concepts.

Semisupervised techniques (e.g., bootstrapping) begin with known information and elicit linguistic patterns underlying the known information. In the context of an information extraction task, for instance, we may begin with specific instances of two entities—for example, Shaila Miranda and OU. Searching a large corpus for these entity instances appear in proximity to each other may reveal headlines such as "Shaila Miranda teaches at the University of Oklahoma" or "Shaila Miranda from University of Oklahoma" ("FACULTY *teaches at* INSTITUTION" or "FACULTY *from* INSTITUTION"). Based on these connecting words, we ascertain that "teaches at" and "from" signals a faculty and institution.

Supervised, unsupervised, and semisupervised algorithms address text classification problems—for example, the geeks versus nerds problem from Figure 9.1, spam filtering, and sentiment analysis. Classification algorithms include rule-based classifiers, decision trees, nearest neighbor classifiers, maximum margin classifiers, and probabilistic classifiers. As we evaluate the models developed by different classifiers, it is advantageous to have a yardstick by which to compare them. The "Assessing Performance of Discovery-Based Methods" insert identifies five different yardsticks that we can use. Weka, named for the institution from which it originated (The University of Waikato) and for a flightless species of bird from the same area, is a machine learning toolkit. It has capabilities for both unsupervised and supervised learning.

Assessing Performance of Discovery-Based Methods

For the classification tasks underlying information extraction and document categorization, we need to know well our mining algorithms perform. Below are the metrics we can use to assess performance and how the decision tree in Figure 9.6 performs on those metrics.

Metric	Description
Accuracy	Percent correctly classified
Kappa	Rate of agreement between human coder and computer-based classification algorithm
Precision	Percent correct positives out of identified positive instances
Recall	Percent correct positives out of all positive instances
F-1	Geometric mean of precision and recall
Lift	Improvement in prediction of an outcome based on classification

Tutorial 9.1. Sentiment Analysis of Movie Tweets via Machine Learning

In this tutorial, we will use Weka to develop a supervised machine learning model of sentiment. In contrast to the previously static dictionary applied to discerning the sentiment underlying texts, this approach will organically surface cues that reveal sentiment in a corpus. Our problem domain is tweets about movies. We begin by creating a model developed from a training data set of tweets about the Star Wars movie. For this training data set, we have manually categorized the tweets as reflecting positive and/or negative sentiment. This categorization is depicted in a T|F (True|False) being assigned to each tweet in the data set for positive emotion and T|F being assigned for negative emotion. The data in the training set thus comprises the text of the tweet, a positive sentiment category, and a negative sentiment category. Once we have developed supervised learning models for positive and negative sentiment from this training data set, we will use these models to classify the tweets about the Kung Fu Panda movie (i.e., our test data set) as containing positive and negative sentiment.

We begin using the program by selecting Explore from the initial Weka interface, depicted in Figure 9.7A. This will bring up the Weka Explorer, which will be the main console for our interactions with Weka.

Next we will open up a file, as depicted in Figure 9.7B. From the **Preprocess** tab, click the Open file button and select your file. Weka can accept different types of input files, including *.csv*, but works best with an *.arff* file. The structure of a Weka training *.arff* file, StarWars.arff, is depicted in Figure 9.8. This file has three areas. The first area, *@relation*, declares the data set name. The second area, in which each line begins with *@attribute*, declares our variables or columns (called attributes in machine learning terminology), listing them along with their data types. Weka permits four data types: (1) numeric; (2) nominal, specified as a factor list within curly brackets (e.g., {T,F} or {BBA,MBA,PhD} or {0,1}); (3) string; and (4) date, which must be followed by the date format (e.g., date "yyyy-MM-dd HH:mm:ss"). Attribute data type specification is not case sensitive (i.e., DATE=date and numeric=NUMERIC). The third area of the *.arff* file, preceded by *@data*, marks the beginning of the set of instances or rows in our data set. We can view these areas by opening the file in Notepad or another text editor.

When specifying our test file, the *@relation* and *@attribute* areas must be identical to those in our training file. To create the test file, we simply replace values of the attributes to be classified in the *@data* area

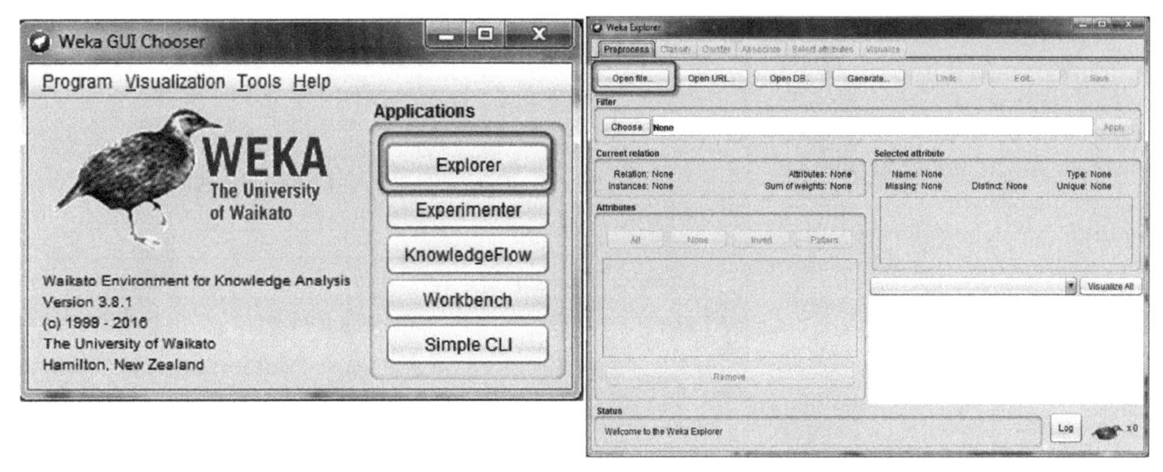

A. Initial Weka Interface

B. Weka Explorer

Figure 9.7 The Weka Interface

with question marks—for example, *'I like the new Star Wars movie!'*, *?* in the @data area. **Note that Weka gets persnickety about data that is not completely alphanumeric. Use a combination of the CLEAN() and SUBSTITUTE() functions in Excel to clean up text data prior to creating the *.arff* file. If you get an error message telling you that Weka is unable to determine the structure as an *.arff* file, it probably is because the file contains some Unicode characters. The swiftest way past this problem may be to delete and recreate the file because the offending Unicode character(s) may not be visible.**

Once our training data is loaded, we can inspect the frequencies of the values for an attribute by selecting it. This will produce a bar chart, as depicted in Figure 9.9. While our example uses attributes with Boolean values only (i.e., the presence or absence of positive and negative sentiment), it certainly is possible for Weka to work with more than two categories of an attribute.

We are about embark on a journey of machine learning with Weka. The objective of our journey is to have Weka discover features of the Tweet attribute from our training .arff file that are associated with T versus F values of Positive and Negative sentiment that we have assigned. Once these features have been discovered, Weka will be able to accurately categorize tweets reflecting Positive and Negative sentiment in future data sets. This is a supervised learning journey because we have provided Weka with a training data set. Note we do not tell Weka *which* Tweet features are likely to be associated with the occurrence of Positive or Negative sentiment, but allow Weka to discover these features itself from our tweet classifications in the training data set.

First, since we want Weka to discover features of the Tweet attribute associated with Positive and Negative sentiment, not have it use our classification of Positive sentiment to predict Negative sentiment and vice versa, we will remove the Negative sentiment before we assign Weka to develop a model for Positive sentiment. We can do so by selecting the Negative sentiment attribute and clicking the Remove button as shown in Figure 9.9. If we do not do this, Weka will model positive sentiment in tweets based not only on the content of the tweet, but also on our designation of tweets as containing negative sentiment. Since this information will be unavailable in our test data set, we want to make sure it is not used to construct the model that determines whether or not the tweet contains positive sentiment. Later, we can reload our file and remove Positive sentiment before asking Weka to develop a model for Negative sentiment.

We then move over to the **Classify** tab to specify the nature of the classification task. First, we choose our classifier. To do so, we click the Choose button, and then the options ***Classifiers***, ***meta***, ***FilteredClassifier***, as depicted in Figure 9.10A. In order to specify our classifying algorithm and preprocess our text data in preparation for classification, we click on the FilteredClassifier, which will produce the pop up dialog depicted in Figure 9.10B.

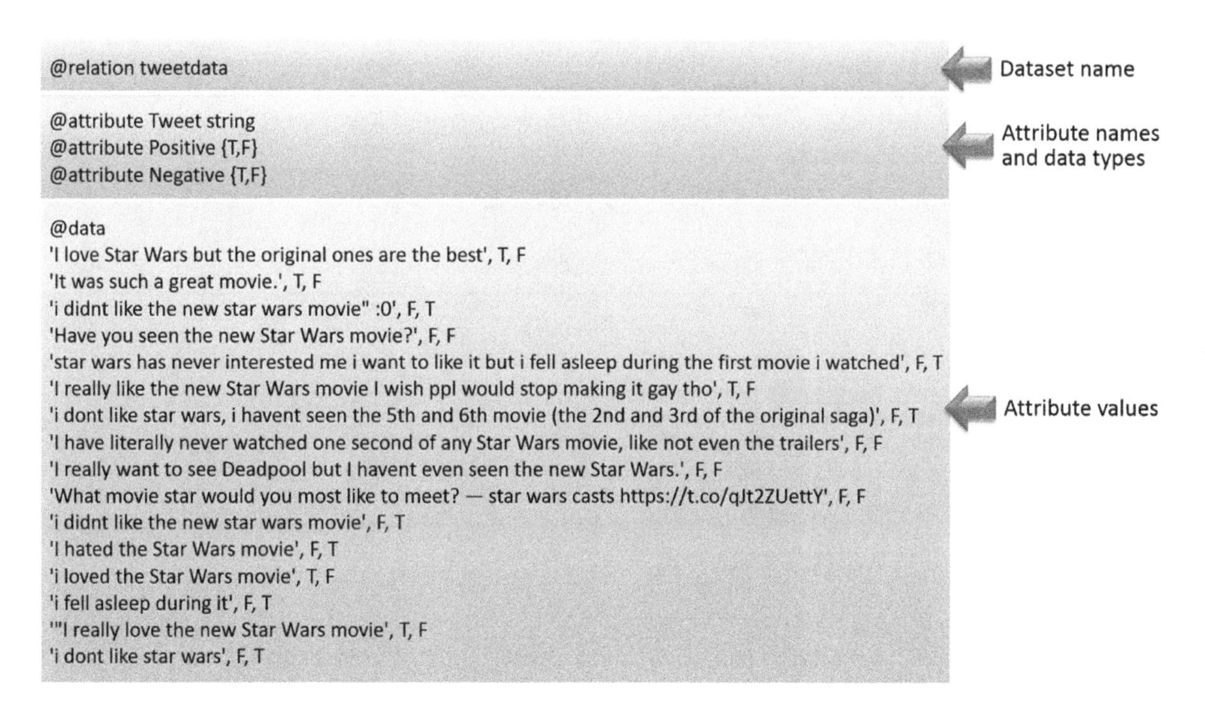

```
@relation tweetdata

@attribute Tweet string
@attribute Positive {T,F}
@attribute Negative {T,F}

@data
'I love Star Wars but the original ones are the best', T, F
'It was such a great movie.', T, F
'i didnt like the new star wars movie" :0', F, T
'Have you seen the new Star Wars movie?', F, F
'star wars has never interested me i want to like it but i fell asleep during the first movie i watched', F, T
'I really like the new Star Wars movie I wish ppl would stop making it gay tho', T, F
'i dont like star wars, i havent seen the 5th and 6th movie (the 2nd and 3rd of the original saga)', F, T
'I have literally never watched one second of any Star Wars movie, like not even the trailers', F, F
'I really want to see Deadpool but I havent even seen the new Star Wars.', F, F
'What movie star would you most like to meet? — star wars casts https://t.co/qJt2ZUettY', F, F
'i didnt like the new star wars movie', F, T
'I hated the Star Wars movie', F, T
'i loved the Star Wars movie', T, F
'i fell asleep during it', F, T
'"I really love the new Star Wars movie', T, F
'i dont like star wars', F, T
```


Figure 9.8 Areas of a Weka Training .arff File

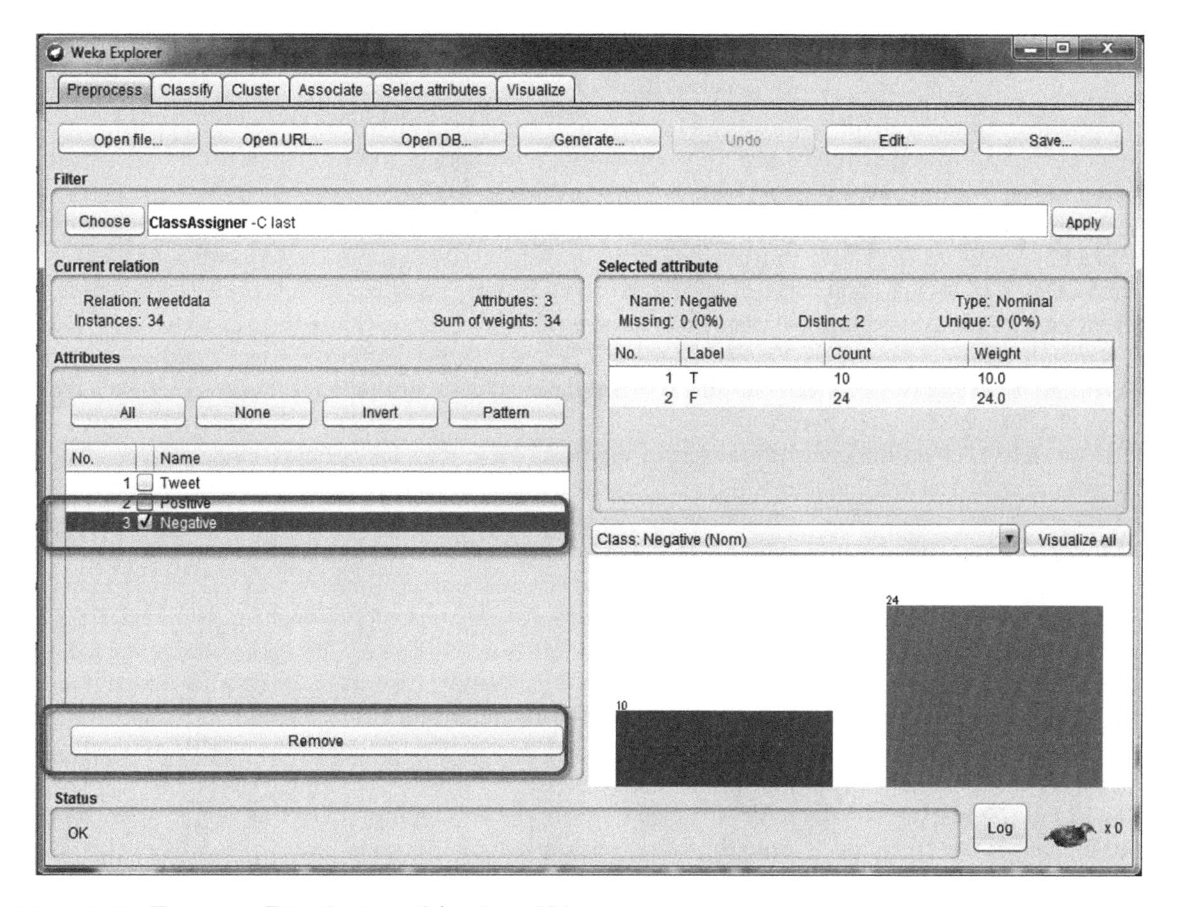

Figure 9.9 Frequency Distribution of Attribute Values

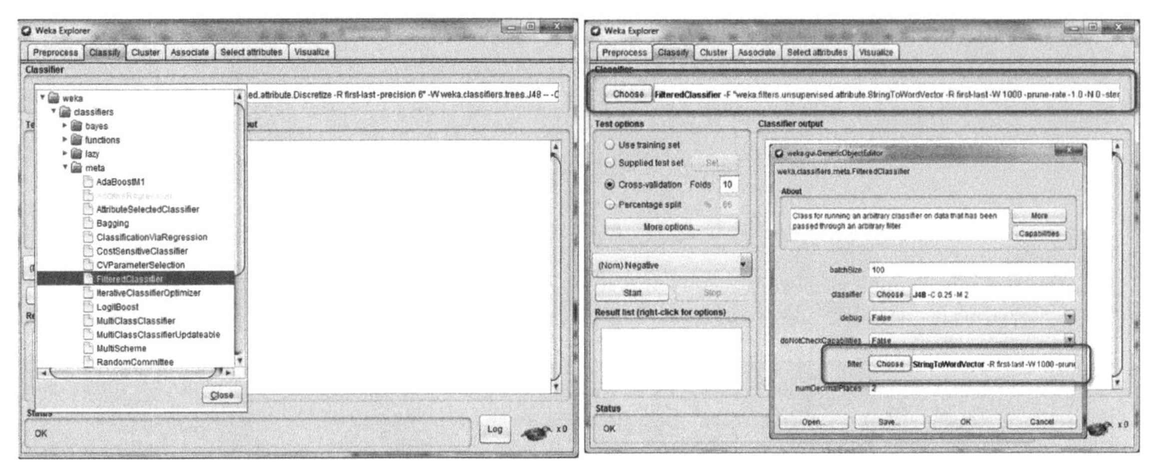

A. Choosing a Classifier B. Starting Pre-processing

Figure 9.10 Choosing a Weka Classifier

From the pop-up dialog, we leave **J48** as our classifier algorithm. (See the insert on "Classifier Algorithms" for more information on this algorithm.) We click the filter's Choose button and set the filter to ***Unsupervised***, ***Attribute***, ***StringToWordVector***. This will enable us to preprocess our data as shown in Figure 9.11. Click on the StringToWordVector filter to bring up the preprocessing options for the corpus. We set ***lowerCaseTokens*** to True, ***normalizeDocLength*** to Normalize all data, choose ***IteratedLovinsStemmer*** for our stemmer, and choose ***WordTokenizer*** for our tokenizer. We then choose ***WordsFromFile*** for our stopwordsHandler and click on ***WordsFromFile***, then on the input box alongside stopwords, and select the custom stopwords.txt file.[2] These choices normalize, stem, tokenize, and remove stop words, respectively. Notice, we're leaving the default number of wordsToKeep of 1000. Later, we can play with other options to determine whether we can obtain a better model. For now, we will click OK to return to our Weka Explorer window.

Back at our Weka Explorer window, we select ***Use training set*** under Test options, and click Start, as depicted in Figure 9.12A. Doing so will produce the output seen in Figure 9.12B. According to the output, there was fairly good agreement between Weka's classification of tweets as expressing positive sentiment or not and my classification. Specifically, Weka correctly classified 97% of the instances and has a Kappa of 0.9312. Its precision was 97.3%, recall 97.1%, and F1 score 0.971. The *Confusion Matrix* is particularly informative, though, telling us that Weka correctly classified twenty-three out of twenty-four non-Positive sentiment tweets and all ten Positive sentiment tweets.

If we right-click on the model to the left of the Weka pane and click the Save model option from the shortcut menu, as depicted in Figure 9.13, we can save our model to apply it to future classification tasks. Let's save the model as PosSent. Weka will append the file extension *.model* to it. If we select Visualize tree, we will see Weka's decision tree, which should resemble (but not necessarily be identical to) the one in Figure 9.5A.

Now, can we use our saved PosSent model to classify tweets about other movies as reflecting positive sentiment? Figure 9.14 depicts a test data set, which includes hypothetical tweets about the movie Kung Fu Panda (KungFuPanda.arff). Notice I have only two attributes in this data set. This is because I retained only two attributes in my training data set—recall we deleted the Negative sentiment attribute from our training data set to prevent WEKA from using it in the model. **It is important that the names and number of the attributes in the saved model (not the training *.arff*) and their data types match those in the test data set.**

To test our KungFuPanda data set against the model derived from the StarWars data set, we begin at the **Classify** tab. **(Note if you closed the WEKA explorer between developing and testing your PosSent model, you will have to use Open file . . . from the Preprocess tab before you can advance to the Classify tab. Then**

2 Obtained from http://www.lextek.com/manuals/onix/stopwords1.html.

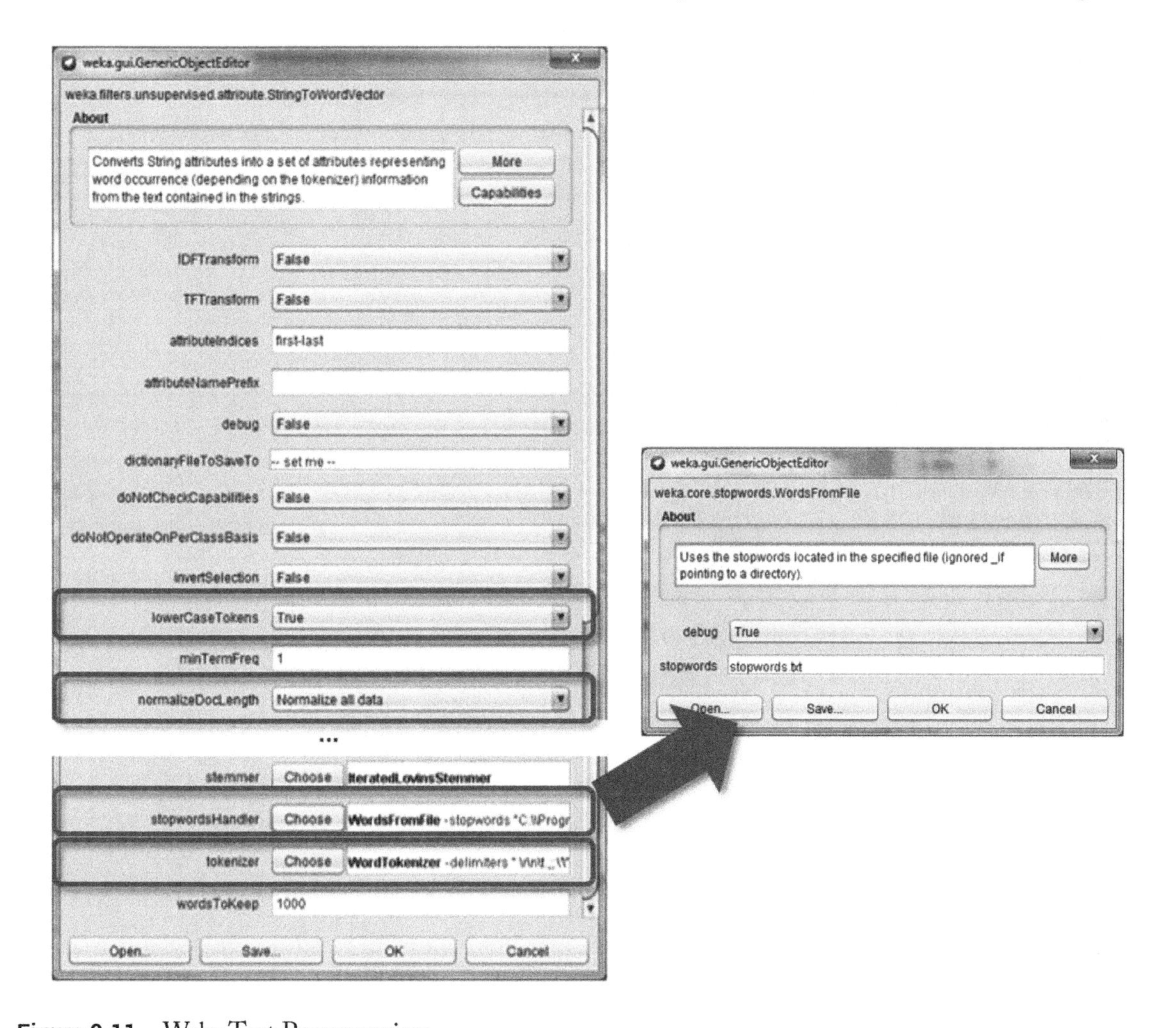

Figure 9.11 Weka Text Preprocessing

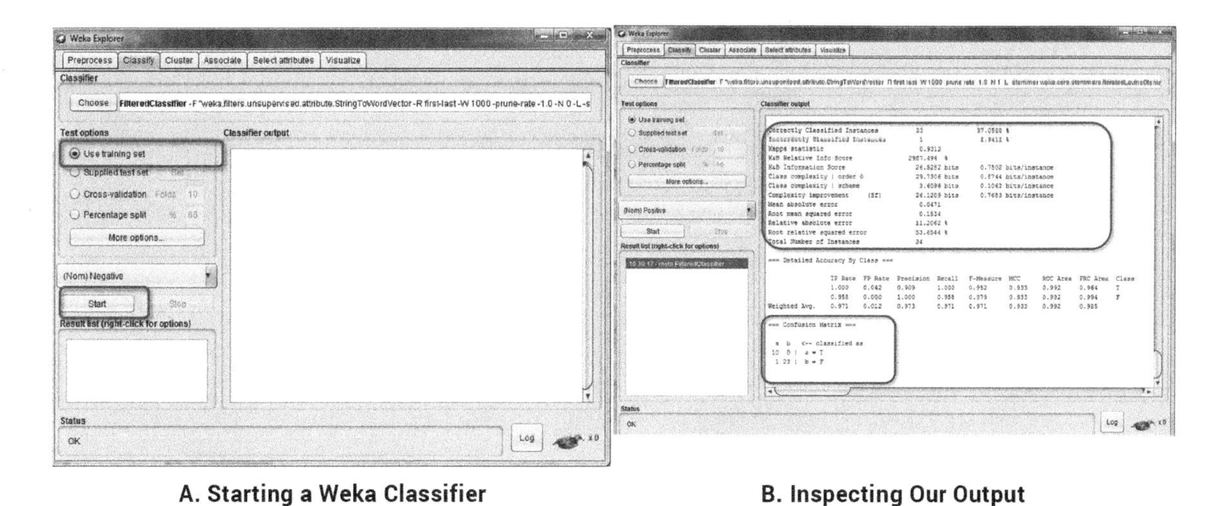

A. Starting a Weka Classifier

B. Inspecting Our Output

Figure 9.12 Obtaining a Classification Model in Weka

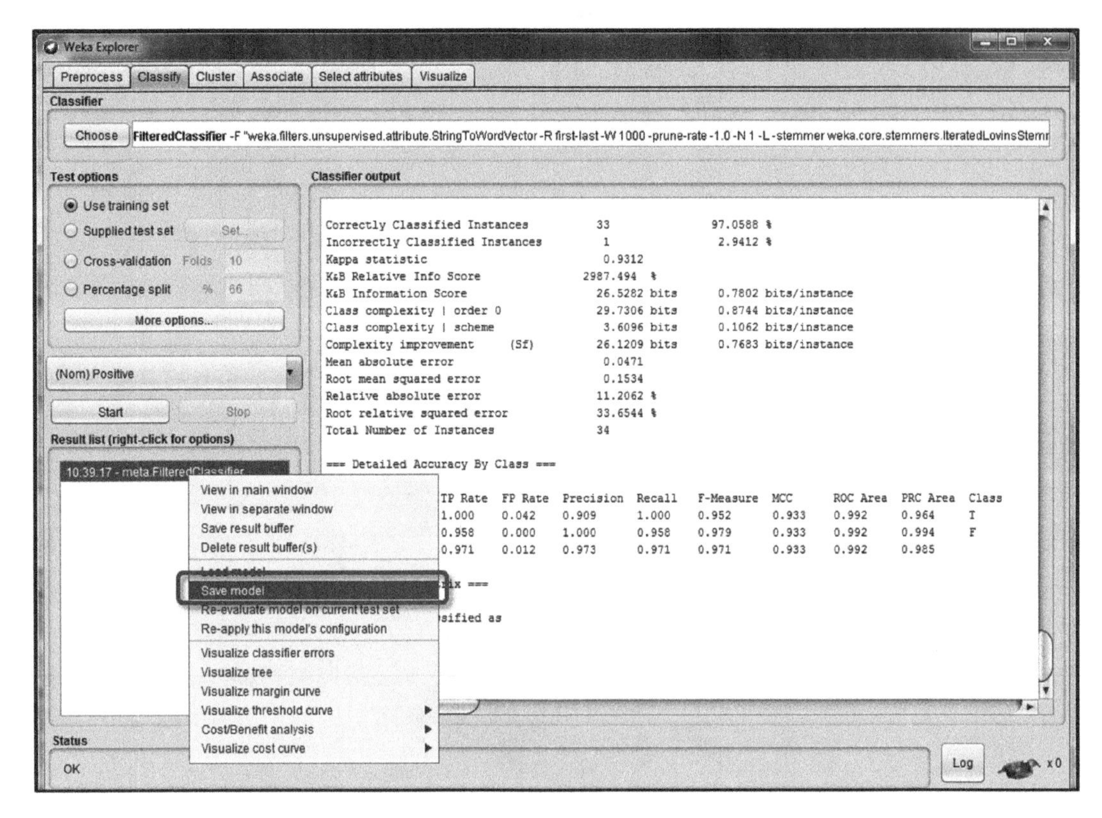

Figure 9.13 Saving and Viewing Our Weka Model

```
@relation tweetdata

@attribute Tweet string
@attribute Positive {T,F}

@data
'I really like Kung Fu Panda.  You should see it too.', ?
'I hated Kung Fu Panda.  What a waste of time!', ?
'I loved Kung Fu Panda.', ?
'What a great movie!  Definitely worth seeing.', ?
'Another Kung Fu movie that put me to sleep.', ?
```

Figure 9.14 Weka Test Data Set

reopen the StarWars.arff file.) From the **Classify** tab, we will select ***Supplied test set*** from Test options, as seen in Figure 9.15. We then click on the Set button (for data set), click Open file . . . , and choose our KungFuPanda.arff file. Then, click Close.

Next, from More Options, alongside ***Output predictions***, we click Choose; then select PlainText, and click OK, as depicted in Figure 9.16.

Now, in the bottom left pane, we right-click to bring up the shortcut menu, and then select Load model, and pick our saved PosSent.model. We then right-click again and select Re-evaluate model on current test set. On our test set, the important portion of the output is the *Predictions on test set*. The third column of this output—***predicted***—provides Weka's classification of each instance in our test data set. Weka expresses this as the category number, followed by a colon, followed by the category value to which each instance was assigned.

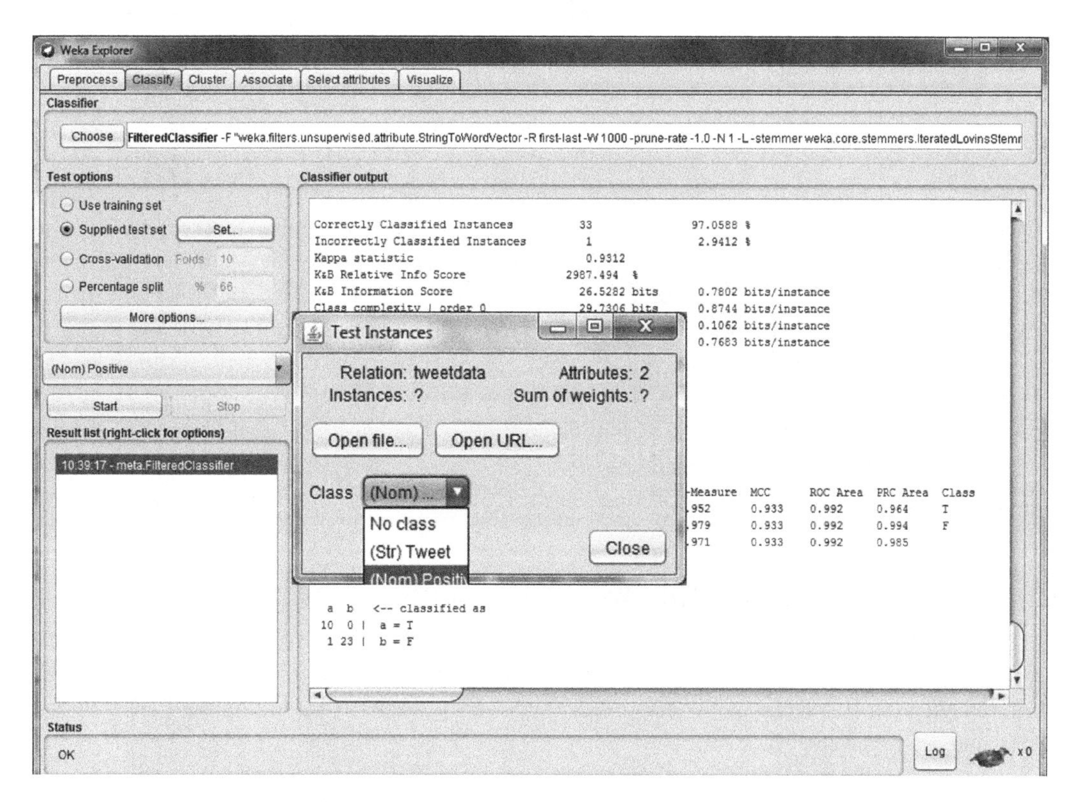

Figure 9.15 Applying Our PosSent Model to the KungFuPanda Data

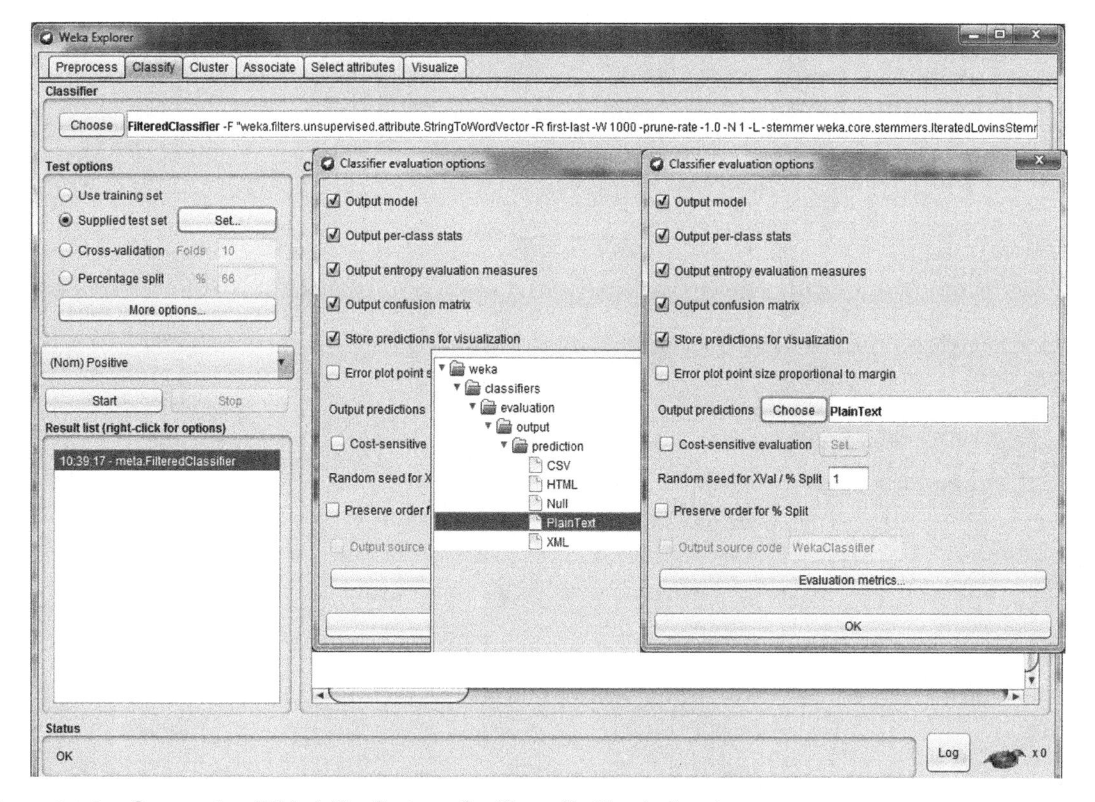

Figure 9.16 Outputting Weka's Predictions for Kung Fu Panda Sentiment

Category numbering is based on the training data set used to develop the classification model. From Figure 9.17, we see that the category ordering declared for the Positive @attribute is {T, F}. So instances seen to reflect positive emotion are assigned a 1:T. In Figure 9.17, we also see that Weka has classified the first, third, fourth, and fifth tweets as expressing positive sentiment about the Kung Fu Panda movie. Comparing these results against the tweets in Figure 9.14, we see it should not have classified the fifth tweet as positive. On our test data, we therefore find our PosSent model to be 80% accurate. The fourth column—***error prediction***—provides an estimate of Weka's confidence in its classification. For the first three tweets, Weka is 100% sure that they should be assigned to 1:T, 2:F, and 1:T, respectively. For the fourth and fifth instances, Weka is only ~80% sure that they reflect positive sentiment, but has ~20% doubt that perhaps they should be assigned to 2:F.

It would be useful to combine this output with our NodeXL and/or LIWC data. To do so, we copy the Weka output table highlighted in Figure 9.14 to an Excel worksheet. There, we can separate the table into its component columns using Excel's Text-to-Columns option (available off the Excel **Data** tab). Next, we can parse the ***predicted*** column using the formula *=LEFT(C2,FIND(":",C2)-1)*1*, if we wish the category number, or *=RIGHT(C2,LEN(C2)-FIND(":",C2))*, if we wish the category value (assuming our category numbers and names are in column C).

Tutorial 9.2. Sentiment Analysis via Machine Learning and LIWC

If we drew upon LIWC for our model features, would we get a better model than with Weka alone? To answer this question, we begin by subjecting our movie tweets to LIWC. First, we will see whether LIWC features alone improve the performance of our Weka model. Then, we will see whether combining LIWC with Weka's native text analysis yields a superior model.

To determine how LIWC-based features perform alone, we have incorporated ten LIWC concepts that correlated best with positive and negative sentiment in our test data set into *StarWarsLIWCFeatures.arff* and

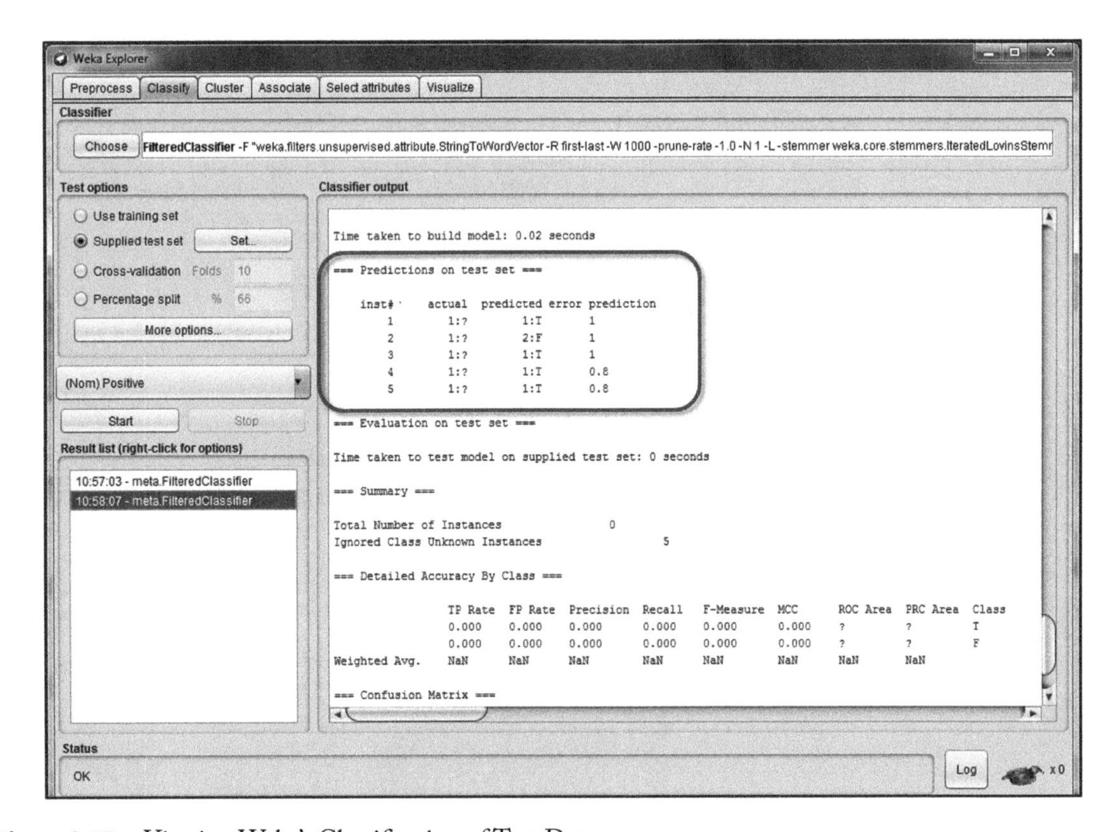

Figure 9.17 Viewing Weka's Classification of Test Data

KungFuPandaLIWCFeatures.arff. We open the StarWars training data set and once again remove the Negative sentiment attribute at the preprocessing stage, so it is not used to develop the classification model. From the Classify tab, we once again choose FilteredClassifier. When we select FilteredClassifier, we set the **filter** once again to StringToWordVector so Weka can parse and use the words in the tweets. Let's use the preprocessing options from Figure 9.11.

Classifier Algorithms

Weka provides a multitude of classifier algorithms for supervised (and in some cases, unsupervised) learning. Below are a few commonly-used classifiers.

Category	Algorithm	Description
Trees	J48	Permits missing values, pruning, continuous attribute values
	RandomForest	Higher number of trees increases processing time, but also accuracy
Bayesian	NaïveBayes	Probabilistic classifier based on Bayes theorem, assuming feature independence
	NaiveBayes-Multinomial	Bayes classifier for nonbinary categories
Functions	SimpleLogistic	Logistic regression classifier for binary classification
	Logistic	Logistic regression classifier for multinomial classification
	SMO (support vector machine)	A nonprobabilistic, binary classifier that, along with RandomForest, is considered a superior algorithm that "wins contests"

We then experiment with the different **classifier** algorithms. Several algorithms misclassify all T values. MultiClassClassifier gives us the best model, perfectly classifying all tweets. This algorithm is not based on a decision tree, but rather on logistic regression. It discovers the logistic model that best predicts whether or not our tweets reflect positive sentiment. Since the model consists of 152 parameters (our 10 LIWC features, 141 token features extracted from the text of the tweets, plus an intercept term), Table 9.3 represents only eight of the parameters modeled—the two best LIWC features and the two best token features that help classify the tweets as Positive sentiment being T(rue) and the two best LIWC features and the two best token features that help classify the tweets as Positive sentiment being F(alse). With logistic regression, negative coefficients and odds ratios less than one signal contraindications, while positive coefficients and odds ratios above one signal indicators. Features with very large or very tiny odds ratios play stronger roles in the classification algorithm. From the coefficients and odds ratio, we can see the LIWC features *negate* and *negemo* are modeled as contraindications of Positive sentiment in the tweets, while *we* and *risk* are modeled as indicators of Positive sentiment. Of the tokenized features, *hate* and *rey* are modeled as the best contraindications of Positive sentiment, while *gay* and *real* are modeled as the best indicators of Positive sentiment. The negative intercept, also depicted in Table 9.3, is attributable to the greater proportion of nonpositive than positive tweets in our training data set.

Let's save the MultiClassClassifier model and see how it performs on our test data set—*KungFuPandaLIWCFeatures.arff.* Once again, we find our model correctly classifies the first four tweets, but misclassifies the last, yielding an accuracy rate of 80%.

Conclusion

While this Weka journey appears to have been incredibly successful, in fact, obtaining a high-performing classification model through unsupervised learning requires a vaster training data set than the meager thirty-four Star Wars tweets we provided. A diversity of training data that approximates the diversity of data against which the model will be applied is highly desirable. In other words, if we plan to use our sentiment classification model on social media posts other that those emanating from Twitter and on movies other than Star Wars, the more social media platforms and movies represented in our training data set, the better the performance of the model developed.

Table 9.3 MultiClassClassifer Algorithm Results for LIWC Features

Coefficients		Odds Ratios	
	Class		Class
Variable	T	Variable	T
hat*	-31.9295	hat*	0.0000
rey	-22.7432	rey	0.0000
LIWCnegate	-0.8983	LIWCnegate	0.4072
LIWCnegemo	-0.5787	LIWCnegemo	0.5606
LIWCwe	1.6296	LIWCwe	5.1016
LIWCrisk	2.8128	LIWCrisk	16.6569
gay	16.4411	gay	13812293.0191
real	20.7091	real	985922252.8895
Intercept	-5.537		

Exercise: What Are the Attributes of a Positively Rated Movie?

We have a total of 50,000 IMDB movie reviews. The *TrainingReviews.arff* file contains 25,000 reviews that have been classified as reflecting positive (1) or negative (0) reviewer sentiment. The *TestReviews.arff* file contains 25,000 reviews that are to be classified as positive or negative. The purpose of this exercise is twofold. First, we would like to classify movie reviews as positive or negative as accurately as possible. Second, we would like a better understanding of why movie-goers respond positively or negatively to a movie.

Individual Assignment

1. Use the text of the reviews in the *TrainingReviews.arff* file to develop a model that determines whether a movie is positively rated. Experiment with at least three different classifier algorithms.
2. Record the differences in accuracy, kappa, precision, recall, and the F-1 metrics.
3. Use your models to classify the reviews in the *TestReviews.arff* file. Save your predictions to an Excel file.
4. Now, randomly select and read at least ten of the reviews in the *TestReviews.arff* file. Would you classify them as positive or negative? Are your WEKA model classifications consistent with your opinion?
5. Comment on the review features that were salient to your three classification models. Which features appear consistently across the models?

Team Assignment

Put together your team's analyses into a PowerPoint that reports on your team's text mining experiences and tells a story about what movie-goers care about.

1. Compare model metrics within your team. Which models produced the best metrics on your training data? Which models were most consistent with your subjective assessments of the test data?
2. What patterns of movie-goer expectations do the model features reveal? Are they all specific to the movie (script, cast, effects, etc.) or are there other aspects of the movie-going experience (e.g., theater environment or screening experience) involved? Are there certain expectations, when violated, more likely to lead to a negative movie review?

Your first slide should name all team members. Your story should reveal at least five insights that explain or predict and lead you to tangible recommendations.

Works Cited

1. Braun, M., "This Machine Turns Trump Tweets into Planned Parenthood Donations: And It's Open Source So You Can Help Make It Better," 2017, https://github.com/maxbbraun/trump2cash.
2. Landauer, T.K., et al., "How Well Can Passage Meaning Be Derived without Using Word Order? A Comparison of Latent Semantic Analysis and Humans," in *Proceedings of the 19th Annual Meeting of the Cognitive Science Society*. Palo Alto, CA: 1997.
3. Berry, M.W., and M. Browne, *Understanding Search Engines: Mathematical Modeling and Text Retrieval.* Philadelphia, PA: SIAM, 2005.
4. Broder, A., et al., "A Semantic Approach to Contextual Advertising," in *Proceedings of the 30th Annual International ACM SIGIR Conference on Research and Development in Information Retrieval.* Amsterdam: ACM, 2007.
5. Paul, M.J., *The Potential of Latent Semantic Analysis to Identify Themes in Online Forums.* Tacoma, WA: University of Washington, 2007, 92.
6. Spomer, J.E., *Latent Semantic Analysis and Classification Modeling in Applications for Social Movement Theory.* New Britain, CT: Central Connecticut State University, 2009.
7. Paul, M.J., and M. Dredze. "Drug Extraction from the Web: Summarizing Drug Experiences with Multi-Dimensional Topic Models," in *HLT-NAACL*. Atlanta: NAACL, 2013.
8. Settles, B., "On 'Geek' Versus 'Nerd,'" *Slackpropagation: A Web Journal about Machine Learning, Music, and Other Mischief,* https://slackprop.wordpress.com/2013/06/03/on-geek-versus-nerd/.
9. Aggarwal, C.C., and C. Zhai, *Mining Text Data*. New York: Springer Science & Business Media, 2012.
10. *Stanford Named Entity Tagger*. Stanford, CA: Stanford University, 2017.
11. Eftimov, T., B.K. Seljak, and P. Korošec, "A Rule-Based Named-Entity Recognition Method for Knowledge Extraction of Evidence-Based Dietary Recommendations." *PloS one*, 12(6; 2017): e0179488.
12. Blei, D.M., "Probabilistic Topic Models." *Communications of the ACM*, 55(4; 2012): 77–84.
13. Lohr, S., and N. Wingfield, "When Mr. Gates Went to Washington," *New York Times*, April 14, 2018.
14. *Stanford Parser*. Stanford, CA: Stanford University, 2016.

CHAPTER 10

Information Extraction with R

> **Learning Objectives**
>
> The purpose of this chapter is to provide you with a deeper understanding of two information extraction tasks and their uses, and develop your ability to conduct those tasks in R:
>
> 1. named entity recognition; and
> 2. part-of-speech tagging.

In 1950, Alan Turing offered the defining standard for artificial intelligence: imagine you are interacting with another entity electronically; if, through the course of that interaction, you cannot determine whether that that entity is a machine, then it possesses intelligence. As you might imagine, language, fundamental to our ability to communicate, is the first hurdle to demonstrating intelligence. In 1966, Joseph Weizenbaum completed one of the earliest applications that passed Turing's test—at least in initial or short-term interactions. The psychotherapy application, called Eliza, was patterned on Carl Rogers's client-centered therapy. It empathetically and iteratively probed users' statements to help them reflexively surface and understand their circumstances. If you told Eliza "I've had a rough morning with my mother," she might have said, "Tell me more about your mother." Typical Rogerian psychotherapy. If, however, you said to her "Necessity is the mother of invention," she also was liable to respond with "Tell me more about your mother" [2]. At this point, you would realize you were not talking with an intelligent being, and Eliza failed the Turing test.

Eliza, which we can still experience at the Computer History Museum in Boston [3] or in modified form at some introductory psychology course websites [e.g., 4], brings home the challenge of communicating with a machine using natural language—that is, the languages that we speak as opposed to the programming language that computers understand. Today, with voice assistants like Siri, Alexa, and Google Assistant, it seems that we have attained a level of success with natural language processing. Researchers at MIT Media Labs are even experimenting with technology that permits us to verbally, but inaudibly, query computers [6]. Yet challenges persist. For example, a HowStuffWorks post [7] notes that Siri responds to the direction "Tell Bill he's going to have to leave without me" by texting Bill from your contact list, "He's going to have to leave without me."

In this chapter, we will use natural language processing for two information extraction tasks: named entity recognition and part-of-speech tagging. Extracting named entities permits us to identify salient content words, such as organization names and names of people mentioned in a text. The tremendous advantage of computer support for recognizing such named entities is our ability to quickly process large volumes of text and discover salient content words, even those that occur infrequently enough to not appear salient using tools such as word clouds. Part-of-speech tagging identifies the different types of content and function words in a text and is a precursor to other types of information extraction and text mining tasks. Instead of the LIWC-type dictionary-based approach to identifying function words, we will look at extracting both salient content words as well as part-of-speech information using natural language processing in R.

Information Extraction Packages

For our foray into text analytics with R, we will need the following R packages: **NLP** and **openNLP**. If you get the following message when trying to load the **openNLP** package, your Java version is inconsistent with your R version (i.e., 32-bit on one and 64-bit on the other). Uninstall and reinstall Java.

```
Error : .onLoad failed in loadNamespace() for 'rJava', details:
  call: fun(libname, pkgname)
  error: No CurrentVersion entry in Software/JavaSoft registry! Try re-
installing Java and make sure R and Java have matching architectures.
Error: package or namespace load failed for 'openNLP'
```

We also will need a set of models from the **openNLPmodels.en** package ("en" for English—other language models also are available [8]). This package supplies a set of models to be used with NLP and openNLP to perform named entity recognition and parts-of-speech tagging. To install openNLPmodels.en, use:

```
install.packages('openNLPmodels.en',
   repos='http://datacube.wu.ac.at/',
   type='source')
```

After running this statement, check the following directory for the pretrained model files *en-chunker*, *en-ner-organization*, *en-ner-person*, *en-ner-date*, *en-ner-location*, *en-ner-money*, *en-ner-percentage*, *en-ner-time*, *en-parser-chunking*, and *en-pos-perceptron*:

\R\win-library\R_VERSION_NUMBER\openNLPmodels.en\models

If missing one or more of these model files, or if you need annotators for another language, you can download them directly from http://opennlp.sourceforge.net/models-1.5/. Put them into the folder noted above.

An alternative to the NLP package is the **monkeylearn** package. This R package is an interface to the monkeylearn API, a machine learning platform. It requires the user register to use the API and permits users up to 10,000 free requests monthly [9]. The R interface to the monkeylearn utility currently is not formally supported.

Information Extraction with Natural Language Processing

In Chapter 9, we considered a variety of information extraction tasks. Here, we will explore information extraction using R's natural language processing packages. The data for this task is the StarWars.txt file, depicted in Figure 10.1. We scan this text file in into a string variable using `s=scan('StarWars.txt', what='character')`. (We can ensure it is of a text data type using `s=as.String(s)`.)

Before we can tag words in our text as named entities or parts-of-speech, we need to tokenize words, which requires that we first identify sentences. To do so, we use the OpenNLP sentence and word tokenizers, ***Maxent_Sent_Token_Annotator()*** and ***Maxent_Word_Token_Annotator()***. Annotators tag tokens such as sentences, words, or bigrams with their types (e.g., sentence, word, entity type, part of speech). We use these tokenizers in conjunction with the ***annotate(STRING, TOKENIZER)*** function, which iteratively calls the designated tokenizers against the input string, annotating each token with its token type. We apply our sentence and word tokenizers to our text to generate a list of tokens called tokenizedS from the string s, using `tokenizedS = annotate(s, list(Maxent_Sent_Token_Annotator(), Maxent_Word_Token_Annotator()))`. The tokenizedS data object contains all sentence and word tokens, annotated with whether they are a sentence or word. We will use this annotated set of tokens in our two information extraction tasks—recognizing named entities and identifying parts of speech.

Star Wars is an American epic space opera franchise, centered on a film series created by George Lucas. It depicts the adventures of various characters "a long time ago in a galaxy far, far away".

The first film in the series, Star Wars (later subtitled Episode IV: A New Hope), was released on May 25, 1977 by 20th Century Fox. It was followed by the similarly successful sequels The Empire Strikes Back (1980) and Return of the Jedi (1983); these three films constitute the original Star Wars trilogy. A prequel trilogy was later released between 1999 and 2005, which received a more mixed reaction from critics and fans, compared to the original trilogy. All seven films were nominated for or won Academy Awards, and were commercial successes, with a combined box office revenue of $4.38 billion, making Star Wars the fourth highest-grossing film series. The series has spawned an extensive media franchise—the Star Wars expanded universe—including books, television series, computer and video games, and comic books, resulting in significant development of the series' fictional universe. Star Wars also holds a Guinness World Records title for the "Most successful film merchandising franchise." In 2012, the total value of the Star Wars franchise was estimated at USD $30.7 billion, including box-office receipts as well as profits from their video games and DVD sales.

In 2012, The Walt Disney Company, located in Burbank, California, acquired Lucasfilm, located in San Francisco, California, for $4.06 billion and announced three new Star Wars films; the first film of that trilogy, Star Wars: The Force Awakens, was released on December 18, 2015. 20th Century Fox retains the physical distribution rights to the first two Star Wars trilogies, owning permanent rights for the original 1977 film and holding the rights to Episodes I-III, V and VI until May 2020. The Walt Disney Studios owns digital distribution rights to all the Star Wars films, excluding A New Hope.

Daisy Ridley (born April 10, 1992) is an English actress. She began her acting career by appearing in minor television roles, before being cast as the main protagonist, Rey, in the Star Wars sequel trilogy—first appearing in Star Wars: The Force Awakens (2015).

Four of the 50 highest-grossing films - i.e., 8% - listed by Wikipedia were from the Star Wars franchise. The four films were Star Wars: The Force Awakens, at third position, Star Wars: The Last Jedi, at ninth position, Rogue One: A Star Wars Story, in 24th position, and Star Wars: Episode 1 - The Phantom Menace, in 29th position.

Legend:
Information to be extracted

Figure 10.1 Text for Information Extraction Task

Named Entity Recognition

The objective of our named entity recognition task is to tag the words in our text with the type of term they represent. The NLP package permits us to tag six types of terms: organization names, names of persons, dates, locations, percentages, and money. We use the ***Maxent_Entity_Annotator(kind='EntityType')*** to generate a set of entity annotations, derived from the **openNLPmodels.en**, which we will apply to *tokenizedS* later. Of course, we could also apply the annotators directly to our string data set as we did with the sentence and word annotators above.

```
org_annotator=Maxent_Entity_Annotator(kind='organization')
person_annotator=Maxent_Entity_Annotator(kind='person')
date_annotator=Maxent_Entity_Annotator(kind='date')
percent_annotator=Maxent_Entity_Annotator(kind='percentage')
loc_annotator=Maxent_Entity_Annotator(kind='location')
money_annotator=Maxent_Entity_Annotator(kind='money')
```

Note that regenerating the annotators may yield the following error. If this occurs, restarting R will remediate the problem.

```
Error in .jnew("opennlp.tools.namefind.TokenNameFinderModel", .jcast(.jnew("java.
     io.FileInputStream",   :
  java.lang.OutOfMemoryError: Java heap space
```

We now apply the annotators to tokenizedS, where each word that matches a word in the annotator models receives its associated entity annotation:

```
swTokens = annotate(s, list(org_annotator, person_annotator, date_annotator,
          loc_annotator, money_annotator), tokenizedS)
```

Inspecting the annotations associated with words from Figure 10.1, using **`View(data.frame (swTokens))`**, provides the token annotation in Figure 10.2.

	id	type	start	end	features
1	1	sentence	1	103	list(constituents = 17:36)
2	2	sentence	105	195	list(constituents = 37:55)
3	3	sentence	197	327	list(constituents = 56:87)
4	4	sentence	329	502	list(constituents = 88:121)
5	5	sentence	504	656	list(constituents = 122:149)
			...		
523	523	word	2572	2572	list()
524	524	entity	1118	1125	list(kind = "organization")
525	525	entity	1270	1272	list(kind = "organization")
526	526	entity	1365	1367	list(kind = "organization")
527	527	entity	1389	1407	list(kind = "organization")
528	528	entity	1874	1892	list(kind = "organization")
529	529	entity	91	102	list(kind = "person")
530	530	entity	381	383	list(kind = "person")
531	531	entity	385	403	list(kind = "person")
532	532	entity	1886	1892	list(kind = "person")
533	533	entity	1977	1988	list(kind = "person")
534	534	entity	295	300	list(kind = "date")
535	535	entity	406	409	list(kind = "date")
			...		
550	550	entity	1488	1497	list(kind = "location")
551	551	entity	1661	1671	list(kind = "location")
552	552	entity	785	797	list(kind = "money")
553	553	entity	1274	1286	list(kind = "money")
554	554	entity	1504	1516	list(kind = "money")
555	555	entity	2287	2288	list(kind = "percentage")

Showing 542 to 555 of 555 entries

Figure 10.2 Results of Tokenization and Annotation

The "features" column of Figure 10.2 indicates which tokens of entity type have been tagged as organization, person, date, location, money, or percentage. We don't know how certain the annotator is of the tags assigned. Adding a "probs=T" to the Maxent_Entity_Annotator function supplies this information, if necessary. For example, setting `org_annotator= Maxent_Entity_Annotator(kind='organization', probs=T)` produces the organization entity annotations depicted in Figure 10.3.

Obviously, Figure 10.2 (and Figure 10.3) is not the most user-friendly output. We can extract subsets of *swTokens* corresponding to the different entities using the code below:

```
swOrg=subset(swTokens,swTokens$features=='list(kind = "organization")')
swPerson=subset(swTokens,swTokens$features=='list(kind = "person")')
swDate=subset(swTokens,swTokens$features=='list(kind = "date")')
swLocation=subset(swTokens,swTokens$features=='list(kind = "location")')
swPercent=subset(swTokens,swTokens$features=='list(kind = "percent")')
swMoney=subset(swTokens,swTokens$features=='list(kind = "money")')
```

Note if we annotated the tags with their probabilities too, we would need to use something like `swOrg= subset(swTokens,substr(swTokens$features,1,26)=='list(kind = "organization"')` to subset the tokens. This would compare the first twenty-six characters of each features value with 'list(kind = "organization"'. We dropped the closing parenthesis following "organization" because, when annotated also with the probabilities, the parenthesis does not immediately follow the tag for the entity kind.

Next, we can extract portions of the original string corresponding to the different entity annotations and tag them with the entity annotations. We begin by initializing a data frame that will contain each tagged Entity, its Position in the text, and the entity Type using `SWEntities=data.frame(Entity=character(), Position=numeric(), Type=character())`.

For each entity tagged, we then extract substrings of our text from the starting position of that token to the ending position of that token from Figure 10.2. To do so, we use the ***substring(TEXT, STARTCHARACTER, ENDCHARACTER)*** function. However, since the scan() command essentially tokenized our text into a list of tokens, we need to collapse this list back into our original text. We do this with the ***paste(LIST, collapse='CHARACTER')*** function. For example, we extract the first tagged token from Figure 10.2, which is an organization beginning at character number 1117 and finishing at character number 1124 in our text corpus, using `substring(paste(s, collapse=' '), 1117, 1124)`, which returns `"Guinness"`.

It is inefficient to have to manually inspect entity positions and extract them individually. We therefore can automate them with a series of loops, as seen below. The loop uses the ***nrow(DATAFRAME)*** function to capture the number of rows in each of the entity token subsets we created earlier (i.e., swOrg, swPerson, swLocation, swDate, and swMoney). We then use the number of rows thus extracted as the upper bound in each loop, and append each subsequently extracted set of entities into a single data frame using rbind().

524	524	entity	1118	1125	list(kind = "organization", prob = 0.912569453896878)
525	525	entity	1270	1272	list(kind = "organization", prob = 0.657766527077986)
526	526	entity	1365	1367	list(kind = "organization", prob = 0.624510433802049)
527	527	entity	1389	1407	list(kind = "organization", prob = 0.847443972675483)
528	528	entity	1874	1892	list(kind = "organization", prob = 0.762222213737348)
529	529	entity	91	102	list(kind = "person", prob = 0.989279525779542)
530	530	entity	381	383	list(kind = "person", prob = 0.792585841059634)

Figure 10.3 Including Probability Assessments in the Token Annotations

```
for (i in 1:nrow(as.data.frame(swOrg)))
{
 SWEntities=rbind(SWEntities, cbind(substr(paste(s, collapse=' '),
    swOrg$start[i],swOrg$end[i]),swOrg$start[i], 'Organization'))
}
for (i in 1:nrow(as.data.frame(swPerson)))
{
  SWEntities=rbind(SWEntities, cbind(substr(paste(s, collapse=' '),
    swPerson$start[i],swPerson$end[i]),swPerson$start[i], 'Person'))
}
for (i in 1:nrow(as.data.frame(swLocation)))
{
  SWEntities=rbind(SWEntities, cbind(substr(paste(s, collapse=' '),
    swLocation$start[i],swLocation$end[i]),swLocation$start[i], 'Location'))
}
for (i in 1:nrow(as.data.frame(swDate)))
{
  SWEntities=rbind(SWEntities, cbind(substr(paste(s, collapse=' '),
    swDate$start[i],swDate$end[i]),swDate$start[i], 'Date'))
}
for (i in 1:nrow(as.data.frame(swPercent)))
{
  SWEntities=rbind(SWEntities, cbind(substr(paste(s, collapse=' '),
    swPercent$start[i],swPercent$end[i]),swPercent$start[i], 'Percent'))
}
for (i in 1:nrow(as.data.frame(swMoney)))
{
  SWEntities=rbind(SWEntities, cbind(substr(paste(s, collapse=' '),
    swMoney$start[i],swMoney$end[i]),swMoney$start[i], 'Money'))
}
colnames(SWEntities)=c('Entity', 'Position', 'Type')
```

Invoking `SWEntities` reveals the following entity tagging:

```
                   Entity Position         Type
1                Guinness     1118 Organization
2                     USD     1270 Organization
3                     DVD     1365 Organization
4  Walt\nDisney\nCompany     1389 Organization
5  Walt\nDisney\nStudios     1874 Organization
6           George\nLucas       91       Person
7                     The      381       Person
8  Empire\nStrikes\nBack      385       Person
9                 Studios     1886       Person
10          Daisy\nRidley     1977       Person
11           Century\nFox      316     Location
12                Burbank     1421     Location
13             California     1430     Location
14         San\nFrancisco     1473     Location
15             California     1488     Location
16           Century\nFox     1661     Location
17               May\n25       295         Date
18                   1980      406         Date
```

```
19                 1983    436      Date
20        between\n1999    541      Date
21                 2005    558      Date
22                 2012   1204      Date
23                 2012   1379      Date
24  December\n18,\n2015   1637      Date
25                 1977   1793      Date
26            May\n2020   1860      Date
27     April\n10,\n1992   1996      Date
28                 2015   2234      Date
29                   8%   2287   Percent
30      $4.38\nbillion     785     Money
31      $30.7\nbillion    1274     Money
32      $4.06\nbillion    1504     Money
```

Comparing the output against Figure 10.1 reveals some errors and omissions. For example, the named entity annotator has tagged "USD" and "DVD" as organizations, and "The" as a person, but omitted "Lucasfilm" as an organization. Also, "Walt Disney Studios" was correctly identified as an organization, but "Studios" was tagged also as a person. Further, while it tagged "Empire Strikes Back" as a person, it failed to tag any other movie titles in the text, raising the issue of tagging consistency. Dates, too, while accurately tagged, are tagged somewhat incongruously (e.g., "between 1999").

Table 10.1 depicts the recall and precision performance for each type of entity extracted and across all types of entities. From Chapter 9, remember that recall is the percentage of tagged entities that are correctly tagged, and precision is the percentage of correctly tagged entities relative to the entities in our text. Table 10.1 indicates considerable disparity in the performance across the different types of entity tags, with an abundance of false positives and false negatives. Performance for the Date and Money tags seems particularly good, but tagging for Organizations is problematic in terms of both recall and performance. With regard to tagging Persons, we can expect R to identify people within our text, but also to falsely tag a number of words that are not people. Yet, for parsing large texts, this approach can provide insights otherwise unavailable except through laborious reading.

Tutorial 10.1. People Named in the *Black Panther* Conversation

Six weeks after its release, *Black Panther* was the highest grossing movie of all time, though ranking twelfth after adjusting for inflation [10]. Well in advance of its February 2018 release, the trailer debuted on social media during the NBA Finals in June 2017. The trailer's exposure of stars Lupita Nyong'o, Michael B. Jordan,

Table 10.1 Summary of R's Entity Tagging Performance

Entity Type	Recall	Precision
Organization	60% (3 out of 5)	50% (3 out of 6)
Person	100% (2 out of 5)	40% (2 out of 5)
Location	– (4 out of 6)	0% (4 out of 4)
Date	100% (12 out of 12)	100% (12 out of 12)
Percent	100% (1 out of 1)	100% (1 out of 1)
Money	100% (3 out of 3)	100% (3 out of 3)
All	78% (25 out of 32)	81% (25 out of 31)

and Chadwick Boseman created considerable social media buzz for the movie [11]. *To what extent did the cast contribute to the movie buzz?* To answer this, we first must identify people's names in the social media posts.

The BlackPantherMovie.csv file contains two hundred Facebook posts obtained from the official Facebook page for the movie, and dating from December 25, 2017, to April 26, 2018. The message column in the file contains the Facebook posts. After we read this file into a data frame called BP, we will identify the names of people mentioned in the messages.

We first create a person annotator with

```
person_annotator=Maxent_Entity_Annotator(kind='person')
```

Next, we create an empty dataframe using

```
BPEntities=data.frame(Post=numeric(), Entity=character(), Position=numeric())
```

To this, we will append the annotated person words from our two hundred Facebook posts using the code below. This code is similar to the code we used to recognize entities in the Star Wars text, with one major modification: Since we have two hundred posts to analyze, we put our code into a loop, which will run two hundred times—or as many times as there are rows in the BP data frame.

```
for (post in 1:nrow(BP))
{
 BPText=as.String(BP$message[post])
  BPTokens=annotate(BPText, list(Maxent_Sent_Token_Annotator(), Maxent_Word_Token_Annotator()))
  BPOrgPersTokens=annotate(BPText, list(person_annotator), BPTokens)
  BPPerson=subset(BPOrgPersTokens,BPOrgPersTokens$features=='list(kind = "person")')
  for (i in 1:nrow(as.data.frame(BPPerson)))
  {
    if (nrow(as.data.frame(BPPerson))>0) {
    BPEntities=rbind(BPEntities, cbind(post, substr(paste(BPText, collapse=' '),
       BPOrg$start[i],BPOrg$end[i]),BPOrg$start[i]))
    }
  }
}
```

We added an if statement prior to the rbind() to exclude rows for post instances when the BPPerson data frame was empty. Next, we reset column titles in our data frame using

```
colnames(BPEntities)=c('Post', 'Entity', 'Position')
```

When we inspect our BPEntities data frame, we notice many instances in which "Studios" has been tagged as a person. We can eliminate these by obtaining the subset of entries in which the tagged word is not "Studios" using

```
BPEntities=subset(BPEntities,BPEntities$Entity!='Studios')
```

Finally, we would like to have our extracted person names side-by-side with the posts from which they were extracted. We accomplish this by merging the two data frames and retaining only the second and eight columns from the merged data frame with

```
BPPeople=merge(BPEntities, BP, by.x='Post', by.y='Post')[c(2,8)]
```

The extracted names and the posts from which they were extracted are depicted in Table 10.2. With names being identified in only twelve of the two hundred Facebook posts, we see that openNLP fell woefully short in identifying the people named in the posts. For example, the second post, *"You need a hero."—Kendrick Lamar #BlackPanther (via Chadwick Boseman)*, contained two unrecognized names. Even within the twelve posts appearing in Table 10.2, we see unrecognized person names: Lupita Nyog'o, Chadwick Boseman, Zoe Saldana, Kendrick Lamar, Dangeroo Kipawaa, Winston Duke, and Crowezilla. We also see Hurricane Harvey incorrectly tagged in row 5 (though perhaps understandably so!) and Music in row 9.

Why did openNLP perform so much worse when tagging Facebook posts about the *Black Panther* movie than when tagging the paragraphs of text about the Star Wars movies? To understand this, we must understand part-of-speech tagging.

Table 10.2 *Black Panther* Facebook Posts with Tagged Named Entities

Recognized Entity		Facebook Post Highlighting Person Entities Mentioned
1	Angela Bassett	Wakanda Forever. Angela Bassett, Danai Gurira, and Lupita Nyong'o surprised fans at a screening of Marvel Studios' "Black Panther"! Watch our Instagram Story to see more.
2	Danai Gurira	Wakanda Forever. Angela Bassett, Danai Gurira, and Lupita Nyong'o surprised fans at a screening of Marvel Studios' "Black Panther"! Watch our Instagram Story to see more.
3	Sterling K. Brown	Congratulations to Chadwick Boseman, Sterling K. Brown, and Ryan Coogler of Marvel Studios' "Black Panther" for being recognized in TIME's 100 Most Influential People of 2018 list! Read Chadwick's profile:
4	Ryan Coogler	Congratulations to Chadwick Boseman, Sterling K. Brown, and Ryan Coogler of Marvel Studios' "Black Panther" for being recognized in TIME's 100 Most Influential People of 2018 list! Read Chadwick's profile:
5	Hurricane Harvey	Join the Marvel team on this #DayofGiving to help those affected by Hurricane Harvey. Visit RedCross.org/ABC, or call 1-855-999-GIVE. Anything helps! (via Zoe Saldana)
6	Ryan Coogler	Discover what makes Wakanda the best-kept secret in this all-new featurette with interviews from Director Ryan Coogler and the cast. Get tickets to see Marvel Studios' "Black Panther" now: www.fandango.com/blackpanther
7	Ruth Carter	Witness the fashion of Marvel Studios' "Black Panther." See the looks that inspired the designs with costume designer Ruth Carter. In theaters Friday: http://www.fandango.com/blackpanther
8	Ruth Carter	Explore the fashion of Marvel Studios' "Black Panther." See the looks that inspired the designs with costume designer Ruth Carter.
9	Music	Kendrick Lamar, Dangeroo Kipawaa, and Top Dawg Entertainment will curate and produce "Black Panther: The Album, Music from and Inspired by the Film," including lead single "All the Stars" by SZA. Listen to the single now: http://bit.ly/2qlT9HN
10	Hulk	"Puny god." Marvel Studios' "Avengers: Infinity War" comes to theaters April 27. #Hulk
11	Daniel Kaluuya	Selfie time with Winston Duke and Daniel Kaluuya! #SAGAwards #BlackPanther (via Lupita Nyong'o)
12	Ryan Coogler	The cast of Marvel Studios' "Black Panther" and director Ryan Coogler are all smiles at the black carpet fan event in Seoul!
13	Shani Crowe	Shani Crowe, AKA Crowezilla, gives her own take on #WakandaStyle. Share your look using the hashtag. #BlackPanther #ad
14	Maria Beltre	Maria Beltre flaunts her #WakandaStyle. What are you wearing to see Marvel Studios' "Black Panther"? Share your photos using the hashtag.

Part-of-Speech Tagging

Part-of-speech tagging is a precursor to other natural language processing tasks. It is necessary for the named entity recognition we saw above. Because social media posts are rarely well-structured grammatically, openNLP has trouble recognizing parts of speech. Given this difficulty, performing the subsequent named entity recognition task is challenging. If the named entity recognition program is unable to recognize a word as a noun, it will not consider it to be an entity of noun form (i.e., a person or an organization), thereby reducing precision in the recognition of these entities. Note that the Facebook posts appearing in Table 10.2 conformed to the conventional sentence subject-verb-object structure, thereby helping openNLP identify people's names.

A second text mining task for which part-of-speech tagging is necessary is ***lemmatization***. Lemmatization is a more intelligent, but computationally intensive, alternative to stemming. While R provides packages that perform lemmatization, should we wish to create a custom lemmatizer, parsing parts of speech would be our first step. See the "Text Normalization via Lemmatization versus Stemming" insert for more information.

The openNLP package provides a part-of-speech annotator. We can access it using `pos_annotator=`**`Maxent_POS_Tag_Annotator`**`()`. We can apply this annotator to our tokenized text using `swPOSTokens = `**`annotate`**`(s, `**`list`**`(pos_annotator), tokenizedS)`. Using `swPOS= `**`subset`**`(as.data.frame(swPOSTokens),swPOSTokens$type=='word')` permits us to obtain a list of word tokens only. Figure 10.4 depicts a partial set of these tagged tokens.

Since Figure 10.4 provides no information about which word from the original text is tagged NNP, NNPS, or VBZ, we need to extract the words from the text using the start and end markers appearing in Figure 10.4. Below, we begin by creating an empty data frame, labeled SWPartsOfSpeech, with three columns: Term, which will contain character or text data; Position, which will hold numeric data; and the PartOfSpeech, which also will contain character data. Next, we set up a loop to append each annotated word to the data frame with the

Text Normalization via Lemmatization versus Stemming

As seen in Chapter 7, stemming is one way to normalize conjugationally different or otherwise inflected forms of a term in a corpus to the same base. Stemming uses a simple rule-based algorithm—for example, replacing the end of all terms ending with "*sses*" to "*ss*," those ending with "*ies*" to "*i*," and deleting the "*s*" from terms ending with "*s*" [1]. While efficient, this reduction often is inaccurate. For example, truncating "*passes*" to "*pass*" using the "sses" to "ss" rule produces an accurate stem, but truncating "*assess*" does not. Some stemming algorithms use rule qualifiers, such as considering term length, to improve stemming accuracy. For example, the rule deleting "*ement*" from the end of terms of length larger than six characters reduces "*replacement*" to "*replac*," but leaves "*cement*" intact [1]. This rule qualifier also alleviates the problem with truncating "*assess*."

Even with these enhanced rules, though, stemming results can be problematic. First, not all words with the same stem mean the same thing. For example, the Porter stemmer reduces "*organize*" and "*organization*" to "*organ*," which also could mean an anatomical part or a musical instrument. Here, stemming is overly reductive. Second, stemming rules fail to recognize semantically related terms with different stems or prefixes. For example, stemming would not recognize "*was*" as a conjugated form of "*be*," or "*better*" and "*best*" as the relative and superlative forms of "*good*," and therefore would treat them differently. Additionally, stemming imposes a cognitive overhead when results are being interpreted, because the stem could be a nonsensical word such as "*hav*" (the stem for "*have*" or "*having*").

Lemmatization is a contextually-sensitive approach to text normalization that works in two stages [5]. In the first stage, it contextualizes a word based on its part of speech in a sentence. For example, consider the word "bearing" in the following two sentences: "*She comes bearing gifts*" and "*She lost her bearing*." In the first sentence, openNLP tags "bearing" as VBG—or verb gerund. In the second, it tags "bearing" as NN—or noun singular. In the second stage of lemmatization, the algorithm looks up a word in its part-of-speech dictionary or lexicon. A lemmatization routine therefore would look up the VBG form of "*bearing*" that appears in the first sentence in a verb dictionary, which would equate it to its lemma of "*bear*"; however, it would consult the noun dictionary to lemmatize the NN form encountered in the second sentence, and subsequently return the lemma of "*bearing*." Finally, while the stem of a word can be nonsensical, the lemma always is a meaningful word. Thus, by incorporating part-of-speech into normalization, lemmatization improves on stemming.

rbind() function, cycling through the loop as many times as there are rows in the swPOS data frame. (Recall this data frame contains the subset of word annotations.) We obtain the entry to be appended by combining the substring with the start and end character numbers from Figure 10.4, which will be our Term column, with the start character number, which will be our Position column, and the part-of-speech tag, which will be the PartOfSpeech column. Finally, we relabel the columns in the SWPartsOfSpeech data frame, as these may have been lost in our multiple data combinations.

	id	type	start	end	features
17	17	word	1	4	list(POS = "NNP")
18	18	word	6	9	list(POS = "NNPS")
19	19	word	11	12	list(POS = "VBZ")
20	20	word	14	15	list(POS = "DT")
21	21	word	17	24	list(POS = "JJ")
22	22	word	26	29	list(POS = "NN")
23	23	word	31	35	list(POS = "NN")
24	24	word	37	41	list(POS = "NN")
25	25	word	43	51	list(POS = "NN")
26	26	word	52	52	list(POS = ",")
27	27	word	54	61	list(POS = "VBN")
28	28	word	63	64	list(POS = "IN")
29	29	word	66	66	list(POS = "DT")
30	30	word	68	71	list(POS = "NN")
			...		
511	511	word	2518	2521	list(POS = "NNPS")
512	512	word	2522	2522	list(POS = ":")
513	513	word	2524	2530	list(POS = "NNP")
514	514	word	2532	2532	list(POS = "LS")
515	515	word	2534	2534	list(POS = ":")
516	516	word	2536	2538	list(POS = "DT")
517	517	word	2540	2546	list(POS = "NNP")
518	518	word	2548	2553	list(POS = "NNP")
519	519	word	2554	2554	list(POS = ",")
520	520	word	2556	2557	list(POS = "IN")
521	521	word	2559	2562	list(POS = "JJ")
522	522	word	2564	2571	list(POS = "NN")
523	523	word	2572	2572	list(POS = ".")

Showing 494 to 507 of 507 entries

Figure 10.4 Results of Parts-of-Speech Annotation

```
SWPartsOfSpeech=data.frame(Term=character(), Position=numeric(),
  PartOfSpeech=character())
for (i in 1:nrow(as.data.frame(swPOS)))
{
  SWPartsOfSpeech=rbind(SWPartsOfSpeech, cbind(substr(paste(s, collapse=' '),
    swPOS$start[i],swPOS$end[i]),swPOS$start[i],swPOS$features[i]))
}
colnames(SWPartsOfSpeech)=c('Term', 'Position', 'PartOfSpeech')
```

We then can view the parts-of-speech tags for our text by invoking `SWPartsOfSpeech`. A partial list of tags appears below, along with the definitions of the tags. For definitions of additional tags that may appear with other terms, see the Penn TreeBank tagset [12].

We used the default openNLP part-of-speech tagger to identify the parts of speech associated with each term appearing in the text about the Star Wars movies. The openNLPmodels.en package provides two alternative part-of-speech tagging models—en-pos-perceptron.bin and en-pos-maxent.bin. To access either of these models, we specify the model when creating our annotator. For example, we can use en-pos-perceptron.bin with `pos_annotator = Maxent_POS_Tag_Annotator(model= system.file('models', 'en-pos-perceptron.bin', package='openNLPmodels.en'))`. For the most part, the three models tag the parts of speech consistently. One exception is with regard to the number "1" in "Episode 1" in the last line of the text, which the perceptron model correctly tags as a cardinal number (CN), while the other two models tag as a list item marker (LS).

	Term	Position	PartOfSpeech
1	Star	1	NNP
2	Wars	6	NNPS
3	is	11	VBZ
4	an	14	DT
5	American	17	JJ
6	epic	26	NN
7	space	31	NN
8	opera	37	NN
9	franchise	43	NN
10	,	52	,
11	centered	54	VBN
12	on	63	IN
13	a	66	DT
14	film	68	NN
15	series	73	NN
16	created	80	VBN
17	by	88	IN
18	George	91	NNP
19	Lucas	98	NNP
20	.	103	.
21	It	105	PRP
22	depicts	108	VBZ
23	the	116	DT
24	adventures	120	NNS
25	of	131	IN
26	various	134	JJ
27	characters	142	NNS
28	a	153	DT
29	long	155	JJ
30	time	160	NN
31	ago	165	RB
32	in	169	IN
33	a	172	DT
34	galaxy	174	NN
35	far	181	RB
36	,	184	,
37	far	186	RB
38	away	190	RB
39	.	195	.
40	The	197	DT
41	first	201	JJ
42	film	207	NN
43	in	212	IN
44	the	215	DT
45	series	219	NN
46	,	225	,
47	Star	227	NNP
48	Wars	232	NNPS
49	(	237	-LRB-
50	later	238	RB
51	subtitled	244	VBN
52	Episode	254	NNP
53	IV	262	NNP
54	:	264	:
55	A	266	DT
56	New	268	JJ
57	Hope	272	NNP
58	)	276	-RRB-
59	,	277	,
60	was	279	VBD
			...

Legend:			
,	*comma*	NNS	*common noun, plural*
:	*semicolon*	PRP	*personal pronoun*
DT	*determiner*	RB	*adverb*
IN	*preposition or subordinating conjunction*	RBR	*adverb, comparative*
JJ	adjective	-RRB-	*)*
-LRB-	*(*	TO	*to*
NN	*noun, singular or mass*	VBD	*verb, past tense*
NNP	*proper noun, singular*	VBN	*verb, past participle*
NNPS	*proper noun, plural*	VBZ	*verb, present tense third person singular*

Lest you come away with the impression that the openNLP part-of-speech annotators are 100% accurate on grammatically well-structured texts, I caution you that this is not the case. Consider, for example, the word "*stranger*" in the following two sentences: "*Truth is stranger than fiction,*" and "*A stranger is a friend we have yet to meet.*" In the first instance, "*stranger*" should be tagged JJR, for a comparative adjective. In the second, it should be tagged NN, for a singular noun. In fact, all openNLP models tag both instances of "*stranger*" as NN. As with named entity tagging, though, we can add the "probs=T" argument to obtain a model's certainty in its part-of-speech classification. The default part-of-speech openNLP annotator assigns the NN tag for the first (incorrectly classified) instance of "stranger" a probability of 0.2172, but the second (correctly classified) instance a probability of 0.9783.

Conclusion

Natural language processing, especially named entity recognition, is a powerful tool in our text mining quiver. With little advance understanding of the knowledge domain of the texts to be mined, we can surface salient insights about key actors, timing, locations, and quantities being discussed. While the atypical grammatical structure of social media posts currently poses substantial challenges for natural language processing, absent an alternative (such as applying supervised learning [13]), even the incomplete insights afforded by natural language processing may be useful.

In interpreting and strategizing based on those insights, it is important to recognize the limitations of insights extracted mainly from formally-structured posts. More educated people tend to write more grammatically correct sentences. Research suggests that socioeconomic status and educational attainment influence individuals' facility with language [14], which includes vocabulary and grammar. Further, younger people use more individualized and informal language (i.e., netspeak and leetspeak) [15]. Until natural language processing algorithms advance to account for the language patterns unique to social media, insights gleaned through natural language processing of social media posts therefore are liable to reflect systematic demographic biases.

Exercise: Retrieving Information about Blockchain

The BlockchainPressRelease.txt file contains a press release about Skuchain's involvement with the blockchain technology. The BlockchainTweets.txt file contains 64 tweets mentioning blockchain from a single Twitter account.

Individual Assignment

1. Extract all named entities from the two files.
2. Compare the information extraction accuracy and recall across the two files. What conclusions do you draw?

Copy all R code and salient output into a Word file, and annotate it with your observations and comments. Submit this file.

Team Assignment

Discuss your observations regarding the accuracy and recall of automated information retrieval. Can you think of ways of improving performance (e.g., preprocessing of the text or preliminary/combined use of other algorithms)?

Works Cited

1. Manning, C.D., P. Raghavan, and H. Schütze, *Introduction to Information Retrieval.* Cambridge, UK: Cambridge University Press, 2008.
2. Meyer, M., *Explorations in Computer Science*, 2nd edition. Sudbury, MA: Jones & Bartlett Learning, 2005.
3. Computer History Museum, 2018, http://www.computerhistory.org.
4. Wallace, M., and G. Dunlop, "Eliza, The Rogerian Therapist," http://psych.fullerton.edu/mbirnbaum/psych101/Eliza.htm.
5. Toutanova, K., and C. Cherry, "A Global Model for Joint Lemmatization and Part-of-Speech Prediction," in *Proceedings of the Joint Conference of the 47th Annual Meeting of the ACL and the 4th International Joint Conference on Natural Language Processing of the AFNLP*: Volume 1. Singapore: Association for Computational Linguistics, 2009.
6. Pelley, S., "Making Ideas into Reality at MIT's 'Future Factory,'" *60 Minutes*, 2018, https://www.cbsnews.com/news/mit-media-lab-making-ideas-into-reality-future-factory/.
7. Johnson, B., "How Siri Works," 2013, HowStuffWorks.com.
8. "Datacube Resource Homepage," 2012, http://datacube.wu.ac.at/.
9. Salmon, M. "monkeylearn, a R Package for Natural Language Processing Using Monkeylearn Existing Modules," CRAN Project, 2010, https://cran.r-project.org/web/packages/monkeylearn/vignettes/monkeylearn_intro.html.
10. Mendelson, S., "'Black Panther' Broke More Box Office Records as It Topped 'Avengers' in Media & Entertainment," *Forbes*, 2018, https://www.forbes.com/sites/scottmendelson/2018/03/26/black-panther-more-box-office-milestones-as-soars-past-the-avengers/#7a30edff61d3.
11. McNary, D., "'Black Panther' Climbs to Top of Social Media Chart with First Trailer," Variety, 2017, https://variety.com/2017/film/news/black-panther-social-media-buzz-trailer-1202462910/.
12. Jurafsky, D., and J.H. Martin, *Speech and Language Processing: An Introduction to Natural Language Processing, Computational Linguistics, and Speech Recognition.* Upper Saddle River, NJ: Pearson/Prentice Hall, 2017.
13. Ritter, A., S. Clark, and O. Etzioni, "Named Entity Recognition in Tweets: An Experimental Study," in *Proceedings of the Conference on Empirical Methods in Natural Language Processing*. Edinburgh, Scotland: Association for Computational Linguistics, 2011.

14. Sullivan, A., "Cultural Capital and Educational Attainment." *Sociology*, 35(4; 2001): 893–912.
15. Androutsopoulos, J., "Language Change and Digital Media: A Review of Conceptions and Evidence," in *Standard Languages and Language Standards in a Changing Europe*, 145–60. Oslo: Novus, 2011.

CHAPTER 11

Association Mining with R

> **Learning Objectives**
>
> The purpose of this lab is to gain awareness of R's association mining tools, specifically those permitting:
>
> 1. word-pair analysis;
> 2. topic modeling, including:
>   a. cluster analysis,
>   b. latent Dirichlet allocation,
>   c. term network analysis, and
>   d. relational class analysis.

A decade or two ago, organizational strategists wishing to understand their competitors' strategic directions could monitor a few personal sources and read their competitors' press releases and annual reports. Political strategists wishing to understand the electorate's concerns relied on personal sources and town-halls. Today these strategists have access to vastly more information and in a more timely fashion. The challenge, however, has become gleaning knowledge and insights from the sea of available information. Association mining is a quick way of accomplishing this.

In this chapter, we examine two types of association mining techniques in R. The objective of such association mining is to glean insight into the content of texts by exploring relationships among terms. We begin the chapter with a simple word-pair analysis. Here, we elicit meaning around on a single focal concept or term. For example, we begin by examining the meaning of the WhereIsRey hashtag via word-pair analysis (i.e., of the terms that correlate with the use of the hashtag). In Tutorial 11.1, we contrast the meanings of a core concept in tweets emanating from two different types of stakeholders.

We then examine various techniques for topic modeling, the purpose of which is to facilitate "finding needles in [a] haystack by shrinking the haystack" [2]. We consider two statistical techniques for topic modeling—cluster analysis and latent Dirichlet allocation (LDA). Next, we apply our social network analysis to analyzing texts, surfacing relationships among terms in our texts and the agglomeration of terms revealed in those relationships. Finally, we examine relational class analysis (RCA), an advanced SNA-based technique that identifies groups of oppositional concepts or terms underlying a corpus.

Text mining is part technique, part art. The more tools we have under our belt, the more creatively we can analyze our data. But knowing our data is paramount. This will inform choices from preprocessing through the approach we use, to the specific variation on the analytic approach we apply. Text mining, at least until we are familiar with our data, also is iterative. As we surface topics with less-than-meaningful terms, we return to the preprocessing stage. Changes at this stage likely will impact the topic models then surfaced.

Packages Relevant to Association Mining

We will require five packages for our forays into association mining with R: **tm**, **cluster**, **topicmodels**, **igraph**, and **RCA**. (Note we will use the topicmodels package for LDA. An alternative to this package is the **LDA** package. I prefer topicmodels to LDA for two reasons: First, the topicmodels package uses preprocessing outputs from the tm package. In contrast, the LDA package has its own preprocessing functions, which we would have to learn. Second, topicmodels implements the two original LDA algorithms [3, 4], while the LDA package implements its own variant of the LDA algorithm.) Let's install any packages we need that we don't already have and then load them.

Word-Pair Analysis

Someone involved with the Star Wars movie or merchandising might, for example, want to know which terms occur most frequently along with the hashtag WhereIsRey. Of course, since we earlier stripped this term from our term-document matrix, we need to put it back before addressing this question. To do so, we create our corpus, *ReyCorp*, and document-term matrix, *ReyDTM*. Apply other data cleansing routines from Chapter 8 that you think are appropriate. (Note I began by converting the corpus to lowercase, removing punctuation, numbers, and white space; stripping URLs, newline characters, and tabs; and ensuring only ASCII characters were retained in the corpus. I then used the custom SearchReplace function developed in Chapter 8 to retokenize and clean the corpus as per the "Data Cleansing Statements for WhereIsRey Word Pair Analysis" insert. I finished by eliminating only standard English stop words and then created my term-document matrix.)

Now, we find the words that co-occur most frequently with a given term using the ***findAssocs(DtmOrTdm, 'Term', CorelationThreshold)*** function, where the correlation threshold specifies the minimum correlation between the frequency with which the specified term and other terms in the term-document matrix occur. Using `findAssocs(ReyTDM, 'whereisrey', 0.20)`, we specify a threshold correlation of 0.20. We discover that the terms "highlight" and "dearth" have the highest correlation with our hashtag, followed by "problem," "sexism," and "merchandise."

```
highlight      dearth     problem      sexism merchandise
     0.26        0.26        0.25        0.24        0.22
```

Tutorial 11.1. Understanding the Different Meanings of Aadhaar

In this tutorial, we will use the findAssocs() function to construct the semantic networks we saw in Figures 2.5 and 2.6. Recall these semantic networks were based on tweets about the newly launched Aadhaar (universal ID) card emanating from government versus citizen accounts. These semantic networks offer insights into how these different interest groups construe the Aadhaar card. The Government.csv and Citizens.csv files contain the text of the tweets emanating from the two constituents. For each of these files, we create an edge list, using the procedures described in Figure 11.1.

We begin by creating a corpus called ACorp from the Text column in the data file and subjecting this corpus to data cleansing. We convert all words to lowercase, remove punctuation and numbers, and eliminate standard stop words. Using our custom search and replace function, we eliminate newlines and ampersands. We clean up the various spellings of "Aadhaar"—adhaar, aadhar, aadhhar, and adhar. We use the custom function also to retokenize newspaper names—like "indian express" and "deccan chronicle"—using the statements that follow.

Data Cleansing Statements for WhereIsRey Analysis

```
ReyCorp=tm_map(ReyCorp,SearchReplace, 'theforceawakens','the force awakens')
ReyCorp=tm_map(ReyCorp,SearchReplace, 'merchsexismproblem','merch sexism problem')
ReyCorp=tm_map(ReyCorp,SearchReplace, 'highlightsdearthfemaletoyhtml', 'highlights dearth female toy')
ReyCorp=tm_map(ReyCorp,SearchReplace, 'forceawakens','force awakens')
ReyCorp=tm_map(ReyCorp,SearchReplace, 'arewereallygoingtostart','are we really going to start')
ReyCorp=tm_map(ReyCorp,SearchReplace, 'makers','maker')
ReyCorp=tm_map(ReyCorp,SearchReplace, 'highlights','highlight')
ReyCorp=tm_map(ReyCorp,SearchReplace, 'figures','figure')
ReyCorp=tm_map(ReyCorp,SearchReplace, 'merchandise','merch')
ReyCorp=tm_map(ReyCorp,SearchReplace, 'merchs','merch')
ReyCorp=tm_map(ReyCorp,SearchReplace, 'merch','merchandise')
ReyCorp=tm_map(ReyCorp,SearchReplace, 'shes','she is')
```

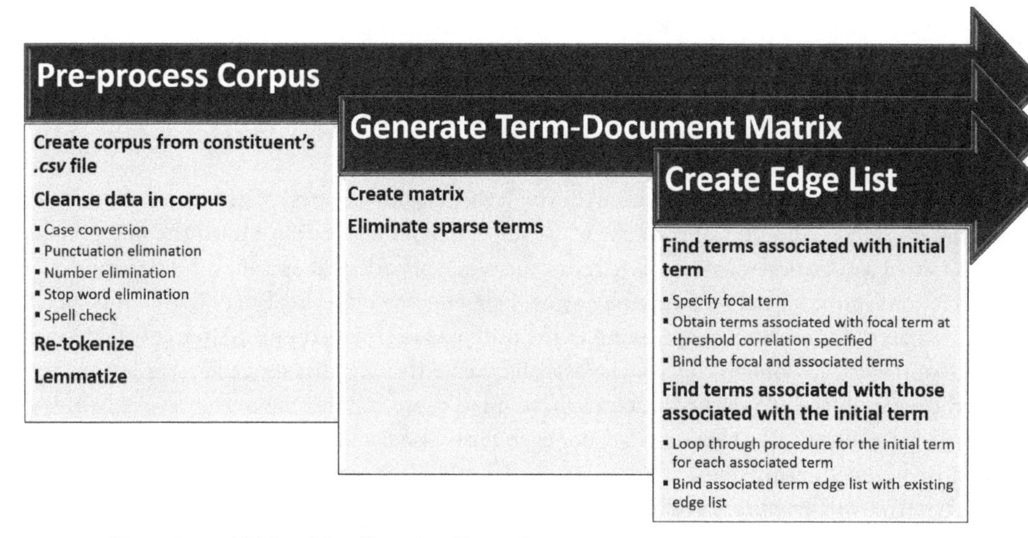

Figure 11.1 Overview of Edge List Creation Procedures

```
ACorp=tm_map(ACorp,SearchReplace,'[\r\n]','')
ACorp=tm_map(ACorp,SearchReplace,'amp', ' ')
ACorp=tm_map(ACorp,SearchReplace,'aadhar','aadhaar')
ACorp=tm_map(ACorp,SearchReplace,' aadhhar ', ' aadhaar ')
ACorp=tm_map(ACorp,SearchReplace,' addhar ', ' aadhaar ')
ACorp=tm_map(ACorp,SearchReplace,' adhaar ', ' aadhaar ')
ACorp=tm_map(ACorp,SearchReplace,' adhar ', ' aadhaar ')
ACorp=tm_map(ACorp,SearchReplace,' asdhar ', ' aadhaar ')
ACorp=tm_map(ACorp,SearchReplace,'indian express','indianexpress')
ACorp=tm_map(ACorp,SearchReplace,'deccan chronicle','deccanchronicle')
```

We also use the custom SearchReplace function to take care of other typos and to lemmatize (i.e., apply identified lexemes), instead of simply stemming. For example, we convert all the conjugations of accuse to a single "accuse" term below:

```
ACorp=tm_map(ACorp,SearchReplace,' accusation ', ' accuse ')
ACorp=tm_map(ACorp,SearchReplace,' accusations ', ' accuse ')
ACorp=tm_map(ACorp,SearchReplace,' accused ', ' accuse ')
ACorp=tm_map(ACorp,SearchReplace,' accuses ', ' accuse ')
ACorp=tm_map(ACorp,SearchReplace,' accusing ', ' accuse ')
```

We create a term-document matrix named ATDM. We set matrix sparsity to 95% to minimize the chance that rarely occurring terms spuriously appear to be correlated.

Now we are ready to create an edge list. In the code below, we first specify "aadhaar" as our initial term of interest. We then look for the terms whose appearance correlates with our specified term and wrap this in a data frame named anet1. To create the edge list, we bind together the specified term, the row names from anet1—which supply the second vertex for the edge list—and the original anet1 data frame, which contains the correlation coefficients for each edge on the list. Later, we will use these correlation coefficients to weight the edges in our graph.

```
term='aadhaar'
anet1=as.data.frame(findAssocs(ATDM, term, 0.20))
anet1=cbind(term,rownames(anet1),anet1)
colnames(anet1)=c('word1','word2','freq')
rownames(anet1)=NULL
```

Next, we assign anet1 to a new data frame, anet2. We will use this second data frame to accumulate the edges extracted by each findAssocs() call.

```
anet2=anet1
```

Now, we look for the terms that correlate with the terms already in anet1, yielding a two-step semantic network around our focal concept: from "Aadhaar" to our first-level associations; from the first-level associations to second-level associations. To do so, we rerun the block of code that specifies the target term, obtains the term associations into the anet1 data frame, forms the edge list in the anet1 data frame, and specifies the row and column names for every term appearing in the original anet1 data frame. (Alternatively, we can write a loop for R to automatically obtain the associations and create the edge list for each term in the anet1 data frame.) When we obtain the edge list for each term, we bind those rows to the rows previously in the anet2 data frame as depicted below, thus adding edges for each term associated with aadhaar. Below, we begin with the most highly correlated term, "takes." (Note that even a minor difference between your preprocessing and mine may change the associated terms identified. Don't let this throw you off—it does not necessarily mean that you did something wrong.)

```
term='takes'
anet1=as.data.frame(findAssocs(ATDM, term, 0.20))
anet1=cbind(term,rownames(anet1),anet1)
colnames(anet1)=c('word1','word2','freq')
rownames(anet1)=NULL
```

We now add the edges just extracted to those previously in the anet2 data frame using

```
anet2=as.data.frame(rbind(anet1,anet2))
```

Then, we rerun the code with the next most highly correlated term, "updation."

```
term='updation'
anet1=as.data.frame(findAssocs(ATDM, term, 0.20))
anet1=cbind(term,rownames(anet1),anet1)
colnames(anet1)=c('word1','word2','freq')
rownames(anet1)=NULL

anet2=as.data.frame(rbind(anet1,anet2))
```

After we have repeated this code segment for every term that correlated with "aadhaar," we will have the necessary edge list. (Challenge: Can you do it with a loop?)

We now can write our edge list to an Excel file for future analyses or visualize the network in R. To do so, we first load our **igraph** package. Then, create the graph data frame based on the first two columns of the anet2 data frame, simplify the graph data frame to eliminate loops, and then plot the graph.

```
AadhaarGraph=graph_from_data_frame(anet2[1:2], directed=F)
AadhaarGraph=simplify(AadhaarGraph)
plot(AadhaarGraph)
```

Alternatively, we can develop our visualizations in NodeXL. Some tips for a sharper depiction of our Aadhaar networks in NodeXL:

1. On the EDGES sheet,
   a. copy the first two columns from AadhaarNetwork.csv into the Vertex1 and Vertex2 columns;

b. copy the third column into a column after "Add Your Own Columns Here" and title that column "Correlation";
c. set the value of the Width column *=-LOG([@[Correlation]])*3*.

2. On the VERTICES sheet,
   a. set the Shape column to *Label* for all rows except the "aadhaar" row;
   b. set the Shape column to *Image* for the "aadhaar" row;
   c. set the Image File column for the "aadhaar" row to *aadhaar.png* (and be sure to copy the .png file into the directory containing your NodeXL file);
   d. set the Label column to *=[@Vertex]*.

Overview of Topic Modeling Approaches

Topic modeling applies the bag of words representation. Recall that in this representation, the order in which terms occur is immaterial. Yet each of the different approaches permits us to surface terms that "go together" to constitute a topic. The fundamental objective of topic modeling is to identify distinct groupings of terms. From these systematic groupings, we can infer the semantic structure of the corpus of documents. Within these parameters, the four different topic modeling techniques model the semantics underlying the corpus slightly differently in terms of relationships among terms within topics, among terms across topics, and between topics and documents. These differences, culminating in topic models that we interpret differently, are depicted in Table 11.1.

While all four approaches identify groupings of terms in our corpus, the meanings of these groupings and the document-related information available from the output differs across the approaches. Cluster analysis yields a hierarchical or a discrete taxonomy of topics and concepts. LDA yields potentially overlapping topics, within which terms have a high probability of co-occurring. The clustering algorithms in SNA attempt to identify weakly interconnected topics, constituted by densely interconnected concepts. RCA identifies topics comprising modules of associated terms (i.e., terms that co-occur), and of oppositional terms (i.e., terms that do *not* co-occur with the terms in other modules in the same topic). The meanings revealed by RCA thus can have a connotation of "A and B, but *not* C and D" lacking in other topic modeling approaches.

Table 11.1 Comparing the Topic Modeling Approaches

Interpreting	Cluster Analysis	Latent Dirichlet Allocation	Social Network Analysis	Relational Class Analysis
Overall topic model	Hierarchical or discrete (k-means) taxonomy of topics and terms	Overlapping topics, with some more unique and some more shared terms	Sparsely connected topic modules composed of densely connected terms	Distinct topic modules comprised of associated and oppositional terms
Topic	Terms that are more proximate to each other than to other terms (hierarchical) or to one centroid than to other centroids (k-means) in the model	Distribution of terms in a fixed vocabulary, with some terms having a high probability and other a low probability of occurrence	Terms that co-occur or correlate more with each other than with terms in other topics	Terms that co-occur and systematically counter other co-occurring terms
Relationships among terms within topics	High incidence of co-occurrence	High probability of co-occurrence	Dense co-occurrence or correlation	Dense absolute (positive or negative) relation
Relationship between topics and documents	NA	Documents contain varying densities of each topic	NA	NA

The clustering procedures covered below do not easily associate documents with topics. However, with a bit of programming, we can do so. Specifically, we can determine the distance of a document from each cluster's center and therefore the cluster to which it belongs. The output of the LDA procedure designates the density of each topic in each document, and a document thus can contain multiple topics. As with cluster analysis, the SNA procedure does not associate documents with clusters without additional programming. A document theoretically may contain multiple related topics, fitting more or less imprecisely with a given topic. Finally, the RCA procedure does not provide a direct way to associate documents with topics either. The presence of the terms representing a topic module in a document is associated with a reduced likelihood of the presence of terms associated with oppositional modules of the same topic.

Topic Modeling via Cluster Analysis of Terms

Cluster analysis is a statistical procedure that groups (or clusters, partitions, or agglomerates) objects—here *terms*—such that objects within a group are more similar than they are to objects in other group [5]. We do so using the **cluster** package. We will look at two major cluster analysis approaches: hierarchical cluster analysis and k-means cluster analysis. ***Hierarchical cluster analysis*** requires no a priori knowledge and therefore often is a good starting point in cluster analysis. Hierarchical clustering is an agglomerative approach in which the algorithm iteratively groups proximate terms, creating the tree-like diagram called a dendrogram. The ***k-means*** clustering algorithm requires prior insight into the number of term groupings, designated as *k*. The algorithm begins with *k* randomly selected centroids (a multidimensional center for each cluster) and iteratively assigns terms to each centroid and updates the centroid to minimize the sum of the distances of terms from their centroids. This process is repeated until further term reassignments or centroid updates result in no improvements in the distance of terms from their centroid. The k-means algorithm then provides the final cluster centers (i.e., the average frequencies of terms in that cluster). If we wish, we can use these centers to determine the distance of each document from each cluster center and then identify the cluster to which documents are most proximate (i.e., documents' association with clusters).

We begin with our preprocessed corpus, from which we create our term-document matrix, and remove sparse terms as necessary. (Because clustering algorithms are resource-needy, I highly recommend avoiding too sparse a matrix. Sparse matrices will be extremely large and contain many terms that are completely uninteresting from the perspective of eliciting actionable insights. For this example, I permitted 95% sparsity in my term-document matrix. As we shall see, this retained twenty terms for further analysis. **Note that even very minor variations in preprocessing steps will yield slightly different results.**)

For a hierarchical cluster analysis, we create a distance matrix using the ***dist(MATRIX, method= 'DISTANCEMETHOD')*** function. The default distance method is "euclidean," which is the sum of squared distances between two vectors; other methods are "maximum" distance, "manhattan" (absolute distances), "Canberra" (sum of ratio of absolute x_i-y_i to x_i+y_i), "binary" (zero elements in the vectors being compared are considered "off," and nonzero elements are considered "on" and assigned 1s), and "minkowski" (a root of the sum of exponentiated differences of the vector elements). Using the method specified in the "method=" argument (e.g., `ReyDist=dist(ReyTDM,method='euclidean')`), the distance function assesses the distance between every pair of terms in the term-document matrix.

We then subject the resulting distance matrix to the ***hclust(DISTANCEMATRIX, method= 'CLUSTERINGMETHOD')*** function, which clusters the terms based on their similarity using the clustering method specified. The default clustering method is the "complete" method, which is based on the minimizing the maximum distance among elements within a cluster. The most recommended [6] clustering method is the "ward.D2" method, an ANOVA-based, sum-of-squares-minimization method. Other methods include "ward.D," "single," "average," "mcquitty," "median," and "centroid". In the example below, we apply the ward.D partitioning method using `ReyClust=hclust(d=ReyDist, method='ward.D')`.

We then can plot the clustering solution as a dendrogram (i.e., a tree diagram that depicts taxonomic relationships) using `plot(ReyClust)`. This produces the dendrogram, clustering the twenty terms, depicted in Figure 11.2.

Partitioning, even with the assistance of the dendrogram, is not an exact science. So, we see where the cuts for different grouping might lie by iteratively specifying different numbers of cuts. We first clean up the

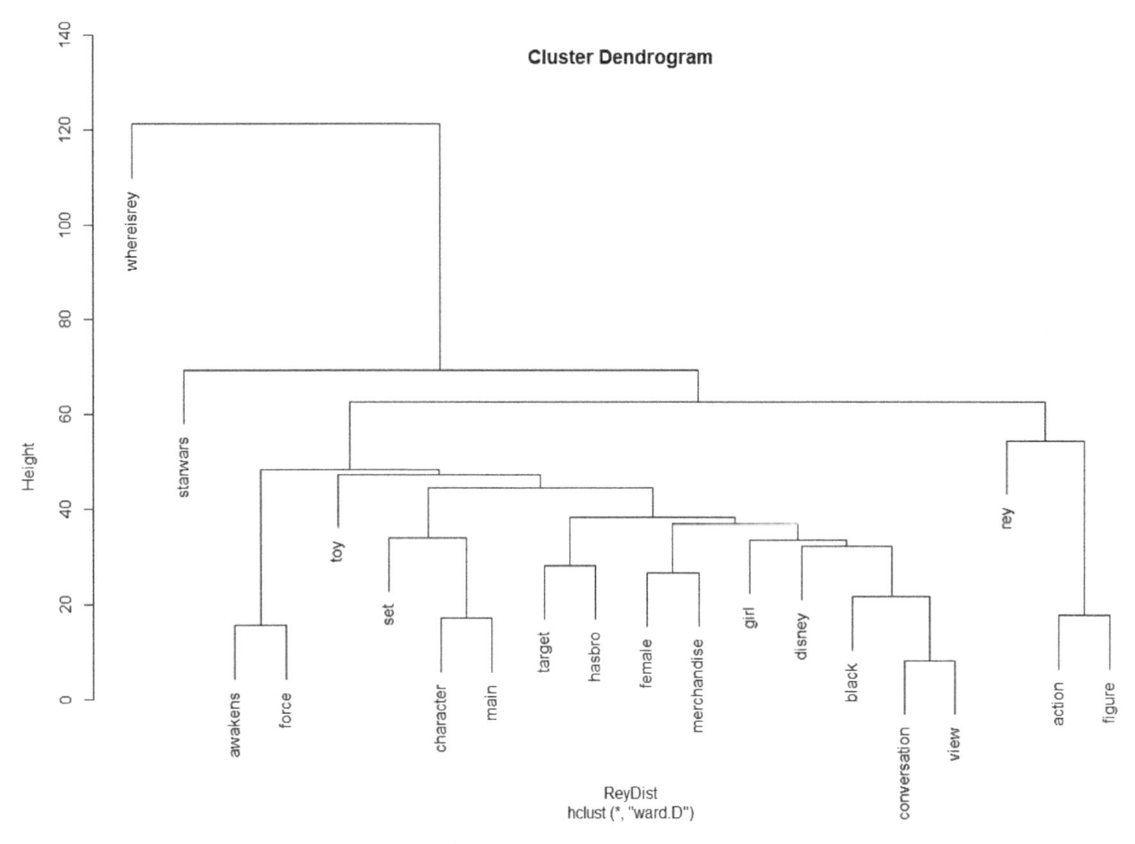

Figure 11.2 Hierarchical Clustering of Terms

plot, eliminating the y-axes and the labels for the x- and y-axes. The hang='' argument specifies the fraction of the plot height by which labels should hang below the rest of the plot. A negative value will cause the labels to hang down from 0. Leaving off this argument positions labels at different levels, as visible in Figure 11.2. Finally, we suppress titles and increase font size of the labels using `plot(ReyClust, yaxt='n', xlab='', ylab='', hang=1, main='', sub='', cex=1.75)`. The ***rect.hclust(ClusterSolution, k=HowManyGroups)*** annotates the dendrogram with rectangles demarcating the specified number of groups or cuts. We specify the number of cuts (values of k) we wish to visualize with `rect.hclust(ReyClust, k=3, border='red2')`. Figure 11.3 depicts between two and five cuts (k=3 to k=6).

Using the ***cutree(ClusterSolution, HowManyGroups)*** function, we can determine which terms were assigned to the different clusters. For example, `ReyTopics=cutree(ReyClust,k=6)` followed by `ReyTopics` produces the following cluster assignment. We can bind this into a data frame and/or export it for further analyses.

```
     female          set     starwars       target          toy   whereisrey
          1            1            2            1            1            3
       girl       hasbro       disney      awakens conversation        force
          1            1            1            4            1            4
       view          rey    character         main        black  merchandise
          1            5            1            1            1            1
     action       figure
          6            6
```

The k-means clustering algorithm surfaces a prespecified number (k) of groups. As with hierarchical clustering, a k-means procedure requires a distance matrix, based on the transposed document-term matrix.

The ***kmeans(DistanceMatrix, HowManyGroups)*** function, with the specified number of groups, allows us to obtain the terms associated with each group. For example, `ReyKClust=`**`kmeans`**`(ReyDist, 6)` assigns terms to the six specified groups in a k-means cluster solution named ReyKClust. To determine which terms were assigned to each of the six clusters, we use `ReyKClust$cluster`. To determine the average incidence of each term in each cluster, we use `ReyKClust$centers`. This produces the output below. For tips on associating documents with clusters, see the "Associating Documents with Clusters" insert.

```
      female          set     starwars       target          toy   whereisrey          girl
           5            6            1            4            5            2             4
      hasbro       disney      awakens conversation        force         view           rey
           4            4            3            4            3            4             1
   character         main        black  merchandise       action       figure
           6            6            4            4            5            5
```

```
       female          set  starwars   target       toy whereisrey      girl    hasbro    disney
1    50.22351     48.82742  27.56810 50.23821  50.11725   72.75993  52.09342  52.33802  50.62370
2    79.21490     81.54140  71.76350 82.35290  76.41989    0.00000  82.89150  80.54191  81.82298
3    34.88565     33.54831  48.27525 31.02353  39.54652   81.74609  32.95980  35.89038  32.63180
4    32.06143     31.64323  52.95097 24.09243  38.94453   82.53021  26.47730  27.91045  25.89911
5    26.98080     37.87520  52.66493 35.56334  30.45110   79.32704  36.37090  39.08958  36.04023
6    34.96715     19.84513  52.42974 31.72978  40.54135   81.37717  33.55877  35.40553  33.14631

      awakens conversation     force     view       rey  character      main     black
1   46.751403     50.05493 47.703959 49.65098  27.56810   49.78756  49.51896  48.38313
2   82.024387     83.43860 81.467785 83.74366  73.75636   80.95678  81.63333  83.47455
3    7.794229     27.56071  7.794229 26.61781  46.18011   32.96804  31.39851  26.95202
4   27.745969     20.29679 33.366081 19.53936  47.64475   30.83877  28.84834  21.16775
5   33.777142     32.34793 38.083954 31.68846  47.61471   36.11526  35.04153  32.08575
6   30.043211     28.12709 35.233364 27.27461  46.32623   15.93210  15.30503  23.40203

  merchandise       action    figure
1    49.00047     50.10404  50.11446
2    81.97561     81.49233  80.18105
3    30.81216     33.45500  35.83502
4    24.53090     32.13079  34.90285
5    32.89302     23.61611  24.92054
6    30.90350     33.76346  36.10402
```

Topic Modeling via Latent Dirichlet Allocation

LDA is a Bayesian approach that addresses the problem: given an observed distribution of terms across documents, what unobserved topics generated the distribution? This technique has been used to cull topics underlying customer service e-mails [7] and video game reviews [8]. LDA presupposes topics that exist beyond the set of documents analyzed and infers the topics based on the distributions of terms observed across documents. The other topic modeling techniques discussed in this chapter originated in domains other than text mining and have been repurposed for the task. In contrast, the original purpose of LDA was to validate and uncover topic models in unstructured texts [3]. It was developed as a counterpoint to then-popular algebraic topic modeling approaches of factor analyzing the *tf-idf* matrix, and latent semantic analysis and the subsequent probabilistic latent semantic analysis. The key limitations of these prior approaches that LDA remedies are the number of topics tended to increase linearly with the size of the corpus, leading to overfitting problems; and how to apply the topic model to corpora beyond the training set was uncertain [3]. Thus many consider LDA the preeminent technique for topic modeling. In an LDA solution, every term has some probability of being associated with each topic surfaced. Thus, a term can have a nonzero—even near-perfect—probability

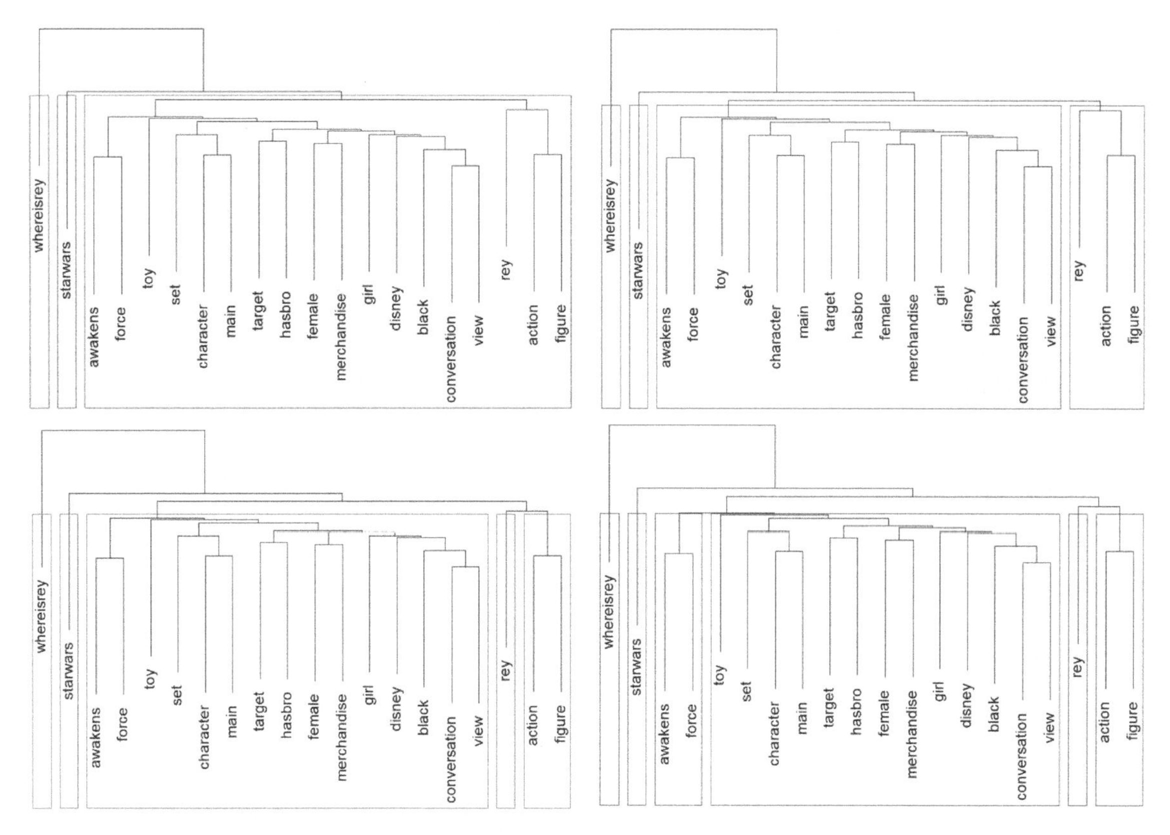

Figure 11.3 Partitioned Dendrograms for k=3 to k=6

Associating Documents with Clusters

Once we have obtained the cluster centers (i.e., the mean values for the incidence of each term across each of the clusters surfaced), we can compute the distance of each document from each of the six cluster centers using the dist() function. Recall that the dist() function computes the distance between every pair of observations in the supplied matrix. So, if we add the output for each cluster center to our transformed term-document matrix using the rbind() function, we then can apply the dist() function to the combined matrix. The term-document matrix must be transposed to be of the same shape as the cluster center matrix. Since we now are unconcerned with the distances between pairs of our original observations, we discard these distance values from the matrix and retain only the first column of the distance scores. Because the first row is redundant with the first column, we also discard the first row, retaining rows 2 through the last row (i.e., number of matrix columns +1). We repeat this for each of the remaining clusters. Lastly, we relabel the columns in the distance vector to designate the distances from each of the six clusters. After this, our resulting DistancesToCenters data frame is ready to output or be used in other procedures in R. We also can use this approach to associate a new corpus of documents with clusters identified based on the documents in the training corpus.

```
DistancesToCenters=as.data.frame(as.matrix(dist(rbind(ReyKClust$centers[1,],
                t(as.matrix(removeSparseTerms(ReyTDM,0.95))))))[1, 2:(ncol(ReyTDM)+1)])
for (i in 2:6)
{
DistancesToCenters=cbind(DistancesToCenters,
                as.data.frame(as.matrix(dist(rbind(ReyKClust$centers[i,],
                t(as.matrix(removeSparseTerms(ReyTDM,0.95))))))[1,2:(ncol(ReyTDM)+1)]))
}
colnames(DistancesToCenters)=c('DistC1','DistC2','DistC3','DistC4','DistC5','DistC6')
```

of being associated with multiple topics. Because LDA permits a term to be associated with more than one topic, it is superior to cluster-based topic modeling in the presence of homonyms (i.e., words that have different meanings depending on the context of their use) [9]. Examples include bank, which may reference a financial institution or the sloping land adjacent to a river, and address, which may reference a geographic location or a speech. This section provides only a rudimentary introduction to LDA, focusing on its use rather than the

LDA Parameters and Dirichlet Hyperparameters

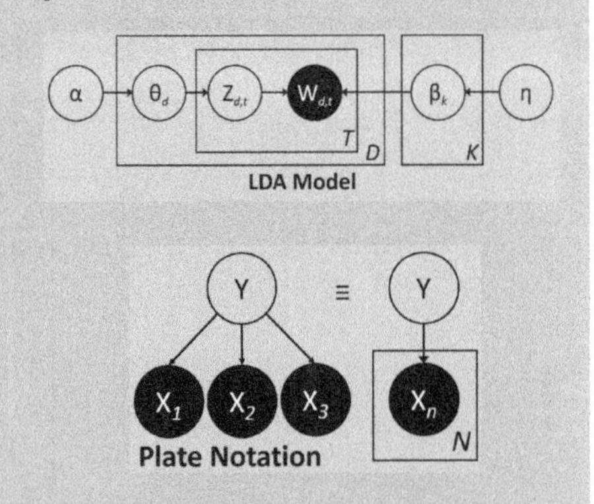

Before we consider the various distributions modeled in LDA, let us look at some notation. In the notation here, we depict the equivalence of the standard $Y=X_1+X_2+X_3$ and the "plate" notation that permits us to represent a variable number (i.e., *N*, X variables).

Each piece in the LDA model represents a random variable. We have three plates in the figure. The document plate, *D*, represents the document replications. The terms plate, *T*, represents the composite set of vocabulary terms represented in the corpus. The topics plate, *K*, represents the collection of topics that are inferred from the distribution of terms over documents.

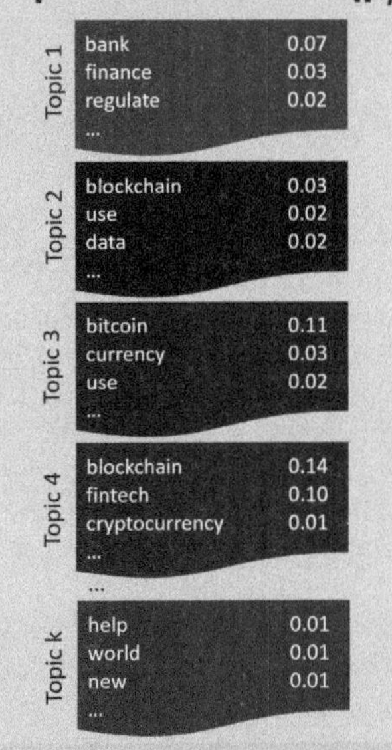

The β_k in the LDA model represents the topics. Every β_k topic (in *K* replications) is a corpus-wide distribution over the fixed vocabulary of terms *T*. So we see each term has a distinct probability of occurrence in each topic (and a nonzero probability in multiple topics). The θ_d in the model represents the topic proportions (for each document in the *D* replications). Notice that this also has *k* dimensions. The probability for each term in the *K*th topic replication of β_k is given by $Z_{d,t}$. This is the probability of vocabulary term *t* being assigned to topic *k*.

Up to now, the distribution of every variable described was theoretical (i.e., inferred from what we observe). The only observed variable in the LDA model is $W_{d,t}$ (i.e., the *t*th word in the *d*th document). As apparent from the LDA model above, the probability of $W_{d,t}$ is dependent on the latent $Z_{d,t}$ and β_k terms (i.e., $p(W_{d,t} \mid Z_{d,t}, \beta_{1:k})$).

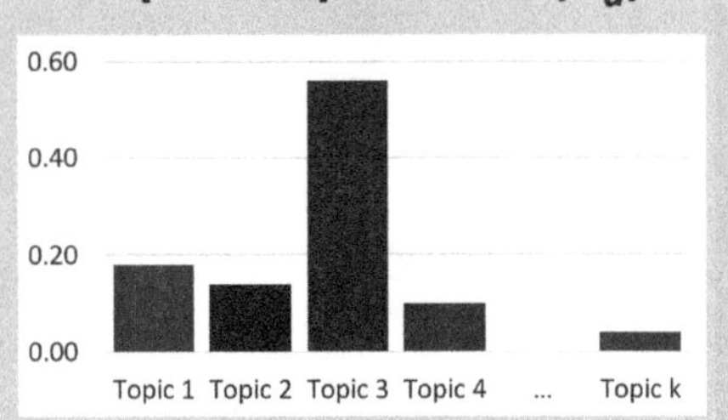

Finally, the α and η in the LDA model are the Dirichlet hyperparameters. These are the Dirichlet distributions from which θ and β respectively are drawn. The α hyperparameter specifies θ (i.e., the sparsity of topic proportions in documents). The η hyperparameter specifies β (i.e., the distribution of topics over terms).

underlying theory. The "LDA Parameters and Dirichlet Hyperparameters" insert provides a brief exposition of the underlying theory [1].

To use LDA to surface topics underlying our WhereIsRey corpus, we conduct our data preprocessing through creation of a document-term matrix. We then will use the ***LDA(DocumentTermMatrix, method='Method', k=NumberOfTopics)*** function from the topicmodels package. This LDA() function does not accept a document-term matrix in which any rows (documents) have only zero term counts (i.e., a document does not use *any* of the terms that commonly appear across the corpus). We therefore must leave the matrix at its original sparsity. (Alternatively, we can drop the documents for which no terms have been retained following preprocessing by removing stop words or sparse terms. For example, `ReyDTM=ReyDTM[rowSums(as.matrix(ReyDTM))>0,]` will retain only documents with nonzero term counts.)

The LDA() function offers two methods: Gibbs sampling and variational expectation-maximization (VEM). While the former is preferable for surfacing "ground truths" under standard assumptions and unconstrained computation time, the latter is computationally efficient. Given our relatively small WhereIsRey corpus, we will stick with the Gibbs sampling method. While not required, the "seed=" argument ensures that rerunning the function on the same data set will produce the same outputs. This is because the algorithm is iterative and different starting points can produce different outcomes. We request the topic model for six topics using `ReyTopics=LDA(ReyDTM, method= 'Gibbs', k=6, control=list(seed = 1234))`.

We then can inspect the terms assigned to the different topics using the ***terms(LDAObject, NumberOfTerms)*** function. For example, `terms(ReyTopics,10)` extracts the top ten terms associated with each of the topics surfaced. Our first observation is that, unlike the output of cluster analyses, some terms (e.g., whereisrey) repeat across the different topics.

```
      Topic 1     Topic 2  Topic 3       Topic 4      Topic 5        Topic 6
 [1,] "starwars"  "rey"    "whereisrey"  "whereisrey" "whereisrey"   "whereisrey"
 [2,] "force"     "figure" "toy"         "hasbro"     "disney"       "found"
 [3,] "character" "action" "starwars"    "target"     "girl"         "fans"
 [4,] "set"       "get"    "female"      "really"     "conversation" "right"
 [5,] "rey"       "one"    "merchandise" "characters" "view"         "hero"
 [6,] "main"      "find"   "sexism"      "going"      "can"          "wheres"
 [7,] "awakens"   "want"   "dearth"      "leia"       "just"         "also"
 [8,] "missing"   "cant"   "highlight"   "start"      "like"         "people"
 [9,] "widow"     "buy"    "problem"     "phasma"     "boys"         "still"
[10,] "black"     "even"   "lead"        "toys"       "dont"         "daughter"
```

We can obtain the Dirichlet parameter for the a priori density of topics discussed in documents by invoking the alpha parameter (e.g., `ReyTopics@alpha`), which we find to be 8.33. To obtain the density of each term in each topic, we invoke the beta parameter (e.g., `ReyTopics@beta`). For a more useful output, we can extract our term names from the row names of the term-document matrix (or transposed document-term matrix) and combine them with the transposed matrix of beta parameters for the ReyTopics: `data.frame(row.names(t(as.matrix(ReyDTM))), t(as.matrix(ReyTopics@beta)))`.

Of the topic modeling approaches discussed in this chapter, LDA provides the most accessible association between documents and topics. To inspect the density of each topic within each document, we can invoke the gamma parameter (e.g., `ReyTopics@gamma`). LDA uses these densities to assign each document to a dominant topic. We can determine these topic assignments using the ***topics(LDAObject)*** function (e.g., `topics(ReyTopics)`). For example, in the first five documents in the gamma parameter matrix below, we that document 1 has the highest density—0.2022—of topic 3. In Figure 11.4, we see that document 1 has been assigned to topic 3.

	topics(ReyTopics)
1	3
2	4
3	3
4	1
5	1

Figure 11.4 Topics for First 10 WhereIsRey Documents (Tweets)

	X1	X2	X3	X4	X5	X6
1	0.16939891	0.15300546	0.20218579	0.16939891	0.16939891	0.13661202
2	0.13888889	0.15555556	0.15555556	0.23888889	0.17222222	0.13888889
3	0.15053763	0.15053763	0.18279570	0.15053763	0.18279570	0.18279570
4	0.18407960	0.13930348	0.15422886	0.16915423	0.18407960	0.16915423
5	0.21637427	0.16374269	0.14619883	0.14619883	0.18128655	0.14619883

In the presence of ties for the highest probability, though, LDA simply assigns the document to the first topic with the highest probability. For example, if we inspect the third document, we note that the densities of topics 3, 5, and 6 are equal in document 3. If we look at the topic to which topics(ReyTopics) assigned document 3 in Figure 11.4, we note that it was assigned to the third topic. Depending on how we wish to use the document-topic association output (i.e., the topics() function), we need to be alert to how LDA handles ties.

This is but a rudimentary introduction to the LDA approach, which has more extensive capabilities than those covered here.

Topic Modeling via Social Network Analysis of Terms

Applying the SNA techniques learned in Part II permits us to surface topics based on interrelationships among terms. We can conceptualize our term-document matrix as a two-mode network. The nodes in this network are the terms. Documents (like companies, projects, or teams we saw in Chapter 3) provide the opportunity for terms (like the directors, employees/agencies, or students in Chapter 3) to associate. Edges are constituted by the correlation, co-occurrence, or distance among these terms in the documents in our corpus. Rather than working with an edge list, as we have done in our previous forays into SNA, we will use an adjacency matrix here. By subjecting this adjacency matrix to community analysis, we can determine which terms cluster together, forming "topics." Let's begin by loading the **igraph** package and the WheresRey.csv file, preprocessing our corpus as done in Chapter 8, and constructing a term-document matrix. Let's also remove terms that do not occur in at least 99% of the WhereIsRey posts from the term-document matrix. This will give us a more manageable set of terms to analyze.

We have several different options in representing the relationship among terms as an adjacency matrix. One simple approach extends the association analysis we saw earlier in this chapter. Here edges are determined by the ***correlations among terms***. Instead of using the findAssocs() function iteratively to develop an edge list as we did in Tutorial 11.1, we can simply use the correlation function (i.e., ***cor(DocumentTermMatrix)***) to obtain an adjacency matrix. We need the document-term matrix, rather than the term-document matrix, to develop the correlation matrix, because calculating correlations requires our variables—here *terms*—to appear as columns. We create our correlation matrix with `ReyCorrel=cor(as.matrix(t(ReyTDM)))`. If we inspect ReyCorrel, as we might expect, some correlations are negative. Values in the adjacency matrix may not be negative, though. We therefore set all negative correlations to zeros using `ReyCorrel[ReyCorrel<0]=0`.

Now we can create our graph data object just as we did before, but with our ReyCorrel matrix: `ReyGraph=simplify(graph.adjacency(ReyCorrel, weighted=T, mode='undirected'))` followed by `plot(ReyGraph, layout=layout.gem(ReyGraph))`. As before, we can obtain various centrality metrics on our terms. For example, `evcent(ReyGraph)$vector` produces the eigenvector centrality measures for the terms, revealing the most central term to be "character." We can visualize this term graph with `V(ReyGraph)$color='yellow'`, and `plot(ReyGraph, layout=layout.davidson.harel(ReyGraph))` produces the graph depicted in Figure 11.5. Notably, "view" and "conversation" are disconnected from the rest of the term network.

Running `mc=multilevel.community(ReyGraph)` identifies groups of related terms. My preprocessing yielded a six-group solution, with a modularity coefficient of 0.49. Visualizing the partitions with `plot(mc, ReyGraph, layout=layout.auto)` produced Figure 11.6. Notice the grouping of the three companies salient to the WhereIsRey discourse.

The correlations among terms approach to topic identification can produce misleading results in data sets with small document sizes, such as tweets. This is because infrequently occurring terms may appear to correlate perfectly because they happen to co-occur in a single document. If using the correlations among terms approach to analyze such data sets, we may wish permit only a low level of sparsity in the term-document matrix.

A second option that can serve as the basis for an adjacency matrix is a ***distance matrix***. Earlier, we used the distance matrix to identify clusters of terms. Since the dist() function returns a matrix of how removed from each other each pair of terms is, we need to convert this distance matrix to a nearness matrix for use with SNA. Subtracting the distance matrix using the "binary" method from one provides an easy nearness matrix—that is, `ReyDist=1-dist(ReyTDM, method='binary')`. This works because the "binary" method computes distances between 0 and 1, where 0 represents elements with zero values, and nonzero elements in the matrix represent the proportion of nonzero distances that are exactly one, relative to the nonzero distances that are at least one. Subtracting these distance proportions from one gives us a matrix of values where larger numbers indicate nearness and smaller numbers indicate farness.

A third option is constructing a ***term co-occurrence*** matrix. This is the product of the term-document matrix and the document-term matrix (or the transposed term-document matrix). In effect, this provides an average of the co-occurrence of terms across the documents (strictly speaking, the covariance of the terms times the number of documents). To perform this computation, we first must convert our term-document matrix into a regular matrix. Unless we created the document-term matrix, in addition to the term-document matrix, we can obtain the transpose using the ***t(RegularMatrix)*** function. The ***%*%*** operator performs the matrix multiplication. For our WhereIsRey data set, we construct our co-occurrence matrix using `ReyCooccurMatrix=as.matrix(ReyTDM) %*% t(as.matrix(ReyTDM))`.

When constructing our adjacency matrix based on the correlation matrix, we reset all negative correlations in the matrix to zero because edges must be specified as non-negative numbers. For distance-based or co-occurrence-based adjacency matrices, we do not have to contend with potentially specifying edges as negative numbers. Yet it would be prudent to consider whether all nonzero values truly constitute an edge. For example, would we consider two terms that co-occur purely by chance to be related? If the answer is no, we would want to discount chance co-occurrences by resetting all matrix values below a certain threshold (e.g., the mean or the mean plus one or more standard deviations) to zero. We would accomplish this with `ReyDist[ReyDist<mean(ReyDist)+sd(ReyDist)]=0`. Alternately, we could use the median distance as our cutoff with `ReyDist[ReyDist<median(ReyDist)]=0`. Failing such adjustments though, our term network is apt to be overly dense, as terms that co-occur even extremely sporadically forge an edge. Even when specifying our adjacency matrix based on a correlation matrix, we may wish to consider only terms that are positively and significantly correlated with each other to constitute an edge—that is, reset the rest to zero. For example, we may want to stipulate that only correlations significant at the 95% level constitute an edge. The z-score (number of standard deviations from the mean of a normal distribution with mean of zero) below which 95% of normally distributed observations lie is 1.96. We can specify that only correlations higher than those at the ninety-fifth percentile constitute an edge using `ReyCorrel[ReyCorrel<mean(ReyCorrel)+1.96*sd(ReyCorrel)]=0`.

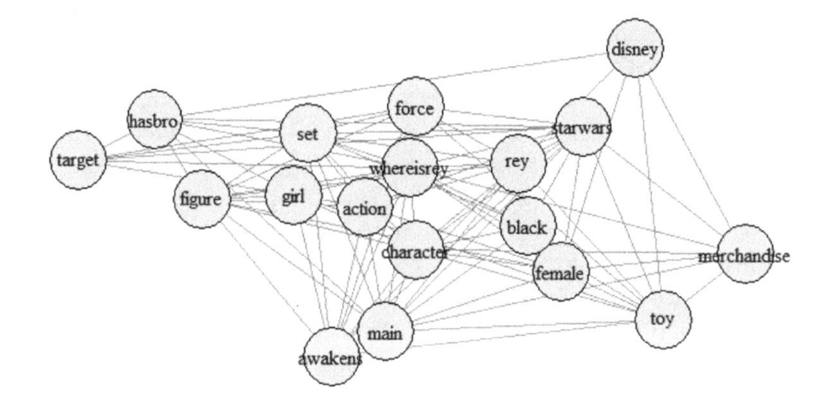

Figure 11.5 Term Correlation Network

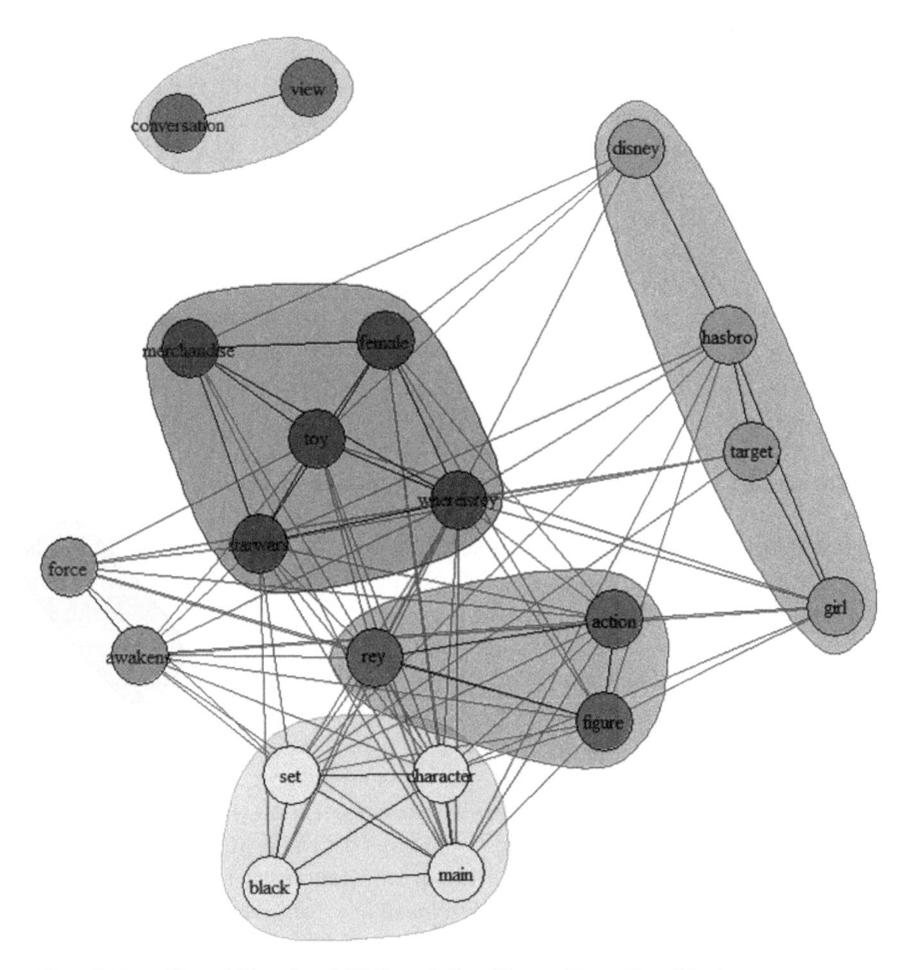

Figure 11.6 Correlation-Based Graph of #WhereIsRey Terms Revealing Topics

Tutorial 11.2. Surfacing Aadhaar Topics and Constituents' Contributions

In this tutorial, we work with the combined tweets about the Aadhaar card emanating from both the Indian government's and citizens' accounts. Our objective is to first surface a topic model of the Aadhaar conversation and then highlight the terms within this model that dominate the government's tweet versus citizen's tweets. We use the Aadhaar.csv file for this tutorial. As we open it, we use the "stringsAsFactors=FALSE" argument to ensure that the Source column—which marks tweets as emanating from either the government or citizens—does not get converted to a factor variable:

```
aadhar=read.csv('Aadhaar.csv', header=T, stringsAsFactors = FALSE)
```

Then we begin with the data cleansing statements from Tutorial 11.1, create our term-document matrix, and specify the sparsity level as 95%. When I inspect this matrix (with `View(as.matrix(ADTM))`), I find it contains fourteen terms.

Next we create a AWhoTerms data frame, combining the transposed term-document matrix with the Source term from the aadhaar data frame. We then derive an AggTerms data frame, aggregating the first fourteen columns (which contain the term frequencies) of the AWhoTerms data frame into means for citizen and government tweets, and then transpose this data frame. (**Note, if your data cleansing has been even slightly different from mine, your ADTM matrix will retain a different number of terms. If so, you will need to change the numbers 14 and 15 in this line of code accordingly.**) We add a column to the AggTerms data frame for the row names (i.e., the terms themselves) and then set the data frame's row names to NULL. We specify the column names for the data frame. Next, we determine whether the mean frequency for citizens' tweets is higher than that for government's tweets for each term.

```
AWhoTerms=data.frame(as.matrix(t(ATDM)),Source=aadhar$Source)
AggTerms=t(data.frame(aggregate(AWhoTerms[1:14], by=list(AWhoTerms$Source),
   FUN=mean))[2:15])
AggTerms=data.frame(row.names(AggTerms),AggTerms)
rownames(AggTerms)=NULL
colnames(AggTerms)=c('Term','Citizen','Government')
AggTerms$Who=ifelse(AggTerms$Citizen>AggTerms$Government,'C','G')
```

This produces the following data frame:

```
      Term Citizen Government Who
1  aadhaar  0.6695     0.3024   C
2     card  0.1559     0.0070   C
3   number  0.0492     0.1309   G
4      get  0.0551     0.0859   G
5    enrol  0.0505     0.2841   G
6     govt  0.0602     0.0025   C
7    pleas  0.0426     0.2432   G
8      can  0.0682     0.1599   G
9     link  0.0974     0.0312   C
10    will  0.0770     0.1788   G
11   share  0.0380     0.2956   G
12   uidai  0.0622     0.0448   C
13   india  0.0609     0.0512   C
14    gtop  0.1103     0.0000   C
```

We create the ACorrel data object as the document-term matrix data frame. Because the graph data object does not permit negative values in the adjacency matrix, we reset all negative correlations to zeros.

```
ACorrel=cor(as.matrix(ADTM))
ACorrel[ACorrel<0]=0
```

The resulting correlation matrix appears below.

	aadhaar	card	number	get	enrol	govt	pleas	can	link	will	share	uidai	india	gtop
aadhaar	1.0000	0.2989	0.0510	0.0792	0.0000	0.0861	0.0000	0.0000	0.1989	0.0000	0.0000	0.0505	0.0117	0.0000
card	0.2989	1.0000	0.0000	0.0469	0.0000	0.0000	0.0000	0.0000	0.0783	0.0000	0.0000	0.0141	0.0000	0.0000
number	0.0510	0.0000	1.0000	0.0000	0.0950	0.0000	0.0751	0.0200	0.0665	0.1072	0.0513	0.0037	0.0000	0.0000
get	0.0792	0.0469	0.0000	1.0000	0.0000	0.0000	0.0000	0.0729	0.0000	0.1279	0.1026	0.0200	0.1292	0.0000
enrol	0.0000	0.0000	0.0950	0.0000	1.0000	0.0000	0.0520	0.2017	0.0000	0.0202	0.0230	0.0120	0.0000	0.0000
govt	0.0861	0.0000	0.0000	0.0000	0.0000	1.0000	0.0000	0.0016	0.0075	0.0008	0.0000	0.0000	0.0000	0.0000
pleas	0.0000	0.0000	0.0751	0.0000	0.0520	0.0000	1.0000	0.0000	0.0029	0.0000	0.4366	0.0000	0.0000	0.0000
can	0.0000	0.0000	0.0200	0.0729	0.2017	0.0016	0.0000	1.0000	0.0000	0.0000	0.0983	0.0035	0.0000	0.0000
link	0.1989	0.0783	0.0665	0.0000	0.0000	0.0075	0.0029	0.0000	1.0000	0.0000	0.0000	0.0000	0.0000	0.0000
will	0.0000	0.0000	0.1072	0.1279	0.0202	0.0008	0.0000	0.0000	0.0000	1.0000	0.0000	0.0000	0.0780	0.0000
share	0.0000	0.0000	0.0513	0.1026	0.0230	0.0000	0.4366	0.0983	0.0000	0.0000	1.0000	0.0000	0.0000	0.0000
uidai	0.0505	0.0141	0.0037	0.0200	0.0120	0.0000	0.0000	0.0035	0.0000	0.0000	0.0000	1.0000	0.0000	0.0000
india	0.0117	0.0000	0.0000	0.1292	0.0000	0.0000	0.0000	0.0000	0.0000	0.0780	0.0000	0.0000	1.0000	0.2008
gtop	0.0000	0.0000	0.0000	0.0000	0.0000	0.0000	0.0000	0.0000	0.0000	0.0000	0.0000	0.0000	0.2008	1.0000

Now, we create the graph data object. Recall that our term graphs are weighted and undirected.

```
AGraph=simplify(graph.adjacency(ACorrel, weighted=T, mode='undirected'))
```

Next, we assign the values of the Who column from our AggTerms data frame to a graph attribute named *Who*. This will permit us to depict the dominant source for each term in our graph. We then request a partitioning of the graph using the multilevel community algorithm. After that, we are ready to plot our graph. We set the vertex shape to a circle. Edge width is set relative to the square root of the edge weight. Node color is based on values of the Who attribute of the term vertices. The "mark.shape=" argument permits us to manipulate the shapes of the different community borders; "mark.col=" allows us to change their colors; and "mark.border=" sets the color of the community borders.

```
V(AGraph)$Who=as.character(AggTerms$Who[match(V(AGraph)$name,AggTerms$Term)])
mc=multilevel.community(AGraph)
plot(mc, AGraph,  vertex.shape='circle', edge.width=sqrt(E(AGraph)$weight)*20,
   col=ifelse(V(AGraph)$Who=='G','plum1', 'cadetblue1'),
   mark.shape=c(-1,-1,-1), mark.col=c('lightblue', 'violetred', 'lightslateblue'),
   mark.border='white', vertex.size=evcent(AGraph)$vector*50, layout=layout.auto,
   sub='blue=citizens; pink=government')
```

Figure 11.7 depicts the resulting graph with three topics. Modularity for this graph was 0.44, indicating reasonable orthogonality of the three topics. The graph indicates one topic dominated by the government, one topic dominated by citizens, and one shared by the government and citizens. The government's topic appears to capture its EXHORTATIONS to citizens to please share information on how they can enroll for the Aadhaar card and get a number. In contrast, the citizens' topic appears to express the CONCERNS regarding linking the Aadhaar card to the tax portal.

Topic Modeling via Relational Class Analysis of Terms

Cluster analysis and network analysis of term-document matrices group terms that "go together" (i.e., that correlate or co-occur). Analogizing terms to people, cluster and network analyses are based on the premise that "agreement" reflects shared meaning. However, Goldberg [10] proposed that people can disagree and still

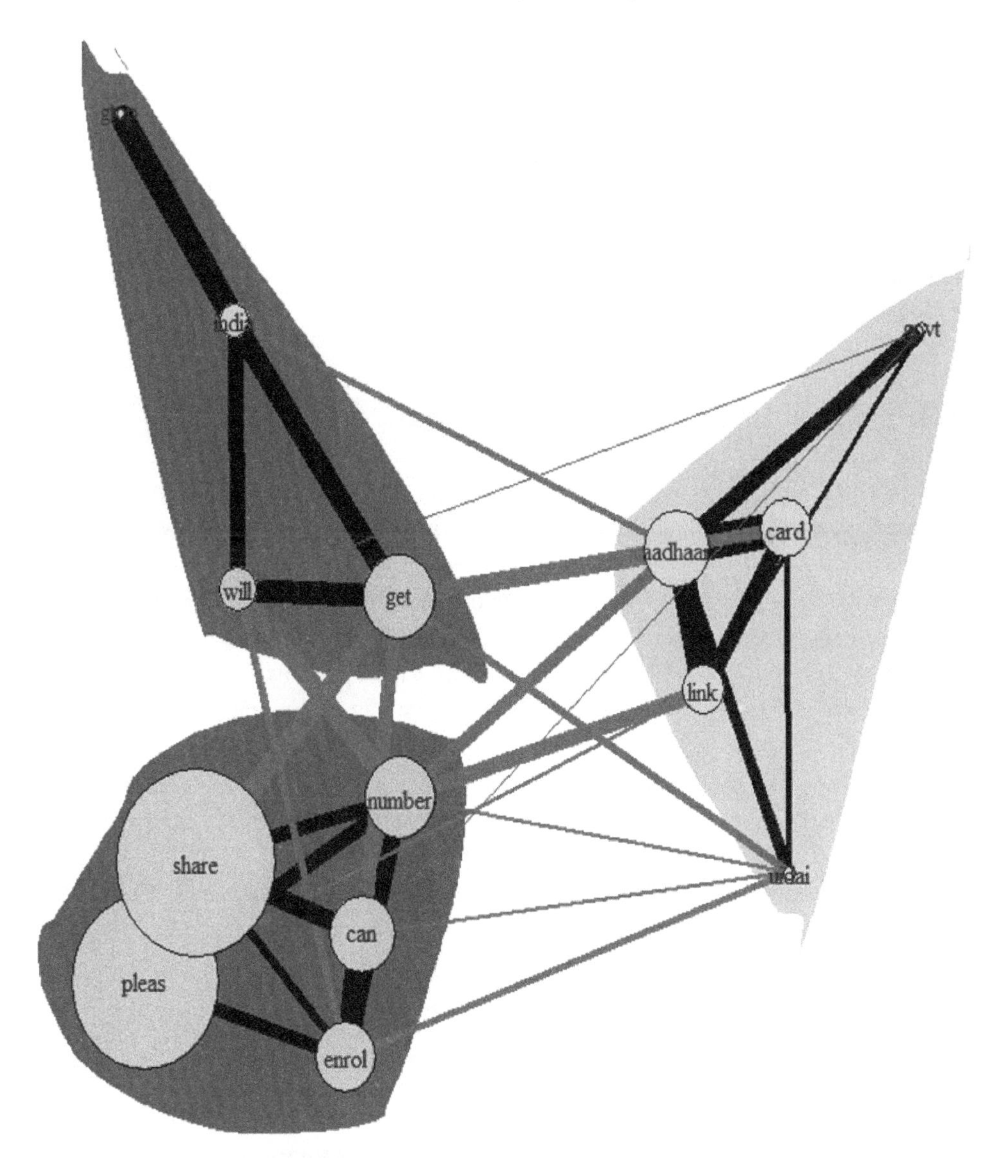

Figure 11.7 Aadhaar Topics as Emphasized by the Government versus Citizens

have shared mental models. For example, while we may disagree on our preferences for who should win the Superbowl, most of us can agree on the criteria that should determine the winner. For Goldberg, differences in meaning—and the negotiability of that meaning—arise when people disagree on the criteria itself. In recent research, my PhD students and I used this approach to surface companies' distinctive visions of social media based on the extent to which the companies' press releases about their social media use reflected each of the following six values: civic, domestic, industrial, inspiration, market, and renown [11]. Companies' systematic juxtapositions of subsets of these values in their different press releases—and systematic eschewing of others—led to our identification of four distinct social media visions: *technology-as-efficiency-engineer*, where social media was used simply to make the firm more efficient at what it already was doing; *technology-as-brand-promoter*, where social media was leveraged to bolster public awareness of and loyalty to the companies' brands; *technology-as-good-citizen*, where social media was used to enable firms to engage the public in their social responsibility initiatives or to represent such initiatives to the public; and *technology-as-master-of-ceremonies*, where social media was used to enable firms to attract attention by giving attention.

An RCA approach to surfacing topics from terms identifies the different criteria underlying the systematic use of some terms in a text and avoidance of others. Mechanically, RCA requires input values between 0 and 1. Weighting the term-frequencies by the inverse-document-frequencies in the term-document matrix accomplishes this. As with the correlation-based network analysis, to apply RCA to our corpus, we need a document-term matrix. For our WhereIsRey corpus, we use

```
ReyDTM=DocumentTermMatrix(ReyCorp, control=list(removePunctuation=T, removeNumbers=T,
  weighting=weightTfIdf))
```

Using the TfIdf weighting requires each document have at least one retained term. This may be an issue with tweets, for example, in which only website links or Unicode characters have been provided and our data cleansing routine has eliminated these links and Unicode characters. For a manageable number of topics and interpretability of those topics, I recommend minimizing the sparsity of the document-term matrix. Once again, I stipulated 95% sparsity for the document-term matrix.

We use the ***RCA(DTMAsRegularMatrix, alpha=SignificanceLevel)*** function from the RCA package to partition the matrix. Once again, we need to convert the document-term matrix to a regular matrix. The alpha argument specifies the significance level to be used for testing the interim relationality coefficients used to partition the matrix. Note that RCA is a computationally intensive technique. This is because it entails partitioning an n × n matrix, where n is the number of observations in our data set. Computations for this n × n matrix are performed iteratively for the number of retained terms. Thus, large, sparse document term matrices will require more computational time. For the WhereIsRey corpus, RCA partitions the 2096 × 2096 matrix, iterating through computations for the twenty terms retained in the document term matrix after specifying the 95% sparsity. So, expect to wait a bit on the analyses. (My computer took about ten minutes to run the procedure.)

We run the RCA, specifying an alpha=0.05 using `rca=RCA(as.matrix(ReyDTM), alpha=0.05)`. We can inspect our results with `summary(rca)`, which produces the following output:

```
              Length  Class  Mode
membership      2096 -none- numeric
modules          777 -none- list
R            4393216 -none- numeric
```

This tells us that RCA identified 777 distinct modules. We can obtain the membership assignment using `rca$membership`. When we inspect this membership roster, we find that only two of those modules (#1 and #777) are assigned more than one tweet—443 and 878 tweets, respectively. The other modules each are assigned only a single tweet. More accurately, RCA was unable to cluster 775 of the 2,096 tweets.

We look at the average use of the twenty terms across tweets assigned to each of the two modules. To do so, we begin by combining the membership assignments with the document term matrix into a ReyMembers data frame using `ReyMembers=as.data.frame(cbind(as.matrix(ReyDTM),RCA=rca$membership))`. We then retain only the tweets assigned to modules 1 and 777 using `ReyMembers = subset(ReyMembers, RCA=="1" | RCA=="777")`. Now, we average the frequencies of the terms across the two modules with `round(aggregate(ReyMembers[1:20], by=list(ReyMembers$RCA), FUN=mean), 4)`. (The round() function permits us to specify the number of decimal places to be displayed.) This produces the following output:

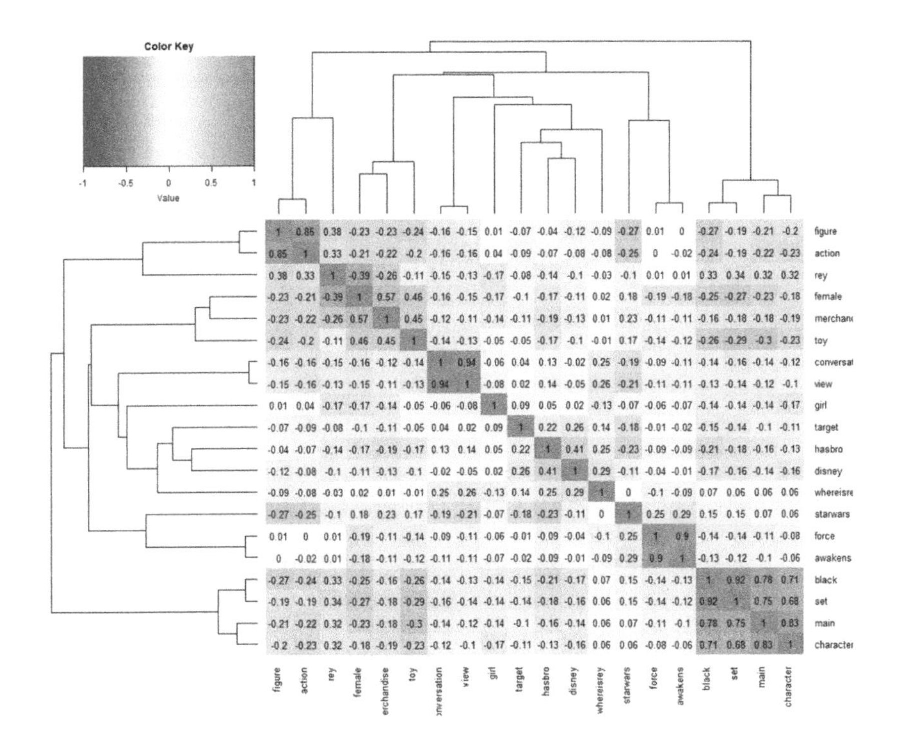

A. Module 1 (443 tweets)

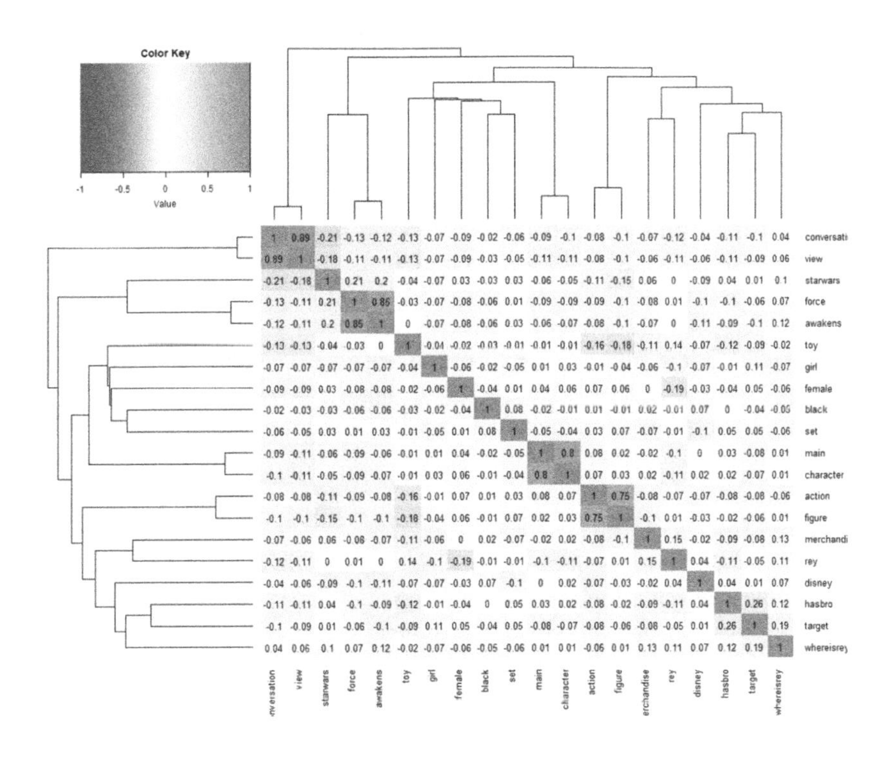

B. Module 2 (878 tweets)

Figure 11.8 Correlation Matrix for RCA Solution

```
  Group.1      female     set starwars        target      toy  whereisrey
1       1      0.0720  0.0801   0.0774        0.0470   0.0662      0.0038
2     777      0.0306  0.0319   0.0659        0.0492   0.0538      0.0037

     girl      hasbro  disney  awakens conversation    force        view
1 0.0448       0.0681  0.0598   0.0419        0.0412   0.0481      0.0409
2 0.0325       0.0487  0.0478   0.0407        0.0377   0.0534      0.0349

      rey   character    main    black  merchandise   action      figure
1 0.0539       0.0498  0.0475   0.0461        0.0432   0.0838      0.0863
2 0.0684       0.0491  0.0464   0.0112        0.0329   0.0294      0.0374
```

The incidence of "starwars," "target," "whereisrey," "awakens," "force," "character," and "main" are comparable across the two modules. But the incidence of "female," "set," "hasbro," "black," "action," and "figure" are considerably lower in the second module. We can glean further insight into the two modules by visualizing how the terms in the two modules are correlated. To do so, we use `plot(rca, module=1, colorblind = FALSE, heat_labels = TRUE)`. Repeating this for module=777 produces the heat maps in Figure 11.8.

From the heat map in Figure 11.8A, we see the correlations in the first module. We see five oppositional groupings of the twenty terms: "rey," "action," and "figure" are strongly correlated; "female," "merchandise," and "toy"; "conversation" and "view"; "target," "hasbro," "disney," and "whereisrey"; "starwars," "force," "awakens"; and "black," "set," "main," "character." The female-merchandise-toy combination consistently correlated negatively with black-set-main-character combination. This suggests that the WhereIsRey tweets in this module either raised concerns about the missing merchandise or discussed the black lead character in *The Force Awakens* movie, but not both. The target-hasbro-disney-whereisrey combination similarly opposed the black-set-main-character combination.

Figure 11.8B depicts the correlations and groupings for the 777th module. The first thing we notice here is that though some similar patterns emerge, neither combinations nor oppositions are as stark as those in Figure 11.8A. In fact, except for view-conversation, starwars-force-awakens, main-character, and action-figure, most combinations are weak. This suggests that the topics underlying the tweets in this module were more inclusive and less compartmentalized than those underlying the tweets in module 1, revealing underlying criteria of CHARACTER/DEMOGRAPHIC-FOCUSED versus BROAD critique of the Star Wars merchandizing strategy. This is useful for Disney, Hasbro, and especially Target to understand. If parents in the vicinity of a Target store contrast pleas for merchandise surrounding the Rey character with pleas for merchandise surrounding the Finn character, Target will want to stock separate merchandise figuring each of the two characters. If, however, parents around a Target store discuss merchandise concerning both characters, Target can offer merchandise on both characters (e.g., action figure sets including both Rey and Finn or linens depicting both characters).

Conclusion

Association mining is a powerful tool for making sense of large corpora. Though beyond the scope of this chapter, association mining permits subsequent predictions. For example, based on the model in Figure 11.7, if we have a tweet from an unknown author with the combination of "please," "share," "number," "can," and "enroll," we can deduce that the tweet is from the Indian government; tweets containing "aadhaar," "card," "link," and "uidai," on the other hand, are liable to be from citizens. In addition to text classification tasks, LDA-based topic modeling has been used in collaborative filtering tasks—that is, where some client preferences are known and the objective of the topic modeling algorithm is to predict unknown client preferences [3]. Further, while our focus has been solely on text data, these mining algorithms can be applied to any data, including image and audio data, enabling us to "learn" complex social patterns from the wealth of data around us.

Exercise: Association Mining of a Twitter Conversation

Use your Twitter data set from the Exercise in Chapter 5 for this exercise—or one provided by your professor. The purpose of this exercise is to glean insights from the associations among terms in your data set.

Individual Assignment

1. Pick one or two terms that are central to your data set. Find the terms associated with these terms and graph them.
2. Pick two topic modeling techniques and use them to analyze your data set. Comment on similarities and differences obtained across the different techniques.

Copy all R code and salient output—including snips of any graphics you generate—into a Word file and annotate it with your observations and comments. Submit this file.

Team Assignment:

Put together your team's analyses into a PowerPoint that tells a story about the associations underlying the terms in your data set. Your first slide should name all team members. Your story should reveal at least five insights that explain or predict and lead you to tangible recommendations.

Works Cited

1. Blei, D.M., "Topic Models," *VideoLectures*, November 2, 2009, http://videolectures.net/mlss09uk_blei_tm/.
2. Zhao, W., J. Chen, and W. Zen, "Best Practices in Building Topic Models with LDA for Mining Regulatory Textual Documents," *Center for Drug Evaluation Research's National Center for Toxicological Research Working Group Presentation*, 2015, http://phusewiki.org/wiki/images/c/c9/Weizhong_Presentation_CDER_Nov_9th.pdf.
3. Blei, D.M., A.Y. Ng, and M.I. Jordan, "Latent Dirichlet Allocation." *Journal of Machine Learning Research*, 3(January 2003): 993–1022.
4. Phan, X.-H., L.-M. Nguyen, and S. Horiguchi, "Learning to Classify Short and Sparse Text and Web with Hidden Topics from Large-Scale Data Collections," in *Proceedings of the 17th International Conference on the World Wide Web*. Beijing, China: ACM, 2008.
5. Hair, J.F., et al., *Multivariable Data Analysis*. Upper Saddle River, NJ: Prentice Hall, 1998.
6. Blashfield, R.K., "Mixture Model Tests of Cluster Analysis: Accuracy of Four Agglomerative Hierarchical Methods." *Psychological Bulletin*, 83(3; 1976): 377.
7. Müller, O., et al., "Using Text Analytics to Derive Customer Service Management Benefits from Unstructured Data." *MIS Quarterly Executive*, 15(4; 2016): 243–58.
8. Müller, O., et al., "Utilizing Big Data Analytics for Information Systems Research: Challenges, Promises and Guidelines." *European Journal of Information Systems*, 25(4; 2016): 289–302.
9. Blei, D.M., "Topic Models," in *Machine Learning*. West Lafayette, IN: P.U. Computer Science Department, 2009.
10. Goldberg, A., "Mapping Shared Understandings Using Relational Class Analysis: The Case of the Cultural Omnivore Reexamined." *American Journal of Sociology*, 116(5; 2011): 1397–1436.
11. Miranda, S.M., I. Kim, and J. Summers, "Jamming with Social Media: How Cognitive Structuring of Organizing Vision Facets Affects IT Innovation Diffusion." *MIS Quarterly*, 39(3; 2015): 591–614.

PART IV

Conclusion

CHAPTER 12

Ethical Social Analytics

> **Learning Objectives**
>
> Throughout this book, we have been exposed to a variety of use cases for social analytics and learned many techniques for analyzing social data. But should we do everything we can? The purpose of this chapter is to consider when we should restrict:
>
> 1. what data we collect/use;
> 2. how we analyze the data; and
> 3. what we do with insights gleaned.

The scope of what we can do with science and technology is growing across a variety of domains. In the area of climate science, geoengineering is being used to obviate the ongoing effects of greenhouse gas emissions [1]. In the medical arena, gene editing is evolving into viable therapy for a variety of inherited diseases [2]; 3D bioprinting and organ fabrication are almost a reality [3]; nanotechnology is being investigated for treatment of cancer [4]. Unmanned aerial vehicles hold the promise of faster pizza deliveries [5] and surveillance of remote pipelines and of wildlife [6]. Ethicists, however, are asking: just because we can, should we? Data science and analytics is not immune to this conundrum.

In early 2012, a story hit the news about a Minneapolis teenager's father discovering her pregnancy after Target mailed the girl some coupons [7]. As the story went, the father, irate about his daughter receiving coupons for baby clothes and cribs, initially challenged a confused Target manager, questioning whether the store was encouraging his daughter, who was still in high school, to get pregnant. A subsequent conversation with his daughter revealed that she indeed was pregnant. Apparently Target "knew" the teen was pregnant before her father did. How was this possible?

To begin with, what data did Target use to "know" the teen was pregnant? Retail firms collect purchase data, which is linked to a unique Guest ID via one of the following: a credit card or loyalty card used at the time of purchase, a survey completed or mail-in rebate used later, or a follow-up customer service call. Purchase data then can be cross-referenced against further customer demographic data obtained from publicly-available census data or from proprietary third-party data aggregators. For online purchases, purchase data also can be cross-referenced against customers' web browsing history, or via cookies and other website traces stored on customers' computers. In this fashion, Target had the raw materials for inferring the teen's pregnancy and for acting on that knowledge.

How did Target analyze the purchase data? In 2002, employees from the marketing department approached newly hired Target statistician, Andrew Pole, with a question: Could Target figure out whether a customer was pregnant, even if she didn't want them to know? In response, Pole began by analyzing the purchase data of women registered with the store's baby-shower registry. In machine learning terminology, this is the training data set, in that it already provides our dependent variables (i.e., pregnancy and due dates). Based on the shopping patterns for women on the registry, Pole developed a statistical model that allotted each shopper a "pregnancy prediction score" and estimated shoppers' due date within a relatively small margin of error. The model included purchases of twenty-five products—for example, fragrance-free lotion was purchased by women beginning their second trimester. It is not the individual purchases that inform the pregnancy score, though, but rather the combination of purchases. For example, purchasing only cotton balls may not be indicative of pregnancy, but purchasing cotton balls along with unscented soap, hand sanitizer, and washcloths apparently is. Thereafter, the model can be applied to predict pregnancy based on customer purchase data.

What did Target do with its model? In charging Pole with developing his model, the goal of Target's Guest Marketing Analytics department was to send you "coupons or things you want before you even know you want them" [7]. People's purchase behavior—the products and brands they buy—generally is relatively resistant to change, except during life status changes such as a new job, marriage, or divorce, at which time purchase behavior can be responsive to targeted marketing [8]. Pregnancy is considered the "holy grail" of life-changing events. Inferring that the teenager was pregnant from her purchase behavior and ascertaining contact information by linking purchase data to customer data via her GuestID, Target sent her the coupon book. Later, Pole acknowledged that "even if you're following the law, you can do things where people get queasy" [7]. Target realized that pregnant women receiving coupon booklets filled exclusively with and baby-related products felt that they were being spied on and tended not to use the coupons. When the booklets contained coupons for random items such as wineglasses and lawnmowers among the coupons for baby items, though, Target found that women were more likely to use the coupons for baby products.

What Data Do We (Not) Collect/Use?

A 2016 *Washington Post* article revealed that Facebook collects ninety-eight different pieces of personal data that it then uses to target advertisements [9]. Twitter has a record of every opinion we have voiced on its platform, every account followed and unfollowed, and locations from which we have tweeted [10]. Google knows the gender, birthdate, cellphone numbers, recent Google search history, websites visited, YouTube videos watched, places visited, and more about most of us [11]. Startling?

Analytics leverages data from two different types of studies. The first is the ***experiment***. This is a scientific procedure in which the researcher manipulates one (or more) "independent" variable(s). Also called "treatments," these variables have different conditions or levels. For example, a pharmaceutical researcher wishing to determine effects of a new drug would assign subjects—study participants—to treatment or placebo conditions. In the treatment condition, the subjects get the drug; in the placebo condition, they think they do, but don't. There may be several treatment conditions, in which subjects are administered different dosage levels of the drug. The effects assessed are the desired (or undesired) outcomes (i.e., the "dependent" variable[s]). For a psychotropic drug, the desired effect may be mood. However, the researcher also will want to assess possible negative side effects. To ensure the relationship between the independent and dependent variable is not contaminated by other variables, the researcher attempts to control variation in other variables by manipulating study conditions or through random assignment of subjects to treatment conditions. For example, to ensure the desired mood change is a function of the new drug, the researcher may select a sample of patients who are not on any other drug; to ensure that the outcome is not a function of the patient's age or gender, the researcher randomly assigns subjects to treatment and placebo conditions.

When attempting to establish a causal relationship between two variables (e.g., education and professional attainment, body temperature and survival), the experiment is the methodological gold standard, permitting the researcher to definitively establish a causal link between the manipulated independent variable and the dependent variable. Without experimentation, our causal conclusions are always suspect because some unknown variable could explain any observed correlation. For example, in lieu of an experiment, the pharmaceutical researcher could correlate drug use by and subsequent hospitalization of people suffering depression. Presumably, a negative correlation would attest to the drug's efficacy. However, such a correlational study could not rule out the possibility that the correlation was attributable to prescribing physician bias. Specifically, physicians may tend to prescribe the drugs for patients with milder cases of depression, who are less likely to require hospitalization, and reserve nonpharmaceutical treatments such as electroconvulsive therapy for patients with more severe depression. When using data to make conclusions with life-and-death consequences such as in the medical arena, being able to establish causality is imperative.

Yet experimental data is not without controversy. For a drug with life-altering potential, is it ethical to lead some study participants to believe they are receiving the drug, when in fact they are receiving a placebo? Controversy sometimes prevails even when data already are collected. Through experiments conducted at the internment camps, the Nazis made available a wealth of medical data that, if used by researchers today, could have life-saving consequences. Some believe that the data itself can never be evil, that using it does not condone the evil through which it was obtained, and not using it does not rectify the evil [12]. Others "fear that insights might replace condemnation of the Nazi evil" [13]. Questionable experiments occurred closer to home and persisted after World War II. In 1932, the US Public Health Service and the Tuskegee Institute began a study of "Untreated Syphilis in the Negro Male." The study included 399 syphilis patients and 201 men without the disease. The men were monitored over a period of 40 years, but went untreated even after penicillin was found effective in treating the disease [14]. With the objective of understanding compliance following the Holocaust, Stanley Milgram experimented with study participants' willingness to administer electric shocks to experimental confederates. He found a startling 65% of participants complied with the experimental rules and administered the maximum possible shock of 450 volts, and no participant opted out of the experiment before administering 300 volts [15]. Milgram thus demonstrated that "if the Nazis were just following orders, then he had proved that anyone at all could be a Nazi" [16]. Confederates were not really subjected to the shocks, and study participants were informed about the deception at the end of the experiment. Yet the belief that they were capable of such evil had to have been emotionally devastating to study participants [17].

But surely such experiments have nothing to do with social analytics? In 2014, researchers at Facebook and Cornell wished to understand the extent to which individuals' emotional states were transmitted via their posts on social media (i.e., the extent to which emotional contagion occurs in large digital social networks) [18]. To do so, they manipulated the emotional content of the news feeds of almost 700,000 Facebook users. With the help of LIWC, they parsed positive and negative Facebook posts, then reducing the positive posts from the feeds of one group of users in the sample and negative posts from the feeds of another group of users in the sample. Control group users had an equivalent number of randomly selected posts held out of their feeds. As seen in Chapter 2, this study yielded the important insight that decreases in negative emotion in users' feeds substantially decreased the amount of negativity users expressed in their own posts, and decreases in positive emotion in feeds substantially decreased the amount of positivity users expressed in their own posts. Unsurprisingly, this experiment raised ethical concerns, though [19, 20]. Many questioned whether the study may have done any harm to study participants. Privacy activist, Lauren Weinstein, quoted in a *New York Times* article, tweeted [20], "I wonder if Facebook KILLED anyone with their emotion manipulation stunt. At their scale and with depressed people out there, it's possible." The key issue was that of ***informed consent*** (i.e., studying subjects' expressed willingness to participate in a study when apprised of its benefits and risks) [21, 22]. This doctrine of informed consent permits researchers to conduct experiments where there are some risks to human participants, as long as those risks are disclosed and subjects have the opportunity to weigh the benefits of the study to themselves and to society against those risks. In the Facebook study, researchers, noting that the study was "consistent with Facebook's Data Use Policy," had failed to notify, much less seek consent from, unwitting—and perhaps unwilling—study participants. The issue of informed consent was raised, once again, with the 2018 revelation that Cambridge Analytica used Facebook data for voter intelligence [23]. Though Facebook itself had not manipulated users, the third-party permitted to access the data had—and for the insidious purpose of influencing the outcome of an election.

So, if we don't manipulate anything, is any social media data fair game? Analytics based on data that do not manipulate any variable to be analyzed are termed ***correlational studies***. Social media opportunities for such studies abound in the spheres of recruiting—corporate and college, insurance, and medicinal analytics. Already, organizations are availing of social media data on a small scale. In 2015, a software engineer, with job offers from Zenefits and Uber, queried Quora, an online Q&A site, for opinions on which offer he should choose. Unfortunately, the CEO of Zenefits encountered his post, responded that the engineer should choose the Uber offer, and promptly withdrew the Zenefits offer [24]. In 2017, Harvard revoked the admissions of ten incoming students who had participated in an online exchange deemed to be offensive [25]. In 2016, insurer Aviva won a case against William Owen [26]. Owen had claimed damages due to a whiplash injury from being rear-ended by an Aviva customer. But insurance investigators found social media posts of Owen competing in a 10k race, placing seventh in a field of two thousand runners, signing up for a half-marathon, and mountain climbing [27].

These are examples of corporate and college recruiter and insurance company reactions to one-off social media posts. Emerging startups are harvesting and analyzing social media data systematically so as to credential applicants and match prospective employees to jobs [28]. Mining text from Facebook profiles and timelines can yield information on prospective recruits' personality traits [29], which together with educational information and job tenure from LinkedIn can be used to predict their likely success on a job [30, 31]. Insurance companies have the ability to use information gleaned from social media posts to determine individuals' premiums based on commonly held risk factors such as smoking and alcohol consumption, but also whether one participates in activities such as hunting or hang-gliding, not typically factored into insurance premiums [32]. Patient and caregiver communities on Facebook or at specialty sites like PatientsLikeMe provide a wealth of information that can be harnessed for medical research [33]. How can such correlational analytics be problematic?

Depending on how the correlational algorithm is implemented, some people may be locked out of job opportunities and incur higher insurance premiums, exacerbating digital divides. This is not a futuristic concern. As part of their Machine Bias investigative initiative, ProPublica "outed" companies such as Amazon, Facebook, UPS, and Verizon for age discrimination. Armed with demographic data mined from its users' profiles, Facebook enabled these companies to target millennials with job advertisements, effectively shutting out older workers [34]. In another Machine Bias expose, ProPublica reported that Facebook permitted housing advertisers to target Facebook users based on race [35].

Mining lifestyle or disease management data from specialty communities such as the National Rifle Association or PatientsLikeMe requires gaining access to the community. Accessing these communities typically entails an active or tacit declaration that one supports a political perspective or has the disease the community supports. Should an analyst desiring access to a community's data make such a declaration if he believes in the need for gun control or if she does not have the disease supported by the community? Is it OK for an analyst who does have the disease to collect data from a support community?

We've Collected the Data—Now How Can We Analyze It?

Explaining his fascination with numbers, when he could rig them, Mark Twain famously quoted the nineteenth century UK prime minister Benjamin Disraeli, saying, "There are three kinds of lies: lies, damned lies, and statistics." Willful data fudging and unmindful analyses yield statistical lies. We all know to avoid the willful fudging. Let's consider the problems endemic with small and large data sets in correlational studies, unmindful analyses of which can produce the misleading results that also constitute statistical lies.

In small data sets, outliers and leverage points can mislead us. ***Outliers*** are observations that are three or more standard deviations away from the average. For example, in Chapter 2, we considered the reciprocation of follower ties among Big XII schools. The average reciprocity for the ten schools in Table 2.1 was 34%. However, the average reciprocity dropped to 28% without Baylor_Business, which is more than two standard deviations from this average. Baylor_Business thus approaches being an outlier with regard to online reciprocity. Relating variables with outlying data points such as reciprocity with other variables can taint our results. For example, if I wished to determine whether BSchools reciprocate more or less as their number of followers increases, I could examine the correlation between reciprocity and number of followers. From Table 2.1, we find a slight positive correlation between the number of followers and reciprocity (i.e., 0.13). Without Baylor_Business, though, the correlation between the number of followers and reciprocity is –0.12. However, without UTexasMcCombs, the correlation between followers and reciprocity is 0.44. Thus both Baylor_Business and UTexasMcCombs are ***leverage points*** (i.e., data points without which the relationship of interest changes considerably). While UTexasMcCombs was not an outlier with regard to reciprocity, at almost three standard deviations from the average, it is an outlier with regard to its number of followers. Thus outlying data points can produce severely misleading results.

Large data sets are not immune to faulty conclusions, either. In fact, big data is especially prone to faulty conclusions in two ways. First, the increased number of observations increases our chances of committing a Type I error—that is, falsely rejecting the null hypothesis of no association between two variables (or no difference across two demographic groups) because our very large sample size renders miniscule differences "statistically significant" [36]. Best practices for big data therefore entail cross-validation, rather than tests of statistical significance. Second, the increased number of variables in a big data set increases the chances of a ***spurious correlation***—that is, one that occurs purely by chance or because of some intervening factor relating to both variables. Spurious correlations result in or propagate a variety of myths and folklore. For example, in a TED talk, Ben Mezrich noted the "strange phenomenon of cattle mutilations" along the path of frequent UFO sightings [37], developing the myth of alien life forms being responsible for cattle mutilation. Another spurious correlation is the one between populations of white storks and the birth of babies in several European countries [38], lending credence to folklore about where babies come from. I have no explanation for the evident correlation between UFO sightings and cattle mutilations. With regard to storks and babies, until the mid-1970s, births in northern European countries such as the Netherlands—where the folklore has strong roots—peaked in March and April [39], because conceptions peaked in June and July, months popular for weddings. Coincidentally, white stork populations in northern Europe surge in March and April, as the birds migrate back from their winter locations [40]. Thus we see that the storks–babies correlation is entirely coincidental.

Perfectly coincidental spurious correlations occur via a practice that Tyler Vigen termed ***data dredging*** (i.e., using computing power to examine correlations across all possible variables available to the analyst) [41]. Using data dredging on a variety of completely-unrelated data such as US spending, suicides, accidental deaths, films, and food consumption over a ten year period, Vigen arrived at some hilarious observations: the number of accidental drownings in pools correlated with the number of films in which Nicholas Cage appeared ($r = 0.67$); commercial space launches correlated with the number of sociology doctorates awarded ($r = 0.79$); per capital cheese consumption correlated with number of deaths by becoming entangled in bedsheets ($r = 0.95$); and the marriage rate in Kentucky correlated with drownings after falling out of fishing boats ($r = 0.95$).

What Should We Not Do with Insights Gleaned?

In the early 1970s, Ford analyzed the relative costs associated with delaying the production of the Pinto to fix the defective fuel tank design that caused the car to ignite following a rear-end collision versus paying out claims following car fatalities. Finding that re-engineering and delay costs far outweighed claims costs, the company went ahead with production and sales of the Pinto, with a consequent death toll estimated as high as five hundred persons [42].

Stories of less shocking, but still dubious, uses of data analytics abound. Creditors mine social media data to ascertain our creditworthiness [43]. The NSA has mined metadata of our phone conversations to profile terrorists [44]. Icelandic company deCODE and US company 23andMe mine genetic data to pinpoint genes associated with different diseases [45, 46]. That data Twitter harvests from our posts is sold to businesses and even the police [10]. What could possibly be wrong with these data uses? In a word—profiling! Analytics permits intelligent profiling. But profiling of any variety can be corrupted into discriminatory practices [47]. Genetic data can be harnessed to make decisions on insurance policies and premiums. Police departments risk harming the citizens they seek to serve. For example, a policing program in Fort Lauderdale evaluated a black teenage girl booked for stealing a bicycle a substantially higher risk than a white forty-year-old man booked for shoplifting merchandise of value equivalent to that of the bicycle. The girl was a first-time offender, while the man previously had been incarcerated for armed robbery. Two years later, the girl had not been charged with any further crimes; the man was subsequently imprisoned for yet another burglary [48]. These risk assessments influence choices made through the criminal justice system—from bond amounts through sentencing. In such decisions, the use of analytics raises issues of human rights, social justice, and public safety. Businesses—such as Target—engaging in profiling-based target marketing risk alienating the very customers they seek out by "creeping out" those customers. Organizations that use analytics in their hiring decisions are susceptible to adverse impact: their choices may appear superficially race, gender, or age neural, but in fact disproportionately disfavor specific subgroups.

Conclusions

Ethical data analysis requires considerable forethought and even more second-guessing of our data collection, analysis, and application choices. Being technically knowledgeable is a good start, as it can preclude unwittingly proffering misleading conclusions. But Target's culpability did not lie in what data they collected, or even in their analyses. There was nothing incorrect in their analyses or misleading in their conclusions. Rather, it was their covert application of their model. In other venues, such as the Fort Lauderdale policing system, reliance on potentially spurious correlations or outlying data engender devastating social problems. However, these analytics applications did not start out as invasive or racist. Rather, well-meaning persons were merely looking to offer better services or to streamline clunky bureaucracies.

How do we remain ethical in the service of evidence-based marketing, health care, government, and so on? Simply foregrounding some of the questions raised in this chapter is a start, as it surfaces disparate perspectives and encourages debate. As Chief Justice Louis Brandeis noted, "Sunlight is said to be the best of disinfectants." Exposing our analytic methods and models to peers in our organization and to external focus groups, even having them challenged by the media and watch groups, can ensure the long-term ethicality of our analytics efforts.

Works Cited

1. Pasztor, J., C. Scharf, and K.-U. Schmidt, *How to Govern Geoengineering?* Boston: American Association for the Advancement of Science, 2017.
2. Kohn, D.B., M.H. Porteus, and A.M. Scharenberg, "Ethical and Regulatory Aspects of Genome Editing." *Blood*, 127(21; 2016): 2553–60.
3. Vermeulen, N., et al., "3D Bioprint Me: A Socioethical View of Bioprinting Human Organs and Tissues." *Journal of Medical Ethics*, 43(2017): 618–24.
4. Oksman, O., "How Nanotechnology Research Could Cure Cancer and Other Diseases," *The Guardian*, June 11, 2016, https://www.theguardian.com/lifeandstyle/2016/jun/11/nanotechnology-research-potential-cure-cancer-genetic-level.
5. Reid, D. "Domino's Delivers World's First Ever Pizza by Drone," Tech Transformers, November 16, 2016, https://www.cnbc.com/2016/11/16/dominos-has-delivered-the-worlds-first-ever-pizza-by-drone-to-a-new-zealand-couple.html.
6. Roos, D., "10 UAV Jobs of the Future," in *How Stuff Works*, July 22, 2017, https://money.howstuffworks.com/10-uav-jobs-future.htm.
7. Duhigg, C., "How Companies Learn Your Secrets," *New York Times Magazine*, February 16, 2012, https://www.nytimes.com/2012/02/19/magazine/shopping-habits.html.
8. Andreasen, A.R., "Life Status Changes and Changes in Consumer Preferences and Satisfaction." *Journal of Consumer Research*, 11(3; 1984): 784–94.
9. Dewey, C., "98 Personal Data Points That Facebook Uses to Target Ads to You," *Washington Post*, 2016, August 19, 2016, https://www.washingtonpost.com/news/the-intersect/wp/2016/08/19/98-personal-data-points-that-facebook-uses-to-target-ads-to-you/?noredirect=on&utm_term=.ef9d03e2b1a6.
10. Garside, J., "Twitter Puts Trillions of Tweets Up for Sale to Data Miners," *The Guardian*, March 18, 2015, https://www.theguardian.com/technology/2015/mar/18/twitter-puts-trillions-tweets-for-sale-data-miners.
11. Haselton, T., "How to Find Out What Google Knows about You and Limit the Data It Collects," Tech Guide, 2017, https://www.cnbc.com/2017/11/20/what-does-google-know-about-me.html.
12. Klosterman, C., "Can Data Be Evil?," *New York Times Magazine*, January 3, 2014, https://www.nytimes.com/2014/01/05/magazine/can-data-be-evil.html.
13. Cohen, B., "The Ethics of Using Medical Data from Nazi Experiments." *Journal of Halacha and Contemporary Society* (1990): 103.
14. US Centers for Disease Control. "U.S. Public Health Service Syphilis Study at Tuskegee," CDC 24/7: Saving Lives, Protecting People, February 22, 2017, https://www.cdc.gov/tuskegee/index.html.
15. Milgram, S., "Behavioral Study of Obedience." *The Journal of Abnormal and Social Psychology*, 67(4; 1963): 371.

16. Romm, C., "Rethinking One of Psychology's Most Infamous Experiments," *The Atlantic*, January 28, 2015, https://www.theatlantic.com/health/archive/2015/01/rethinking-one-of-psychologys-most-infamous-experiments/384913/.
17. Dewey, R.A., "Psychology: An Introduction," 2017, http://www.intropsych.com.
18. Kramer, A.D., J.E. Guillory, and J.T. Hancock, "Experimental Evidence of Massive-Scale Emotional Contagion through Social Networks." *Proceedings of the National Academy of Sciences*, 111(24; 2014): 8788–90.
19. Metcalf, J., E.F. Keller, and D. Boyd, *Perspectives on Big Data, Ethics, and Society*. Council for Big Data, Ethics, and Society, 2016.
20. Goel, V., "Facebook Tinkers with Users' Emotions in News Feed Experiment, Stirring Outcry," *New York Times*, June 29, 2014, https://www.nytimes.com/2014/06/30/technology/facebook-tinkers-with-users-emotions-in-news-feed-experiment-stirring-outcry.html.
21. Metcalf, J., and K. Crawford, "Where Are Human Subjects in Big Data Research? The Emerging Ethics Divide." *Big Data & Society*, 3(1; 2016): 1–14.
22. Faden, R.R., and T.L. Beauchamp, *A History and Theory of Informed Consent*. Oxford, UK: Oxford University Press, 1986.
23. Rosenberg, M., N. Confessore, and C. Cadwalladr, "How Trump Consultants Exploited the Facebook Data of Millions," *New York Times*, March 17, 2018, https://www.nytimes.com/2018/03/17/us/politics/cambridge-analytica-trump-campaign.html.
24. Petrone, P., "CEO Revokes Offer after Candidate Asks the Internet If He Should Take the Job," Talent Blog, LinkedIn, May 12, 2015, https://business.linkedin.com/talent-solutions/blog/2015/05/ceo-revokes-offer-after-candidate-asks-the-internet-if-he-should-take-the-job.
25. Schmidt, S., "Harvard Withdraws 10 Acceptances for 'Offensive' Memes in Private Group Chat," *Washington Post*, June 5, 2017, https://www.washingtonpost.com/news/morning-mix/wp/2017/06/05/harvard-withdraws-10-acceptances-for-offensive-memes-in-private-chat/?utm_term=.cae468784cd8.
26. Connington, J., "Whiplash Fraudster Caught When He Tweeted about His Running Prowess," *The Telegraph*, July 1, 2016, https://www.telegraph.co.uk/insurance/car/whiplash-fraudster-caught-when-he-tweeted-about-his-running-prow/.
27. Hickey, S., "Insurance Cheats Discover Social Media Is the Real Pain in the Neck," *The Guardian*, July 18, 2016, https://www.theguardian.com/money/2016/jul/18/insurance-cheats-social-media-whiplash-false-claimants.
28. Bersin, J., "The 9 Hottest Trends in Corporate Recruiting," Forbes, July 4 ,2013, https://www.forbes.com/sites/joshbersin/2013/07/04/the-9-hottest-trends-in-corporate-recruiting/#6847180492b0.
29. Schwartz, H.A., et al., "Personality, Gender, and Age in the Language of Social Media: The Open-Vocabulary Approach." *PloS one*, 8(9; 2013): e73791.
30. Barrick, M.R., and M.K. Mount, "The Big Five Personality Dimensions and Job Performance: A Meta-Analysis." *Personnel Psychology*, 44(1; 1991): 1–26.
31. Ferris, G.R., L.A. Witt, and W.A. Hochwarter, "Interaction of Social Skill and General Mental Ability on Job Performance and Salary." *Journal of Applied Psychology*, 86(6; 2001): 1075.
32. Ramasastry, A., "Will Insurers Begin to Use Social Media Postings to Calculate Premiums? A Look at Some Startling Trends and the Possible Consequences for Consumers," in Verdict, Justia, January 3, 2012, https://verdict.justia.com/2012/01/03/will-insurers-begin-to-use-social-media-postings-to-calculate-premiums.
33. PatientsLikeMe, March 1, 2016, https://www.patientslikeme.com/.
34. Angwin, J., N. Scheiber, and A. Tobin, "Dozens of Companies Are Using Facebook to Exclude Older Workers from Job Ads," in Machine Bias, December 20, 2017, https://www.propublica.org/article/facebook-ads-age-discrimination-targeting.

35. Angwin, J., A. Tobin, and M. Varner, "Facebook (Still) Letting Housing Advertisers Exclude Users by Race," Machine Bias, November 21, 2017, https://www.propublica.org/article/facebook-advertising-discrimination-housing-race-sex-national-origin.
36. Abbasi, A., S. Sarker, and R.H. Chiang, "Big Data Research in Information Systems: Toward an Inclusive Research Agenda." *Journal of the Association for Information Systems*, 17(2; 2016).
37. Mezrich, B., "Why I Believe in UFOs, and You Should Too . . . ," presented at the TED Conference, New York, 2016.
38. Matthews, R., "Storks Deliver Babies (p = 0.008)." *Teaching Statistics*, 22(2; 2000): 36–38.
39. Haandrikman, K., and L.J. Van Wissen, "Effects of the Fertility Transition on Birth Seasonality in the Netherlands." *Journal of Biosocial Science*, 40(5; 2008): 655–72.
40. Zalakeuicius, M., "Global Climate Change, Bird Migration and Bird Strike Problems." *International Bird Strike Committee*, IBSC25/WP-RS10 (2000): 509–25.
41. Vigen, T., *Spurious Correlations: Correlation Does Not Equal Causation*. New York: Hachette Books, 2015.
42. Matteson, M., and C. Metivier, *Business Ethics*. Greensboro, NC: University of North Carolina, 2018.
43. Sandberg, E., "Social Networking: Your Key to Easy Credit?," Credit Card News, January 13, 2010, https://www.creditcards.com/credit-card-news/social-networking-social-graphs-credit-1282.php.
44. MacCaskill, E., and G. Dance, "NSA Files: Decoded," *The Guardian*, November 1, 2013, https://www.theguardian.com/world/interactive/2013/nov/01/snowden-nsa-files-surveillance-revelations-decoded#section/1.
45. Kirby, E.J. "Iceland's DNA: The World's Most Precious Genes?," BBC, 2014, http://www.bbc.com/news/magazine-27903831.
46. Wilbanks, J.T., and E.J. Topol, "Stop the Privatization of Health Data." *Nature*, 535(7612; 2016).
47. Buytendijk, F., and J. Heiser, "Confronting the Privacy and Ethical Risks of Big Data," *Financial Times*, September 24, 2013, https://www.ft.com/content/105e30a4-2549-11e3-b349-00144feab7de.
48. Angwin, J., et al., "Machine Bias," Machine Bias, May 23, 2016, https://www.propublica.org/article/machine-bias-risk-assessments-in-criminal-sentencing.

PART V

Appendices

APPENDIX A

Introduction to R

R, the "free software environment for statistical computing and graphics" [1], is the analyst's go-to alternative to the more established SAS and IBM's SPSS Modeler. In fact, an analysis of analytics jobs posted on recruiting site, Indeed.com, in 2014 found that demand for R skills already had exceeded demand for SPSS skills [2]. The study further projected that demand for R skills would exceed demand for SAS skills within less than two years.

Learning Objectives

The purpose of this appendix is to introduce you to R and RStudio, and to basic statistical analysis with R. The chapter covers R commands required to:

1. interface with R;
2. understand and work with R data objects and structures;
3. work with dates;
4. load data from external files and other data sources;
5. reorganize and restructure data;
6. export data and outputs from R;
7. perform rudimentary R programming;
8. manage memory and outputs; and
9. get help.

Developed by two statistics professors at the University of Auckland, its academic origins and open source model have ensured R's creative vitality. Researchers across the world implement analytic procedures to analyze phenomena they theorize. About 20% of the code for these procedures is written in the R language itself (yes, R is also a programming language), 50% in C, and 30% in Fortran [3]. To enable other researchers to analyze the phenomenon too, they then "package" these analytic procedures. A ***package*** is a collection "of **R** functions, data, and compiled code in a well-defined format" [4]. Packages are analogous to SAS Procs, but frequently exceed the scope of a Proc. For example, the R *Hmisc* package accomplishes much the same tasks as the SAS Proc Means, but also will provide postregression diagnostics. The power of R lies in the multitude of these packages, which begin as obscure analytic procedures, and then get honed into analytic routines of value to the corporate world. Such is the history of the social network, and text analysis and mining packages we will use in this book. These R packages offer advanced social analytics functionality still under development in competing products.

Legitimacy for using R in the corporate world has been growing steadily. In 2007, Revolution Software was founded. The company aimed to popularize and support R in the corporate world as RedHat did for Linux many years ago. While R initially was handicapped by its ability to process only data sets that fit in main memory, Revolution's 2010 release of ScaleR overcame this limitation [5], enabling it to take advantage of Hadoop and MapReduce [6]. In September 2013, big data giant, Teradata, partnered with Revolution Software to deliver in-database R analytics [7]. With Microsoft's January 2015 acquisition of Revolution Software, R acquired instant corporate credibility [8]. Microsoft's January 2016 announcement of the availability of R with Visual Studio (R Tools for Visual Studio or RTVS) further increased the accessibility of R to corporate users [9].

Finally, being open source, R gives analysts the ultimate flexibility. Someone with R skills can elect to use R in a company that uses SAS or SPSS. The reverse, however, is not possible. Someone with SAS or SPSS skills cannot choose to use them in a company that does not subscribe to the software. Being open source also provides the analyst with a wealth of free resources in learning a new package or troubleshooting an analysis problem.

R provides the data management flexibility of a programming language. While superior to the data management options available with conventional statistical packages such as SAS, SPSS, and Stata, this does create some confusion for novice programmers. This appendix will provide an introduction to interfacing with R, to the unique data management approaches R uses, and to the rudiments of programming with R.

Interfacing with R

R is a command-line driven analytics software. This makes R powerful, giving the analyst complete control of their analytic procedures. However, being command-line driven also makes R not very user-friendly. Most R users therefore use a GUI. As of now, the two most popular GUIs are RStudio and RCmdr. Others such as RATTLE, Red-R, Deducer, RKWard, and JGR also are used frequently by data analysts. In this book, we will use ***RStudio***, the look and feel of which is comparable to using RTVS.

Figure A.1 depicts the four panels in the RStudio interface. The top left panel is the ***Scripting*** panel. We use this area to write our R code. To execute one or more lines of code, we select the line(s) and click the Run button at the top right of the panel as depicted in Figure A.1. Alternatively, we can press Ctrl+Enter. Between one session and the next, RStudio will automatically preserve all commands executed in the Scripting panel unless you delete them. This feature is very useful in saving startup time in each session as you perform tasks such as setting your working directory, loading data, and so on. The bottom left (i.e., the ***Console*** panel) displays the commands executed and associated error messages. This mimics what we would see if we were working directly in R. Note that red does *not* necessarily mean an error in R or RStudio (just a poor design choice). Error messages will be preceded by the word "Error" and warnings by the word "Warning." The top right is the ***Global Environment*** panel, which displays variables in our current RStudio session and facilitates data management. The bottom right panel is the ***Input-Output (IO)*** panel, which facilitates file management and will display loaded Packages, Plots, Help, and so on.

We can use R as a ***calculator*** to do simple things such as adding a couple of numbers. For example, *5+7* will produce the output

```
[1] 12
```

The [1] preceding the output of the 5+7 problem indicates the dimension of the output. (More information on output dimensions will be provided later.) We also can use R in a more sophisticated fashion once we get comfortable with its data objects and structures.

Understanding and Working with R Data Objects and Structures

"Everything that exists is an object. Everything that happens is a function call" [10]. R, after all, is a programming language. So it is helpful to understand the different types of objects, especially data types and structures, and operations on those data objects that are available via base R and the various R packages.

Data structures are ways of organizing data into data objects, such that lower-level objects can be combined into a higher-level object. Table A.1 summarizes general purpose R data objects that we will use. (For further details, please see the Github tutorial [11].) In addition to these commonly used objects, we will see special purpose objects such as the graph data object, which is required for SNA and the corpus data object, which is used for text analysis.

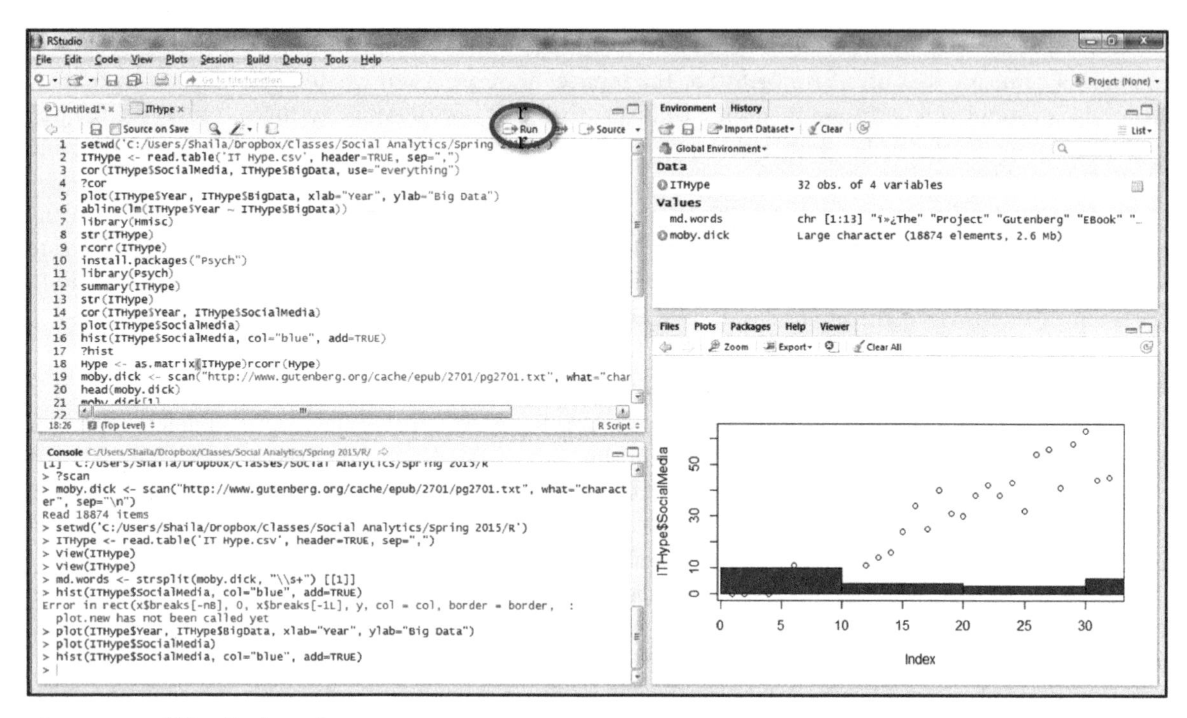

Figure A.1 RStudio Interface

Table A.1 Structuring of Some Basic R Data Objects from Low to High

Object	Description	Types	Examples
Data element	A scalar variable containing a single value	Character	"Shaila," "A sentence"
		Numeric	2, 3.14159
		Integer	2
		Logical	TRUE, FALSE
		Date	"2018-01-16"
Vector	A collection of data elements that are of the same type (atomic vector) or different types (list)	Atomic vector	[1] "Shaila" "Miranda" [1] 3 49 8 56 22
		List	[1] "Shaila" "Miranda" "Fall" 2002
Factor	A special case of a vector that contains categorical data with pre-defined values	Unordered	male, female
		Ordered	low, medium, high
Matrix	A two-dimensional data object with elements of the same data type, typically numeric	—	correlation matrix, distance matrix
Array	A multidimensional data object with elements of the same data type	—	Figure A.2a
Data Frame	A table or two-dimensional data object in which the elements may be of different data types	—	Figure A.2b, Figure A.3, Figure A.7

The smallest general-purpose data object is a variable (i.e., a single piece of data such as the number 5 or my name). As with other programming languages, assigning values to variables (e.g., `x=5` or `x<-5` or `MyName<-'Shaila'`) makes them available for extended processing.

We also can create a vector of atomic values. A vector may be visualized as a row or column of data. We would use the concatenate ***c(Value1, Value2, …)*** function to do so. For example, we could create `a<-c(1,3,5,7,9)` as a vector of odd numbers and `b<-c(0,2,4,6,8)` as a vector of even numbers. Then setting `c<-a+b` would yield a vector, named c, containing values 1, 5, 9, 13, 17 (the solution of 1+0, 3+2, 5+4, 7+6, and 9+8).

The matrix data object typically is used by R in computations. This is a two-dimensional data object and its data elements usually are numeric, but may be character or logical. Some matrix examples we shall encounter are correlation and distance matrices.

R Assignment Notation

R uses the distinctive assignment notation of "<–" instead of the more conventional notation of "=". While *x<–5* and *x=5* both assign the value of 5 to the variable x, the "<–" and "=" notations are not always equivalent. For example, *median(x=1:10)* and *median(x<–1:10)* produce the same result of 5.5. But the latter command also creates a vector named x with 10 integer values, while the former only supplies the result. In this case, choosing between = versus <– should depends on whether we wish the underlying data structure stored for further operations or simply wish the output displayed.

The array is a multidimensional data object, elements of which must be of the same data type. We can combine two vectors into an array using the ***cbind(Vector1, Vector2, …)*** function. For example, we create two vectors, `Universities<-c('UGA', 'FAU', 'Columbia')` and `StartDates<-c(1985,1991,1998)`, and combine them using `History<-cbind(Universities, StartDates)`. This produces the array depicted in Figure A.2a. Notice that R converted all data, including the start dates, to a character data type. In the presence of multiple data types in an array, numeric or logical data is coerced to a character data type.

Alternatively, we can combine the two vectors using the ***data.frame(Vector1, Vector2, …)*** function. This function allows for different data types across dimensions of the resulting data object. For example, `History<-data.frame(Universities,StartDates)` produces the output in Figure A.2b. Notice that StartDates now is a numeric data type. The Universities data type appears to be character, but in fact is a factor data type. This means that R will now expect values of Universities to be one of the current three—UGA, FAU, or Columbia. We can confirm this using `History$Universities`. This produces the following output:

```
[1] UGA       FAU       Columbia
Levels: Columbia FAU UGA
```

The "Levels: Columbia FAU UGA" tell us that Universities is a factor (i.e., categorical) variable and has exactly three possible levels or values. To allow Universities to be a more flexible character data type, we add the "stringsAsFactors=F" argument (i.e., `History<-data.frame(Universities,StartDates, stringsAsFactors=F))`.

We can reference any portion of an array or data frame using ***ArrayOrDataFrameName[Row#, Col#]***. For example, `History[1,2]` produces the following output if History is an array:

```
     Universities StartDates
[1,] "UGA"        "1985"
[2,] "FAU"        "1991"
[3,] "Columbia"   "1998"
```

(a) Array

```
  Universities StartDates
1          UGA       1985
2          FAU       1991
3     Columbia       1998
```

(b) Data Frame

Figure A.2 Combining Vectors

```
StartDates
    "1985"
```

and `[1] 1985` if it is a data frame.

A data frame is simply a named location in primary storage (main memory, similar to a SQL Server "cursor"). This will be the foundational data structure for our analytics tasks. Later, we will look at importing data into a data frame. We can assign or change column names with the ***colnames(DataFrame)*** function. For example, `colnames(History) = c('University', 'Start Date')` relabels the column headers of our History data frame.

The ***rbind(DataFrame1, DataFrame2, . . .)*** function combines data frames, vectors, or matrices horizontally. We can use the rbind() function to add data to our History data frame. Using `History=rbind(History, c('OU', 2002))` produces the output below when we invoke `History`:

```
  University Start Date
1        UGA       1985
2        FAU       1991
3   Columbia       1998
4         OU       2002
```

If we don't want to continually reference a data frame by name when we use one or more of its columns, we can attach the data frame to R's search path using ***attach(DataFrame)*** (e.g., `attach(History)`). Thereafter, we can invoke the columns from the History data frame using just the column names. For example, `University` will produce

```
[1] "UGA"      "FAU"      "Columbia" "OU"
```

Note if we add columns to our data frame, we must rerun our attach() statement for R to recognize the columns without the data frame prefix.

I have another data frame called Roles. This indicates whether I was a student or faculty at each of the universities in my history (created using `Roles=data.frame(University= c('UGA', 'Columbia', 'FAU', 'OU'), Role=c('Student', 'Student', 'Faculty', 'Faculty'), stringsAsFactors=F)`). Now, we want to combine History and Roles into such a way that they line up based on the University column (implementing a basic relational database join). We can do this with the ***merge(DataFrame1, DataFrame2, by.x=ColumnFromDF1, by.y=MatchingColumnFromDF2)*** command. For example, using

```
AcademicHistory=merge(History, Roles, by.x='University', by.y='University')
```

produces the output depicted in Figure A.3. (When working with tables from relational databases, COLUMNFROMDF1 would be the primary key from the first data frame and the MATCHINGCOLUMNFROMDF2 would be the foreign key located in the second data frame.)

When we are done with it, we may want to unload a data object from memory to free up memory. Of course, this happens by default when we exit R. But should we have some data sets we want to clear, we can use the ***rm(DataObject)*** command. For example, we can use `rm(History)`, `rm(Roles)`, and `rm(AcademicHistory)` to unload the three data frames we created earlier. We see that the data no longer shows up in the Global Environment panel. We also can use the Global Environment panel to manage our data, including data imports and exports as shown in Figure A.4.

R provides a series of "as" functions that enable us to convert one data type to another. Some we will encounter are ***as.Date(CharacterString)***, ***as.numeric(NumberStoredAsCharacter)***, ***as.matrix(Table)***, and ***as.data.frame(Table)***, which convert incoming data to dates, numbers, matrix, and data frame objects, respectively.

	University	Start Date	Role
1	Columbia	1998	Student
2	FAU	1991	Faculty
3	OU	2002	Faculty
4	UGA	1985	Student

Figure A.3 Result of Merged AcademicHistory Data Frames

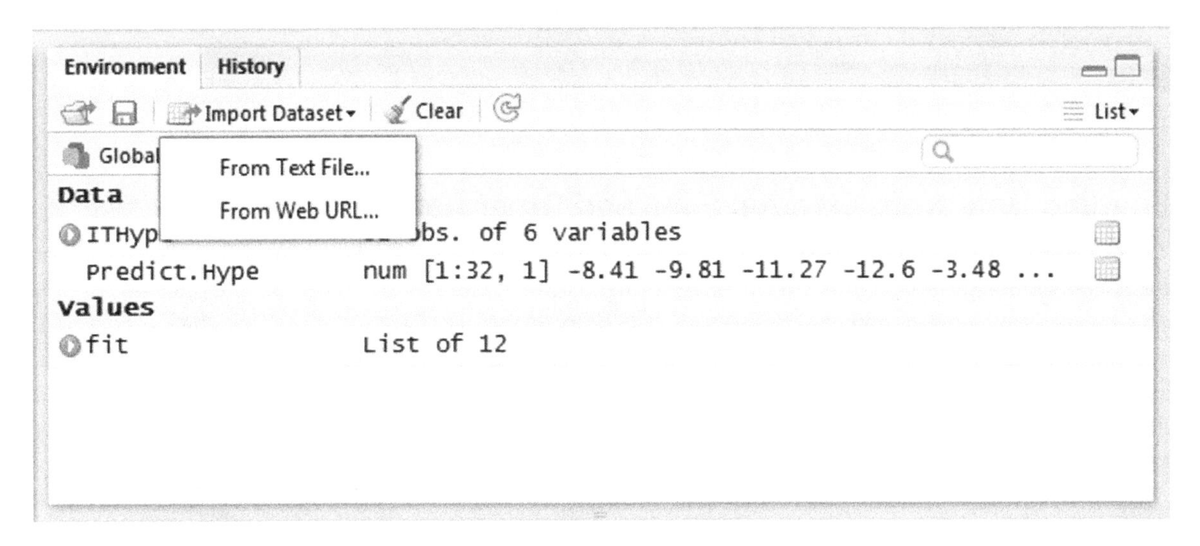

Figure A.4 Data Imports through the Global Environment Panel

Note that not all data types can be coerced to every other data type. R will notify us when we attempt an illegal type conversion.

Working with Dates

Working with dates in R is simple once we understand how R likes dates formatted. We specify an input is a date using the ***as.Date('DateValue')*** function. For example, we can set a semester start date using `SemesterStart=as.Date('2018/01/16')`. Here, our date part separator is a "/". The "-" also is a valid separator. If, however, our date is not formatted as year, month, day, or we have different separators, we need to add a '%DateFormat' argument to our as.Date() function. Let's say our input data was in this hinky format: '01&16&2018'. By specifying the ordering of the month, day, and year date parts, and the date part separator in the '%DateFormat' argument, we can have R read the date accurately: `SemesterStart= as.Date('01&16&2018','%m&%d&%Y')`. Symbols for valid date parts are provided in Table A.2.

To extract a date part, we use the ***format(DateField, '%DatePart')*** function. For example, `format(SemesterStart,'%Y')` extracts the year. Table A.1 provides the symbols for extracting the different date parts and sample outputs corresponding to the input date of 2018-01-16. We can stack date parts as needed. For example, `format(SemesterStart,'%A, %B %d, %Y')` will produce Tuesday, January 16, 2018.

Table A.2 Inputting/Extracting Date Parts

Symbol	Part Information	Input or Output	Sample Output
%Y	Four-digit year	Input and output	2018
%y	Two-digit year	Input and output	18
%m	Month number	Input and output	04
%d	Day number	Input and output	16
%b	Abbreviated month name	Input and output	Jan
%B	Unabbreviated month name	Input and output	January
%a	Abbreviated weekday name	Output only	Tue
%A	Unabbreviated weekday name	Output only	Tuesday

Loading Data from External Files and Other Data Sources

The first thing we typically need to do is to load data. If the files you want to work with are on your local machine, the easiest way to access them is to first set your working directory via the ***setwd(PATH)*** command, and then reference the files by name. For example, I use `setwd('C:/Users/Shaila/Classes/Social Analytics/R')`.

An easy way to obtain your path is to open up the folder in Explorer and copy the path from the path bar at the top. Be sure to replace the back slashes with forward slashes when you do so. You also can check your default directory with the following command: ***getwd()***. Alternatively, as in Figure A.5, we can use the Files tab of the bottom right panel of RStudio to manage our files.

R permits us to work with diverse file types and files from diverse sources. To read data from a tabular file, we can use the ***read.table('FILENAME.EXT')***. Alternatively, we can load data from the clipboard using ***read.table('clipboard')***. For example, `read.table('myfile.txt')` will read the contents of the text file named *myfile*, with the *.txt* extension into the data frame named *MyTable*. The read.table() assumes columns are separated by spaces. If they are not, we would need to add a "sep=" argument—for example, `MyTable=read.table('myfile.txt', sep=';')` lets R know that columns are separated by colons. By default, R assumes that the table has no header and is delimited by any white space. If your data file contains variable names in the first row, use the "header=TRUE" (or "header=T") argument, to let R know (e.g., `MyTable=read.table('myfile.txt', header=TRUE))`. Note that if you see the following warning, "**incomplete final line found by readTableHeader on . . .** ," it is because your text data file must end with a hard return.

The ***read.csv('FILENAME.CSV')*** command permits us to use data from a comma-separated values file. The "sep" argument specifies the character separating the columns (e.g., `read.table('MyFile.csv', header=T, sep=','))`. If you don't get the number of columns you are expecting, check the separator character in your data set against the separator you are indicating in your code. **Remember R is case sensitive. So "true" is not the same as "TRUE" and will yield an error.**

R also permits us to read in data from a website by referencing the URL in the ***read.table('URL')*** or ***read.csv('URL')*** function. In addition to data formatted as tables, we can load and use data formatted as text. To do so, we use the ***scan('URL')*** command.

When loading data from a file, we should direct it to a ***data frame*** so that it is available for further use in our R session. To do so, we use ***DATAFRAMENAME=read.table('FILENAME.EXT')*** or ***DATAFRAMENAME=read.csv('FILENAME.CSV')*** or ***DATAFRAMENAME=scan('URL')***. For example, we can import American Express's (Ticker: AXP) historic stock price data going back to June 1, 1972, with the following command:

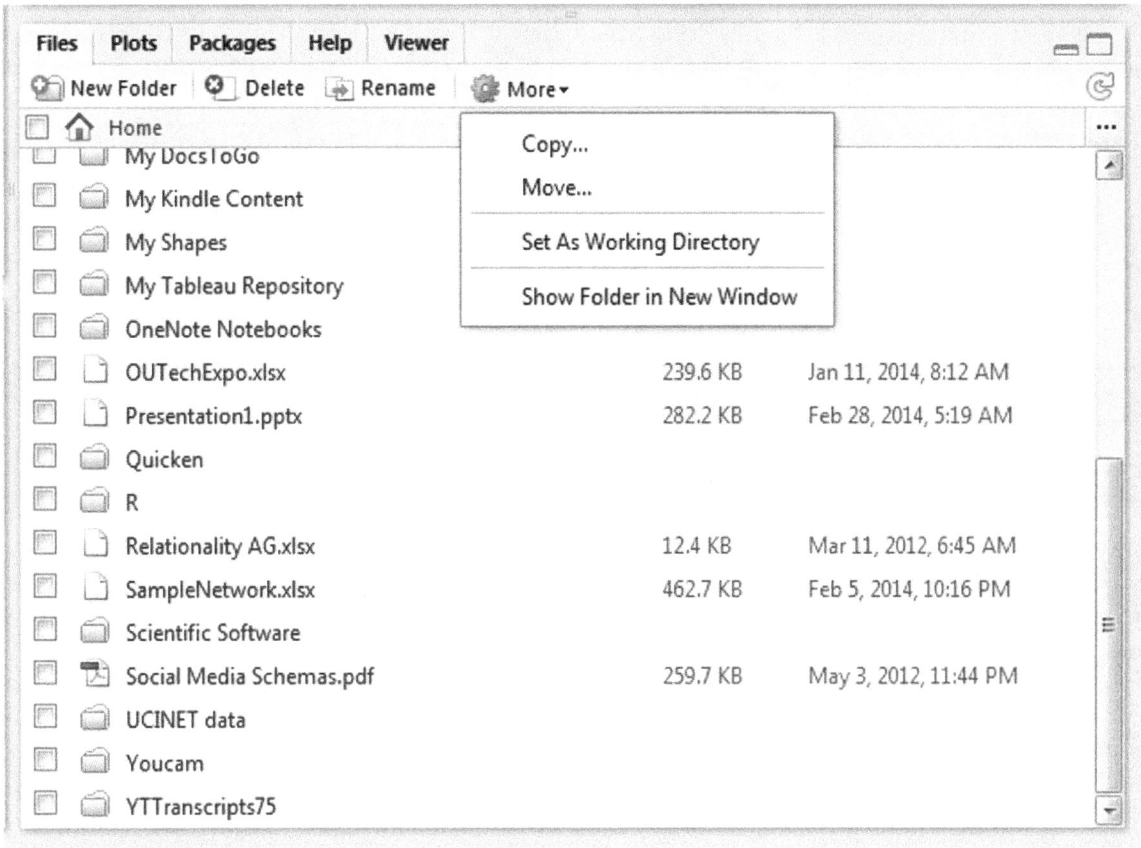

Figure A.5 Using the GUI to Manage Files

```
StockPrices=read.csv('AXP.csv',header=T)
```

Or, we can import the text of the novel Moby Dick from the Gutenberg Project repository.

```
Moby.Dick = scan('http://www.gutenberg.org/files/2701/2701-0.txt', what='character',
     sep='\n')      #separated by new lines
```

We can use the variable assignment operator "<-" instead of "=" to load the file data into the data frame. Once loaded into a data frame, we reference the data set by the data frame name.

When we set a variable equal to something, if all goes well, R does not provide any feedback. In RStudio, we can view a data table by clicking on the name in the Global Environment panel. This opens the data in a new tab in the top left panel as in Figure A.6, which displays the stock prices for American Express. On large data sets, the panel will display only the first thousand rows, but will let you know the total number of rows in the data set.

Alternatively, to see the data we just loaded, we can call the variable or data frame directly. For example, *StockPrices* will display the contents of the data from the StockPrices data frame in the Console. Since this is a bit long, we can request just the top six rows via the ***head(DataFrame)*** command (e.g., `head(StockPrices)` or `head(Moby.Dick)`). Or we can inspect the bottom six rows via the ***tail(DataFrame)*** command. Adding an "n=" argument permits us to specify the number of rows to be displayed. For example, `tail(StockPrices, n=10)` will display the last ten rows of the StockPrices data frame.

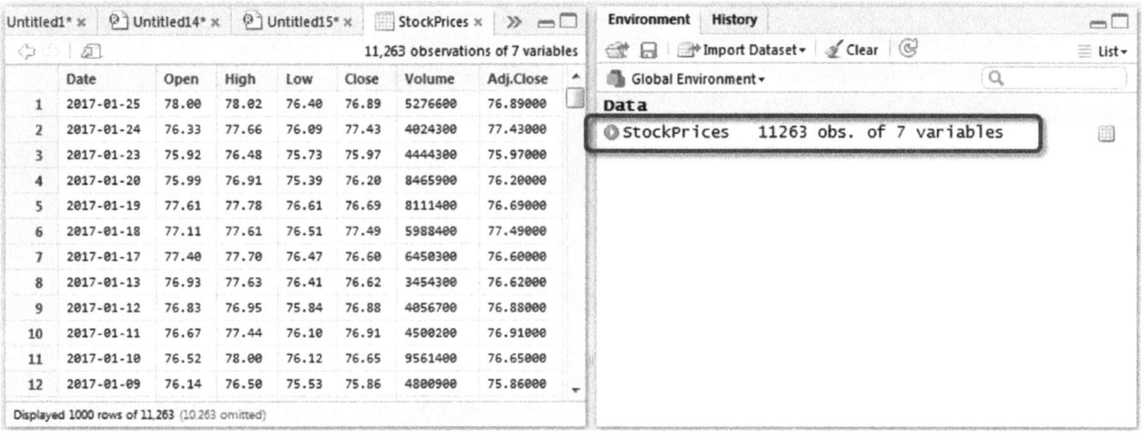

Untitled1* × | Untitled14* × | Untitled15* × | StockPrices ×

11,263 observations of 7 variables

	Date	Open	High	Low	Close	Volume	Adj.Close
1	2017-01-25	78.00	78.02	76.40	76.89	5276600	76.89000
2	2017-01-24	76.33	77.66	76.09	77.43	4024300	77.43000
3	2017-01-23	75.92	76.48	75.73	75.97	4444300	75.97000
4	2017-01-20	75.99	76.91	75.39	76.20	8465900	76.20000
5	2017-01-19	77.61	77.78	76.61	76.69	8111400	76.69000
6	2017-01-18	77.11	77.61	76.51	77.49	5988400	77.49000
7	2017-01-17	77.40	77.70	76.47	76.60	6450300	76.60000
8	2017-01-13	76.93	77.63	76.41	76.62	3454300	76.62000
9	2017-01-12	76.83	76.95	75.84	76.88	4056700	76.88000
10	2017-01-11	76.67	77.44	76.10	76.91	4500200	76.91000
11	2017-01-10	76.52	78.00	76.12	76.65	9561400	76.65000
12	2017-01-09	76.14	76.50	75.53	75.86	4800900	75.86000

Displayed 1000 rows of 11,263 (10,263 omitted)

Environment | History

Import Dataset ▾ | Clear | List ▾

Global Environment ▾

Data

StockPrices 11263 obs. of 7 variables

Figure A.6 Inspecting Loaded Data

We can view attribute (column) names with the ***names(DataFrame)*** command. For example, `names(StockPrices)` will list all attributes of the StockPrices data frame. Or we can get more extensive descriptions of our data with the ***str(DataFrame)*** and ***attributes(DataFrame)*** commands.

We also can use the ***fix(DataFrame)*** command to view our data in a new window (e.g., `fix (StockPrices))`. Unlike interfacing with our data through the Global Environment panel, which permits us to inspect only data frame objects, the fix() command permits us to inspect any of the data objects loaded, including Moby.Dick, and **to edit** them. We must close this data window before doing anything else with R, though.

Exporting Data and Outputs from R

We can export data to a text file with the ***write.table(DataFrame, file=FileName)*** command. For example, the statement

```
write.table(StockPrices,file='stockprices.txt', quote=FALSE, sep=' ')
```

saved with our stock price data to a text file. The "quote=FALSE" lets R know that quotes are not to be output with the data; "sep=' '" stipulates that the values for the different columns are to be separated by a space.

We can write to a csv file with the ***write.csv(DataFrame, file=FileName)*** command. The statement

```
write.csv(StockPrices,file='stockprices.csv', quote=TRUE)
```

outputs our predicted data to a stockprices.csv file, putting quotes around each data value. Note we do not use the "sep" argument with write.csv because csv files are necessarily comma-separated. If used, R simply ignores the argument.

Finally, we can send some output to a PDF file. We do so simply by bracketing commands to produce the output between ***pdf('File.pdf')*** and ***dev.off()***. Note that **this can be only output that we would see in the RStudio IO panel, not the output sent to the console panel.** Typically this output is limited to graphics. We will see examples of this in Appendix B.

Tutorial A.1. Working with Data Files

In this tutorial, we will work with the two files depicted in Figure A.7. The first of these, Bankruptcies.csv, contains four columns of variables—Year, State, Bankruptcies, and Population—and twenty-five rows of observations. The second, Landlocked.csv, contains two columns of variables—State and Landlocked—and five rows.

	Year	State	Bankruptcies	Population
1	2014	Alabama	25245	4849377
2	2013	Alabama	27272	4833996
3	2012	Alabama	28194	4817484
4	2011	Alabama	30379	4801695
5	2010	Alabama	34152	4785822
6	2014	Alaska	456	736732
7	2013	Alaska	593	737259
8	2012	Alaska	753	731081
9	2011	Alaska	999	722572
10	2010	Alaska	1112	713856
11	2014	Arizona	19897	6731484
12	2013	Arizona	23377	6634997
13	2012	Arizona	28497	6556236
14	2011	Arizona	36550	6472867
15	2010	Arizona	42818	6411999
16	2014	Arkansas	11231	2966369
17	2013	Arkansas	12242	2958765
18	2012	Arkansas	12915	2949300
19	2011	Arkansas	14601	2938430
20	2010	Arkansas	16500	2922297
21	2014	California	103362	38802500
22	2013	California	136426	38431393
23	2012	California	187255	38062780
24	2011	California	213861	37701901
25	2010	California	260073	37336011

A. State Bankruptcies

	State	LandLocked
1	Alabama	TRUE
2	Alaska	FALSE
3	Arizona	TRUE
4	Arkansas	TRUE
5	California	FALSE

B. State Topology

Figure A.7 Two Sample Data Frames

Start by setting your working directory using **setwd**('PathToRTutorialFiles'). We can read our two files into two data frames we will use in our R session with

```
Bankruptcies<-read.csv('Bankruptcies.csv', header=T)
LandLocked<-read.csv('Landlocked.csv', header=T)
```

We now can reference individual columns as Bankruptcies$Population and LandLocked$State. But let's use

```
attach(Bankruptcies)
attach(LandLocked)
```

so we can bypass having to reference the data frames and simply inspect the columns with *Population* and *State*. To use these data tables together, we will need to "join" them into a single data frame. To do so, we use

```
StateData=merge(Bankruptcies, LandLocked, by.x='State', by.y='State')
```

	State	Year	Bankruptcies	Population	LandLocked	BkrptPer100
1	Alabama	2014	25245	4849377	TRUE	0.52058233
2	Alabama	2013	27272	4833996	TRUE	0.56417093
3	Alabama	2012	28194	4817484	TRUE	0.58524325
4	Alabama	2011	30379	4801695	TRUE	0.63267242
5	Alabama	2010	34152	4785822	TRUE	0.71360782
6	Alaska	2014	456	736732	FALSE	0.06189496
7	Alaska	2013	593	737259	FALSE	0.08043306
8	Alaska	2012	753	731081	FALSE	0.10299816
9	Alaska	2011	999	722572	FALSE	0.13825612
10	Alaska	2010	1112	713856	FALSE	0.15577371
11	Arizona	2014	19897	6731484	TRUE	0.29558118
12	Arizona	2013	23377	6634997	TRUE	0.35232872
13	Arizona	2012	28497	6556236	TRUE	0.43465488
14	Arizona	2011	36550	6472867	TRUE	0.56466478
15	Arizona	2010	42818	6411999	TRUE	0.66777927
16	Arkansas	2014	11231	2966369	TRUE	0.37861102
17	Arkansas	2013	12242	2958765	TRUE	0.41375371
18	Arkansas	2012	12915	2949300	TRUE	0.43790052
19	Arkansas	2011	14601	2938430	TRUE	0.49689800
20	Arkansas	2010	16500	2922297	TRUE	0.56462433
21	California	2014	103362	38802500	FALSE	0.26637974
22	California	2013	136426	38431393	FALSE	0.35498583
23	California	2012	187255	38062780	FALSE	0.49196354
24	California	2011	213861	37701901	FALSE	0.56724195
25	California	2010	260073	37336011	FALSE	0.69657415

Figure A.8 Denormalized Data Frame

This produces the denormalized StateData data frame in Figure A.8. (A denormalized data set is one contain data redundancies, but is easier to search. Denormalized data can engender storage problems, but is essential for analysis.) We can calculate the bankruptcies per one hundred members of the population using

```
StateData$BkrptPer100=StateData$Bankruptcies/StateData$Population*100.
```

We want to save this denormalized data as a csv file for future use. To do so, we run

```
write.csv(StateData,file='StateBankruptcies.csv', quote=FALSE)
```

We now can determine whether there is a difference in the bankruptcy rate in landlocked versus coastal states. We find the mean difference with

```
aggregate(StateData$BkrptPer100, by=list(StateData$LandLocked), FUN=mean)
```

The following output tells us that landlocked states do have a higher bankruptcy rate than states that are not landlocked.

```
  Group.1         x
1   FALSE 0.2916501
2    TRUE 0.5082049
```

We can determine whether or not this mean difference is significant with

```
t.test(StateData$BkrptPer100 ~ StateData$LandLocked)
```

More on tests of significance in Appendix B, but a t-statistic of 2.777 and a p-value of 0.01623 tells us that the possibility that the difference in bankruptcy rates for landlocked and nonlandlocked states that we see occurs purely by chance is less than 2%, which is pretty low.

```
        Welch Two Sample t-test


data:  StateData$BkrptPer100 by StateData$LandLocked
t = -2.777, df = 12.467, p-value = 0.01623
alternative hypothesis: true difference in means is not equal to 0
95 percent confidence interval:
 -0.38575718 -0.04735233
sample estimates:
mean in group FALSE  mean in group TRUE
          0.2916501           0.5082049
```

Performing Rudimentary R Programming

Using available packages enables us to use R without being too aware of the fact that R is a programming language. So, programming expertise is not required in order to use R effectively for analytics. As you get familiar with R, some programming knowledge can move you quickly from journeyman R user to expert. Because R is command-line driven, understanding a little about R programming also may clarify and contextualize the way R handles analytics tasks. We therefore will take a brief digression through R as a programming language. If the idea terrifies you, feel free to skim past this section for now.

A foundational programming concept is the variable. A ***variable*** is a named storage location. As with any programming language, we assign values to a variable with the "=" operator. An ***operator*** tells the computer what to do with one or more variables, specifically which computational, comparative, or logical tasks to perform. For example, we can set `x = 5` and `y = 8`. The "=" operator loads data into the named memory location (i.e., sets a variable equal to something). Since you undoubtedly will run into it when Googling some R functionality, the "<-" operator is equivalent to the "=" operator; the two are used interchangeably. We will use such assignment statements for a variety of tasks, including loading data to analyze in R. See the "R Operators" inset for more.

We then can use the ***print(WhatToPrint)*** function to display results of our arithmetic manipulations. For example, **`print`**`(x+y)` will produce the output 13. We also can nest functions. For example, **`print(sum`**`(x, y))` also will produce the output 13. Of course, we can leave off the print() command for the same result, as in **`sum`**`(x , y)`.

Since R is a programming language, we need to be cognizant of programs and control structures. A ***program*** is a set of coded instructions issued to a computer directing it to perform a set of activities necessary to complete a desired task. A ***control structure*** determines the order in which statements in a program are executed, which statements are executed, and how many times the statements are executed. These activities correspond

R Operators

Arithmetic

Operator	Description
+	Addition
-	Subtraction
*	Multiplication
/	Division
^ or **	Exponentiation
x %% y	Modulus (x mod y)
x %/% y	Integer division

Logical

Operator	Description
<	Less than
<=	Less than or equal to
>	Greater than
>=	Greater than or equal to
==	Exactly equal to
!=	Not equal to
!x	Not x
x | y	X OR y
x & y	X AND y
isTRUE(x)	Test if X is TRUE

to the three basic control structures: sequence, selection, and repetition. With the ***sequence*** control structure, statements in a program are executed in the order in which they occur. In other words, we can count on line 1 being executed before line 2, which is executed before line 3. Therefore we need to make sure that tasks required for the completion of line 3 have been handled in lines 1 or 2. A ***selection*** control structure determines whether or not a statement (or batch of statements) is executed based on whether or not a stated condition is met. If the condition is met, a batch or statements may be executed; if they are not met, another batch may be executed or nothing may be done. Also referred to as loops, the ***repetition*** control structure determines the number of times a batch of statements will be executed. The repetition control structure may direct the computer to execute a batch of statements a fixed number of times or while or until a particular condition is met.

Unlike the execution of a sequence control structure, which requires no special commands or keywords, executing a selection or repetition control structure does. In R, we can implement the selection control structure using

if (CONDITION) {FIRSTSTATEMENTBATCH} else {SECONDSTATEMENTBATCH}

For example, the following code displays "x is greater than y" if "x>y" evaluates to be true; otherwise, it displays "y is greater than x." Try it out after having assigned values to x and y. Change the values and re-execute the code.

```
if ( x > y ) {
  print("x is greater than y")
} else {
  print("y is greater than x")
}
```

We implement repetitive control structures or loops using

for (COUNTER in N1:N2) {STATEMENTBATCH}

where COUNTER is a variable, and N1 (typically, but not necessarily, 1) and N2 are numbers that set up the bounds for the number of times the statement batch is to be executed. In the example below, the variable i is our counter, which is permitted to assume values from 1 to 10. For each of these 10 values, we print its square, resulting in the outputted number sequence: 1, 4, 9, 16, 25, 36, 49, 64, 81, 100.

```
for (i in 1:10)
{
  print(i^2)
}
```

Working with Packages

To take advantage of the resources provided by the extensive R open source community, we need to be able to install, load, and inspect packages. Of course, it helps to know what packages are available. A complete list of available R packages is available at the CRAN (comprehensive R archive network) site [12]. Select "Packages" from the menu to the left of that page and select the table in your preferred format. To determine what package will help you accomplish your task, you can either scan the descriptions from this table (I do not recommend this until you are vastly more familiar with R) or Google it (way better). We then can install desired packages with the ***install.packages('PackageName')***. A package needs to be installed only once on a given computer.

Being open source, R packages use other packages, creating daisy chains of dependencies. In other words, package A can depend on packages B, C, and D; package B can depend on E, package C on F and G. Using the "dep=T" argument tells R to automatically install all packages required by the requested package. For the most part, the install.packages() command handles dependencies gracefully—sometimes even without the "dep=T" argument, automatically installing all packages upon which the requested package depends. **Sometimes we may experience a glitch in this installation process and receive a message telling us that R was unable to install some required package.** When this happens, first installing that required package using the "dep=T" and then rerunning our command to install the original package should fix the problem, though we may have to do this for more than one package on which the requested package depends.

We make a package available for use during an R session with ***library('PackageName')***. For example, `library(ggplot2)` will enable us to use the ggplot2 package. Whereas install.packages() needs to be run only once for a computer, we need to run the library() command at each R session; packages do not load automatically by default (though we can set this as a preference if we like).

Sometimes different packages overlap in functionality and cause unexpected behavior when both are loaded simultaneously. If you ever want to remove an existing library, use the ***detach(Package)*** command (e.g., `detach(package:ggplot2)`).

R also permits us to "package" our own code and data sets for use by a wider audience. A data package can contain not only data sets, but also associated documentation, enhancing accessibility to any R user. While creating packages will be beyond the scope of our labs, we will want to use data from packages in the future. When data sets are part of an R package, we can inspect them using ***data(package='PackageName')***. We then can load a specific data set using the ***data(DATA_SET, package='PackageName')***.

Reorganizing and Restructuring Data

We may need to sort our data. We can do so with ***DataFrame [order(Column),]***. For example,

```
StockPrices.Sorted = StockPrices[order(-StockPrices$Volume, -StockPrices$High),]
```

sorts the StockPrices data. Because we preceded the StockPrices$Volume and StockPrices$High variables with a minus sign (-), our data is sorted in descending order. Leave off the minus sign to sort in the default ascending order.

In the big data arena especially, we often need to slice our data sets. We can slice a data set horizontally (by rows) by using ***DataFrame[RowNum,]***. For example, we can obtain the last week's data as

```
Week1.Prices=StockPrices[1:7,]
```

Or we could obtain the top twenty most active trading dates using

```
StockPrices.Top20=StockPrices.Sorted[1:20,]
```

To slice data vertically, we use ***DataFrame[,Col]***. We can reference columns by number or name. For example,

```
StockPrices.HighLow=StockPrices[, 3:4]
```

will extract the two columns containing the daily high and low prices.

```
StockPrices.Volume=StockPrices['Volume']
```

will extract only the Volume column. Alternatively, if we want to display only the dates and the transaction volume columns, we could use

```
StockPrices.Top20=StockPrices.Sorted[1:20, c(1,6)]
```

for the first and sixth columns. Note that when indicating discontinuous columns that require a comma, we have to use the concatenation function—c()—to indicate that all columns reference a single dimension of the data frame.

Finally, we may want to cull a data slice based on whether the data meet a certain condition. To do so, we use the ***subset(DataFrame, Condition1, Condition2, …)*** command. For example, to extract only 2016 stock prices for further analysis, we can use

```
AXP2016=subset(StockPrices, format(as.Date(Date,'%m/%d/%Y'), '%Y')==2016)
```

If we wish to add stock history data for other companies to that StockPrices data frame, we can begin by adding a column indicating the company's stock symbol or ticker. `StockPrices$Tick="AXP"` accomplishes this task. Then, we can append records for the next company we wish to analyze—YUM. In the statement below, the cbind() vertically appends a column to the data frame being created—attaching the ticker of YUM to the YUM stock history records being imported with the Tick="YUM". This ensures that the incoming YUM data set has the same number of columns as the AXP data set, to which we had added the Tick column. The rbind() then horizontally appends the YUM records to the AXP records already in the StockPrices data frame:

```
StockPrices=rbind(StockPrices,cbind(read.csv('YUM.csv'),Tick="YUM"))
```

Alternatively, I could stack the data imports for all the companies of interest into one statement with multiple read.csv() statements as below:

```
StockPrices=rbind(cbind(read.csv('AXP.csv'),Tick='AXP'),
      cbind(read.csv('YUM.csv'),Tick='YUM'))
```

The ***melt(DataFrame, id.var=c(Vars))*** function from the rehape2 package provides further data wrangling capabilities. To access this function, remember to first run **`install.packages('reshape')`** (required only once on a machine) and **`library(reshape)`** (required once per R session). The melt() function then enables us to convert wide-format data into long format. In the code below, we first extract the Open, Close, and Tick columns from the StockPrices data frame and the numerically formatted Month. This results in the data frame pictured in Figure A.9A. We then use melt() to create a single column of opening and closing prices. Finally, we use the colnames() function to relabel the column headers to produce the relabeled, melted data frame pictured in Figure A.9B.

```
StockOpenClose=data.frame(StockPrices[c(2,5,8)], Month=
               as.numeric(format(as.Date(StockPrices$Date,'%m/%d/%Y'),'%m')))
StockOpenClose=melt(StockOpenClose,id.vars=c('Tick','Month'))
colnames(StockOpenClose)=c('Symbol', 'Month', 'TimeOfDay', 'Price')
```

	Open	Close	Tick	Month
1	3.693287	3.693287	AXP	6
2	3.677195	3.677195	AXP	6
3	3.604777	3.604777	AXP	6
4	3.411664	3.411664	AXP	6
5	3.371432	3.371432	AXP	6
		...		
16606	82.69	82.67	YUM	12
16607	82.64	81.61	YUM	12
16608	82.15	81.60	YUM	1
16609	81.23	81.53	YUM	1
16610	81.75	82.36	YUM	1

Showing 16,600 to 16,610 of 16,610 entries

A. Wide-Format Data

	Symbol	Month	TimeOfDay	Price
1	AXP	6	Open	3.693287
2	AXP	6	Open	3.677195
3	AXP	6	Open	3.604777
4	AXP	6	Open	3.411664
5	AXP	6	Open	3.371432
		...		
101	AXP	10	Open	3.926632
102	AXP	10	Open	3.958818
103	AXP	10	Open	3.958818
104	AXP	10	Open	3.958818
105	AXP	10	Open	3.950771
		...		
28111	AXP	1	Close	100.849998
28112	YUM	9	Close	5.234543
28113	YUM	9	Close	5.414270
28114	YUM	9	Close	5.436736
28115	YUM	9	Close	5.391805
		...		
33216	YUM	12	Close	82.67
33217	YUM	12	Close	81.61
33218	YUM	1	Close	81.60
33219	YUM	1	Close	81.53
33220	YUM	1	Close	82.36

Showing 33,210 to 33,220 of 33,220 entries

B: "Melted" Long-Format Data

Figure A.9 Data Wrangling with the melt() Function

Managing Memory and Outputs

As noted in Chapter 1, social media data usually is "big." When dealing with big data, it is useful to be able to allocate computing resources based on the size of the data being analyzed. In preparation for doing so, two things are worth noting about R's approach to memory management. First, R does not use virtual RAM. In other words, R holds all working data in RAM and does not offload any loaded data to secondary storage [13]. Second, R does not automatically use all available memory when running an analytics job. By default, R allots a conservative 2GB of RAM on a 32-bit Windows machine (which cannot be expanded) and 4GB on a 64-bit machine (expandable to 8TB or the amount of RAM available on your machine, whichever is lower). This usually is good because R does not hog memory, constraining performance on other processes running concurrently on your computer. Because of R's conservative memory allocation and use, we first want to ensure that we don't retain data objects unnecessarily in our R session using the rm() command. Even so, we will run into memory constraints with larger data sets.

To determine the amount of memory currently allotted, we use ***memory.size(max=T/F)***. To change the amount of RAM allotted to an R session, we use ***memory.limit(size=INTEGER)***.

By default, R will display up to a thousand rows of output in our Console panel. We can determine our current output limits with ***getOption("max.print")***. Given that we are working with "big" data, the output from our R commands often will exceed this limit. When this happens, we may see messages such as

```
[ reached getOption("max.print") -- omitted xxx rows ]
```

The first thing we can try when this happens is to resize our Console. By increasing its width, R will be able to display more columns of tabular output per row, thereby decreasing the number of rows to be displayed. A second option is to reset the max.print limits using ***options(max.print=INTEGER)***.

Of course, increasing our Console limits may not be particularly useful if the size of our output exceeds the Console's scroll limits (a thousand lines). In this case, we can redirect our output to a text file using ***sink('FILENAME.txt')***. Output of all commands run after this sink() command will appear in the specified text file. Within a session, we can redirect our output to the Console using the sink() command without any arguments (i.e., *sink()*).

Getting Help

If (when) you get confused, a good place to start is with R's built-in help functionality. R offers detailed help files for each function and each package. To figure out what functions and data are available with a package, use ***ls('package: PACKAGENAME')***. For example, `ls('package:ggplot2')` will provide us with a list of the functions and data available with the popular *ggplot2* package. To obtain help on a particular function from this list, type ***?FUNCTION*** in the console. For example, for help on the ***sum(WHATTOSUM)*** function, type `?sum`.

Also, because R is an open source product and widely used, there are rich resources across the Internet to help you learn to use a particular package, accomplish a specific task, or figure out a pesky error message. So start Googling . . .

Works Cited

1. "The R Project for Statistical Computing," 2015, https://www.r-project.org/.
2. Muenchen, R.A., "The Popularity of Data Analysis Software," r4stats, 2014, http://r4stats.com/articles/popularity/.
3. Smith, D., "What Language Is R Written In?," in *Revolutions*. Redmond, WA: Revolution Analytics, 2011.
4. Kabacoff, "R. Packages," Quick-R, 2011, http://www.statmethods.net/interface/packages.html.
5. Rickert, J.B., *Big Data Analysis with Revolution R Enterprise*. Redmond, WA: Revolution Analytics, 2010.
6. Rickert, J.B., *Alpha Testing RevoScaleR Running in Hadoop*. Redmond, WA: Revolution Analytics, 2013.
7. Smith, D., *Revolution Analytics and Teradata Bring R into the Database*. Redmond, WA: Revolution Analytics, 2013.
8. Dinsmore, T.W., "Microsoft Buys Revolution Analytics," *The Big Analytics Blog: News and Analysis on High Performance Analytics*, 2015, https://thomaswdinsmore.com/2015/01/26/microsoft-buys-revolution-analytics/.
9. Sirosh, J., "Making R the Enterprise Standard for Cross-Platform Analytics, Both on Premises and in the Cloud," *Machine Learning Blog*, 2016, https://blogs.technet.microsoft.com/machinelearning/2016/01/12/making-r-the-enterprise-standard-for-cross-platform-analytics-both-on-premises-and-in-the-cloud/.
10. Chambers, J.M., *Interfaces, Efficiency, and Big Data*. Los Angeles: UCLA, 2014.
11. Github, "Data Structures," in Introduction to R, Github, 2016, https://ramnathv.github.io/pycon2014-r/learn/structures.html.
12. CRAN, Contributed Packages, 2017, https://cran.r-project.org/web/packages/.
13. Gorjanc, G., "Memory Limit Management in R," R-bloggers, 2008, https://www.r-bloggers.com/memory-limit-management-in-r/.

APPENDIX B

Statistical Analysis with R

In this appendix, we will review some of the basic data preparation, statistical analysis, and reporting tasks required of an analyst and how we perform them with R. The objective of this appendix is to get sufficiently up to speed so we then can interact knowledgeably with social network and text data. This appendix does not provide an in-depth exposure either to introductory descriptive and inferential statistics. If you have not had a statistics course, I strongly recommend you avail of one of the many free online courses. This appendix does not provide a comprehensive survey of R tools and techniques for conducting such analyses, either. But it will provide you a sufficient familiarity with what is available to permit you to continue learning on your own.

Learning Objectives

The purpose of this appendix is to introduce you to statistical analysis with R. The appendix covers R commands required to:

1. handle missing data;
2. perform simple and conditional computation;
3. install code packages for basic statistical analyses;
4. conduct simple exploratory data analysis;
5. generate graphical displays;
6. perform correlation analysis;
7. run t-tests; and
8. run ANOVAs and OLS regression.

Statistical Analysis Packages

We will use the **data.table**, **aplpack**, **psych**, and **Hmisc** packages. These packages will permit us to run exploratory data analysis. Let us load the data.table, aplpack, psych, and Hmisc with the library() function.

Handling Missing Values

One of the data preparation problems analysts have to deal with is the presence of missing data. Prior to analyzing a data set, it is good to inspect it for the prevalence of missing data. In R, we can request information on the presence of missing values using the ***is.na(DataFrameOrColumn)*** command.

An analyst typically deals with missing values in one of three ways. First, we can ***drop the entire observation*** if the value for one variable is missing. This is the easiest-to-implement, but the most stringent method of handling missing values. In the era of big data, though, this may be a perfectly adequate method since we have some many observations. In R, we then can exclude rows with missing data from our analyses using the ***na.omit(DataFrame)*** or the ***na.exclude(DataFrame)*** command.

Second, we can ***retain portions of the observation for which we do have values*** in our analyses. For example, say we are estimating correlations between the amount individuals spent on a product, their annual income, and educational level, and five individuals declined to provide annual income. While we would not be able to use their data to estimate the correlation between spending and income, we could retain their data for estimating the correlation between spending and educational attainment.

The third method entails ***estimating values for the missing data*** and replacing the missing values with the estimated values. This method is trickiest, but most desirable when our sample size (amount of data available) is small. The simplest approach to estimating missing data is to replace missing values with their **column mean** (i.e., the average value for that variable). However, this approach is liable to deflate coefficients of any correlation or regression analysis involving the estimated variable. The next approach is to replace the missing data with the **column mean, grouped by a categorical variable** in the data set. In using this approach, we must be careful that our choice of categorical—or grouping—variable does not have an inflationary impact on the statistical coefficients we will estimate later. For example, if we are interested in predicting spending amount based on minutes spent by a salesperson, estimating missing spending amounts based on the average minutes spent by the salesperson on all other customers in the data set would yield an inflated estimate of the relationship between spending and salesperson minutes. But estimating missing data for the salesperson's minutes spent based on her average minutes spent with other customers should not inflate our correlation or regression coefficients. Finally, we can estimate missing values with a **multiple regression** (i.e., by regressing the column with missing values on other columns for which we have data). Here, too, we will need to be careful not to bias the results of our future statistical analyses in our choice of predictive variables for our missing data regression model. As we learn how to obtain column means, column means by another categorical variable, and regression coefficients, we will revisit estimating missing values with these statistics.

Performing Simple and Conditional Computations

Often, we will need to create new variables from the data available in our data set. Let's reconsider the example we saw in the last appendix, where we imported stock price history using `StockPrices = read.csv('AXP.csv', header=TRUE)`. To be sure R can read the price dates, we set `StockPrices$Date=as.Date(StockPrices$Date,'%m/%d/%Y')`.

We would like to determine daily price volatility as the difference between the daily high and low prices. First, we run `attach(StockPrices)`, so R knows where to look for columns referenced. Then, we can calculate daily volatility with the following formula:

```
StockPrices$Volatility=High-Low
```

This adds a new Volatility column, containing the difference between High and Low, to our StockPrices data frame. Note that if we left off the data frame reference before the name of the new variable (i.e., just used `Volatility=High-Low`), R would generate a new data object—a vector—containing the computed differences between the daily High and Low stock prices. Preceding the variable name with the data frame name lets R know that we wish the new variable appended to the existing data frame.)

Sometimes we may need our computations or assignment of values to a categorical variable to be contingent on the values of another variable(s) in our data set. We can do so with the ***ifelse(CONDITION,DOTRUE, DOFALSE)*** function. For example, we would like to add a new variable called BadDay, with a value of TRUE if Volatility equals or exceeds the average volatility and FALSE otherwise. Let's begin by rerunning `attach (StockPrices)` to ensure our newly created variable is associated with the data frame in R's memory. Then we can use

```
StockPrices$BadDay=ifelse(Volatility>=mean(Volatility),TRUE,FALSE)
```

We also would like to categorize the financial eras as pre-dotcom, bubble, and dotcom. We can do so using

```
StockPrices$Era=ifelse(format(as.Date(Date),'%Y')<1999,'PreDotCom',
        ifelse(format(as.Date(Date),'%Y')<2002,'Bubble','DotCom'))
```

Conducting Simple Exploratory Data Analysis

One of the first ways in which we would want to describe our data is to see the frequencies with which different values occur. We can use the ***table(COLUMN)*** function to do so. After rerunning `attach(StockPrices)` (because we added new columns to the data frame since we last attached it), we can determine the relative frequency of bad days using

```
table(BadDay)
```

This produces the following output:

```
BadDay
FALSE  TRUE
 7070  4431
```

What information does this convey? Recall that we determined that bad days were those with a volatility at or above the mean. So should we not have roughly an equal number of TRUEs and FALSEs? The fact that we do not suggests that volatility is skewed—in fact, right skewed because of the overabundance of FALSEs. Later, we will graph volatility to inspect the distribution and confirm its skewness. (Note if we need to display this one-way table vertically, we can enclose the table() in a cbind() function, thereby tricking R into displaying the horizontal data frame [i.e., a row] vertically [i.e., as a column].)

The ***table(Column1, Column2)*** function can be used to produce a two-way frequency table. Let's say we want to determine whether we have more bad days (higher volatility) in certain months. First, we need to extract the month from the Date column in the StockPrices data frame, after ensuring that R views the Date column as a date data type. We do so with `StockPrices$Month=format(as.Date(Date), '%b')`. Once again, we need to attach our data frame. We can inspect our data frame to confirm we have this new column. Then, `table(Month, BadDay)` produces the following output:

```
Month FALSE TRUE
  Apr   556  373
  Aug   646  374
  Dec   612  358
  Feb   529  334
  Jan   579  360
  Jul   581  389
  Jun   600  385
  Mar   605  380
  May   582  370
  Nov   583  354
  Oct   608  409
  Sep   589  345
```

From this, we can see that we are most likely to have a bad day (i.e., experience high stock volatility) in the months of January, April, and October, and least likely to experience it in August, November, and December.

Next, we want measures of central tendency and variation, beginning with the mean and standard deviation. For individual columns, we obtain these with the ***mean(Column)*** and ***sd(Column)*** functions. To get the mean and standard deviation for all variables in our data set, we can use the ***sapply(DataFrame, Statistic)*** function. For example, `sapply(StockPrices[,2:8],mean)` will get us the averages for columns 2 through 8 (Open—Volatility, which are all the numeric variables) of the StockPrices data frame. To develop a report that includes multiple summary statistics, we can wrap them in the cbind() function. For example,

```
cbind(sapply(StockPrices[,2:8],mean), sapply(StockPrices[,2:8],median),
   sapply(StockPrices[,2:8],sd))
```

will produce the following output:

```
                  [,1]         [,2]         [,3]
Open       2.577274e+01 1.000969e+01 2.580486e+01
High       2.605488e+01 1.013843e+01 2.601553e+01
Low        2.548993e+01 9.913137e+00 2.559433e+01
Close      2.577476e+01 1.000969e+01 2.580702e+01
Adj.Close  2.191569e+01 7.085732e+00 2.462865e+01
Volume     5.198586e+06 4.238200e+06 4.664925e+06
Volatility 5.649479e-01 2.735770e-01 6.497687e-01
```

For descriptive statistics without the fuss of wrapping multiple sapply() functions, we can use the ***summary()*** function. So **`summary(StockPrices)`** produces the following output, also summarizing our date and Boolean data type columns:

```
      Date                 Open              High              Low
 Min.   :1972-06-01   Min.   :  1.151   Min.   :  1.175   Min.   : 1.135
 1st Qu.:1983-10-19   1st Qu.:  4.313   1st Qu.:  4.361   1st Qu.: 4.248
 Median :1995-03-06   Median : 10.010   Median : 10.138   Median : 9.913
 Mean   :1995-03-12   Mean   : 25.773   Mean   : 26.055   Mean   :25.490
 3rd Qu.:2006-08-03   3rd Qu.: 44.930   3rd Qu.: 45.489   3rd Qu.:44.465
 Max.   :2018-01-04   Max.   :100.210   Max.   :101.650   Max.   :99.910
     Close            Adj.Close            Volume            Volatility
 Min.   :  1.135   Min.   :  0.4201   Min.   :       0   Min.   :0.00000
 1st Qu.:  4.313   1st Qu.:  2.1390   1st Qu.: 2547900   1st Qu.:0.09656
 Median : 10.010   Median :  7.0857   Median : 4238200   Median :0.27358
 Mean   : 25.775   Mean   : 21.9157   Mean   : 5198586   Mean   :0.56495
 3rd Qu.: 44.973   3rd Qu.: 37.5799   3rd Qu.: 6372500   3rd Qu.:0.87530
 Max.   :100.850   Max.   :100.8500   Max.   :90336900   Max.   :5.88000
   BadDay              Era                 Month
 Mode :logical     Length:11501        Length:11501
 FALSE:7070        Class :character    Class :character
 TRUE :4431        Mode  :character    Mode  :character
```

The ***describe(DataFrame)*** function from the psych package produces an even more comprehensive set of descriptive statistics, again with little effort. See the "Descriptive Statistics" insert for a description of each of the thirteen outputs produced.

Often we will need to aggregate our data by one or more variables—that is, produce group-by or control-break reports. To do so, we use the ***aggregate(DataFrame, by=list(Column1, Column2, …), FUN=FunctionName)*** function. (Note, in the arguments for the aggregate function, **FUN is not a placeholder to be replaced** with a value, as is the case with other uses of capitalization in discussions of R. Rather, it refers to the function that will be used to aggregate the data. Possible functions include mean, median, sum, var, sd, min, max, length.) If we need multiple group-by variables, they will appear in the "by=list()" argument, separated by commas.

Earlier, we looked at the distribution of bad days by month. Let's say we would like a more direct look at volatility by month (i.e., to determine the average volatility by month). To do so, we can use **`aggregate`** `(Volatility, by=`**`list`**`(Month), FUN=mean)`, which produces the following output, once again confirming that our top three months for volatility are January, April, and October, but the three months with the lowest volatility are June—instead of August, November, and December:

```
    Group.1         x
1       Apr 0.5782983
2       Aug 0.5408602
3       Dec 0.5239170
4       Feb 0.5363432
5       Jan 0.6054443
6       Jul 0.5769500
7       Jun 0.5414086
8       Mar 0.5511105
9       May 0.5468712
10      Nov 0.5448572
11      Oct 0.6569754
12      Sep 0.5716316
```

Generating Graphical Displays

Three types of graphs are particularly useful in data visualization—histograms, bar charts, and scatterplots. The material below provides a brief introduction to these three types of graphs. Obtaining R help on each chart function will acquaint you with arguments that permit you more control over your visuals. ***Histograms*** are a graphical display of a frequency distribution of continuous data. In R, we can generate a histogram with the ***hist(Column)*** function. Adding a "col='' " argument allows us to specify the color of the bars. For example, we can graph volatility to produce the histogram in Figure B.1 with **hist(Volatility, col='blue')**.

A ***bar chart*** typically is used to depict a frequency distribution of categorical data. Visually, whereas histogram bars do not have spaces, bar chart bars tend to have them. In R, we can generate a bar chart with the ***barplot(Column)*** command. To get a bar chart of the daily closing prices for AXP in 2016, we can use

```
barplot(subset(Close, format(as.
Date(Date), '%Y')==2016), col='green',
        xlab='Trading Days',
ylab='Stock Price ($s)', main='Daily AXP
        Closing Prices for 2016',
        ylim=c(0,100))
```

The subset function extracts only observations in the AXP price history for the year 2016. We label the x-axis with the argument "*xlab='Trading Days*" and the y-axis with "*ylab='Stock Price ($s)*". To provide a title, we can add the argument "*main='Daily AXP Closing Prices for 2016*". We can set $100 as our upper limit for the y-axis with the argument "*ylim=c(0,100)*", which specifies the lower and upper bounds for our y-axis. Because the ylim (and xlim) argument assumes a range of values, we must use the c() function to convert those values to a vector. We now have the output depicted in Figure B.2.

A ***scatter plot*** is a graphical display of the association between two variables. To generate a scatter plot,

Descriptive Statistics Produced by Describe()

Statistic	Meaning
vars	Column number
n	Number of observations in data set
mean	Arithmetic average of a column
sd	Standard deviation of a column
median	Median value of a column
trimmed	Column mean, after trimming the data of outliers (with trim default of 0.1)
mad	Median absolute deviation of each column value from the median
min	Minimum column value
max	Maximum column value
range	Range of values
skew	Extent to which distribution of column values is tilted left or right, rather than being centered around the mean
kurtosis	Extent to which distribution of column values is overly tall or flat
se	Standard error of the column

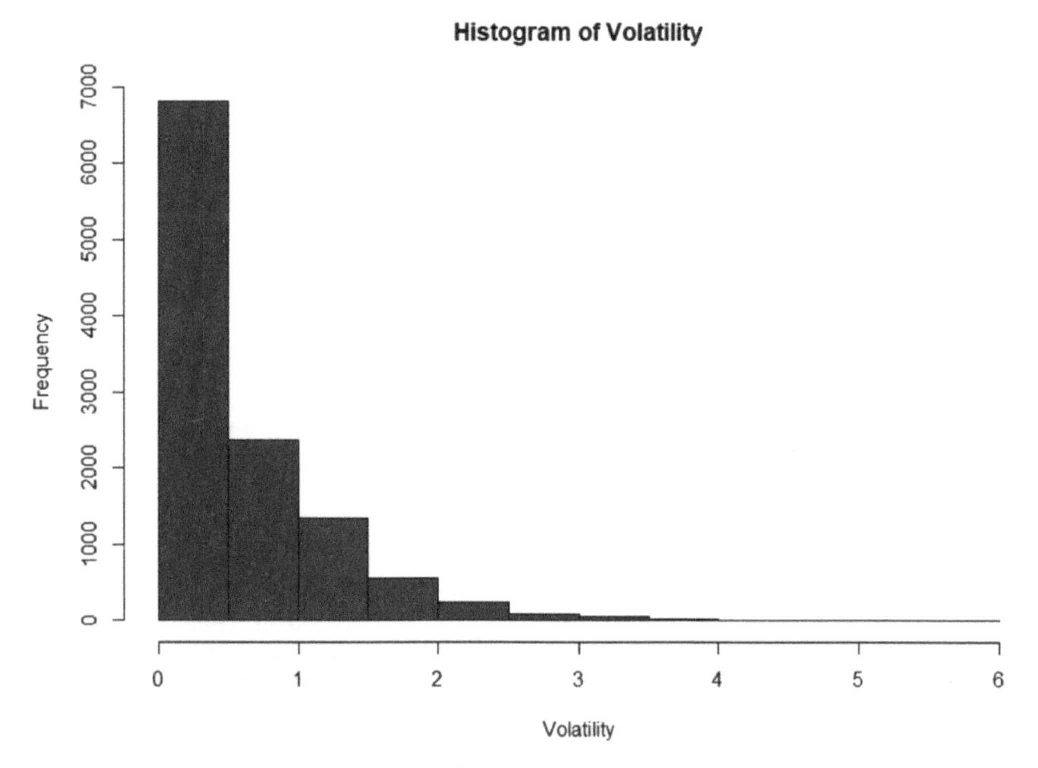

Figure B.1 Distribution of Daily Volatility of AXP Stock Price

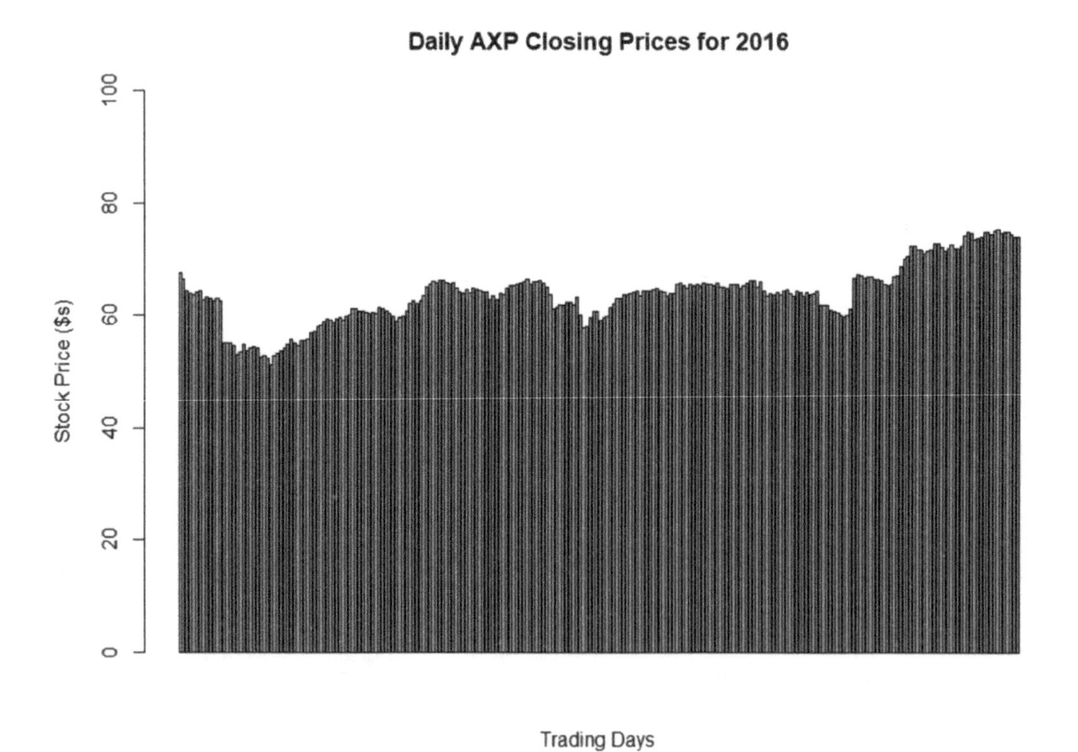

Figure B.2 Bar Chart of One Year of AXP Stock History

we use the ***plot(ByColumn, Column)*** command. For example, to obtain a scatter plot of the closing prices of American Express stock by year, we can use:

```
plot(format(as.Date(Date), '%Y'), Close, xlab='Year', ylab='Closing
     Prices', main='Closing Prices by Year' , col='dark red')
```

where we extract the year from the Date column with *format(as.Date(Date), '%Y')* and define the x- and y-axis labels, and chart title with the "xlab='' ", "ylab='' ", and "main='' " arguments, respectively, and produce the graph depicted in Figure B.3.

Chernoff faces is a novel approach to visualizing multidimensional data. The technique was developed by statistician, Herman Chernoff, in the 1970s [1]. It uses each facial feature to represent a dimension of the data. Because mainstream statistical analysis software does not provide the capability for Chernoff faces, its use typically has been limited to those with strong programming skills. In R, this capability is embedded in the aplpack package, and permits simultaneous representation of up to fifteen data dimensions. If we don't have the aplpack package loaded, let's go ahead and load it.

The ***faces(DataFrameOrColumnList)*** function from aplpack produces Chernoff faces. The function defaults to a visual in which all fifteen facial features are used, regardless of the number of data dimensions we wish to display. This can make for a confusing visual. We can specify which of the fifteen facial features appearing in the "Chernoff Face Dimensions" insert we wish to use to represent our data. In doing so, there are a couple of visual design issues to bear in mind. First, research has shown that the three features easiest for viewers to recognize changes in are smiling, height of face, width of eyes [2]. Second, we need to consider what we are depicting when choosing facial features to represent our data. For example, depicting increases in unfavorable variables (e.g., crime) using a widening smile may be disconcerting to the viewer, detracting from the information the graph otherwise communicates. So it is useful to be able to control the output of the faces() function.

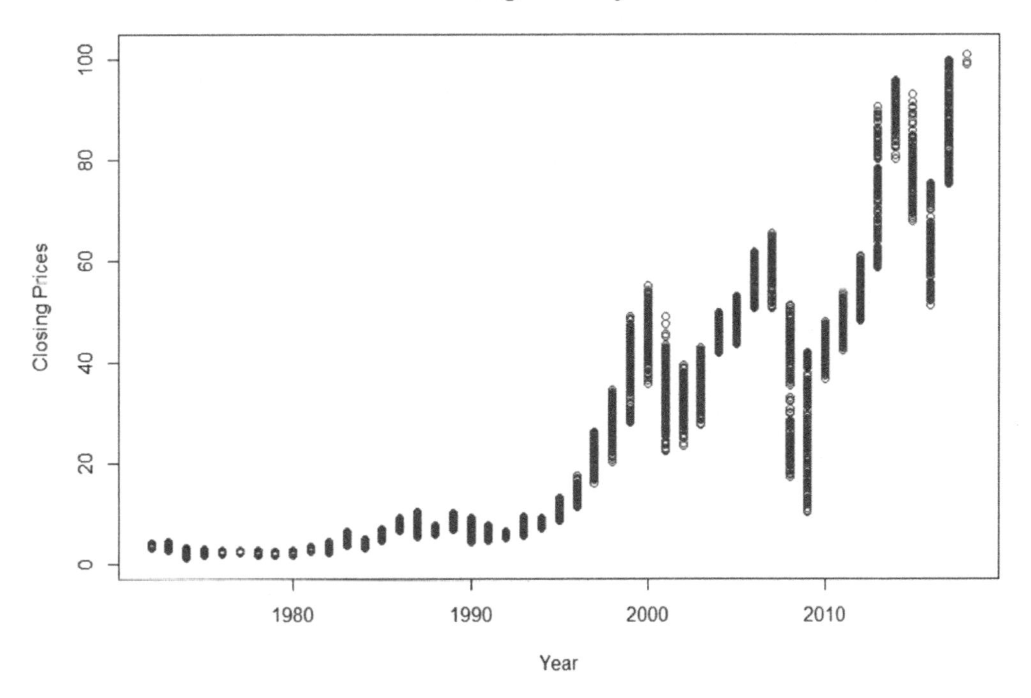

Figure B.3 Scatter Plot Depicting AXP Stock Prices

Chernoff Face Dimensions

1. Height of face	6. Smile	11. Style of hair
2. Width of face	7. Height of eyes	12. Height of nose
3. Structure of face	8. Width of eyes	13. Width of nose
4. Height of mouth	9. Height of hair	14. Width of ear
5. Width of mouth	10. Width of hair	15. Height of ear

We control the facial attributes displayed in the ordering of the data columns (see the "Chernoff Face Dimensions" insert for ordering) appearing in our faces() function. If we are not using all the columns from a data frame, we need to use the cbind() function to assemble the columns we wish to display into a list of columns to be displayed. Columns to be displayed must be of a numeric data type. Features we wish not to use will simply have a zero. The "face.type=" argument determines which one of three types of facial colorings will be used: 0=black and white; 1=multicolor; 2=Christmas. Be socially aware when using Chernoff faces, especially with the "face.type=1" argument. While a powerful way of visualizing multidimensional data, the visuals may generate chagrin if perceived to represent ethnic groups or otherwise are considered socially inappropriate.

In order to depict the high, low, and close average daily stock prices for the last nine years, we first obtain the yearly average high, low, and closing stock prices and then filter the summarized data for the last nine years with

```
ForFaces=aggregate(StockPrices[,3:5], by=list(format(as.Date(Date), '%Y')), FUN=mean)
ForFaces=subset(ForFaces,ForFaces$Group.1>=2007)
```

Then, we run the faces() command, associating two facial attributes with each of the three data columns—annual low, high, and closing prices to produce the output depicted in Figure B.4.

```
faces(cbind(ForFaces$Low, ForFaces$Low, 0, ForFaces$High, ForFaces$High,
     ForFaces$Close, ForFaces$Close, 0, 0, 0, 0, 0, 0, 0, 0, 0, 0, 0),
      labels=ForFaces$Group.1, face.type=2, fill=FALSE)
```

Performing Correlation Analysis

Instead of viewing the relationship between variables graphically, we may want to be able to summarize them with correlations. To investigate the correlation between a single pair of variables, we can use the ***cor(Column1,Column2,...)*** function. For example,

```
cor(Close, Volatility)
```

tells us that volatility of AXP stock relates fairly strongly with closing prices, with a correlation of 0.65. If we want to investigate the correlations among several variables, computing them in pairs can get tedious. We can reference a set of columns from a data frame instead. For example,

```
cor(StockPrices[c(5,7,8)])
```

provides the following output:

```
               Close    Volume Volatility
Close      1.0000000 0.1798125  0.6481396
Volume     0.1798125 1.0000000  0.5469123
Volatility 0.6481396 0.5469123  1.0000000
```

This tells us that the correlation between closing prices and volume traded is negative, that between closing prices and volatility is positive, and that between volume and volatility is positive. However, this matrix tells us nothing about the significance of those correlations. To obtain these, we can use the ***rcorr(Matrix)*** function from the Hmisc package. We need to ensure it is loaded (if not, go ahead and use the library command to do

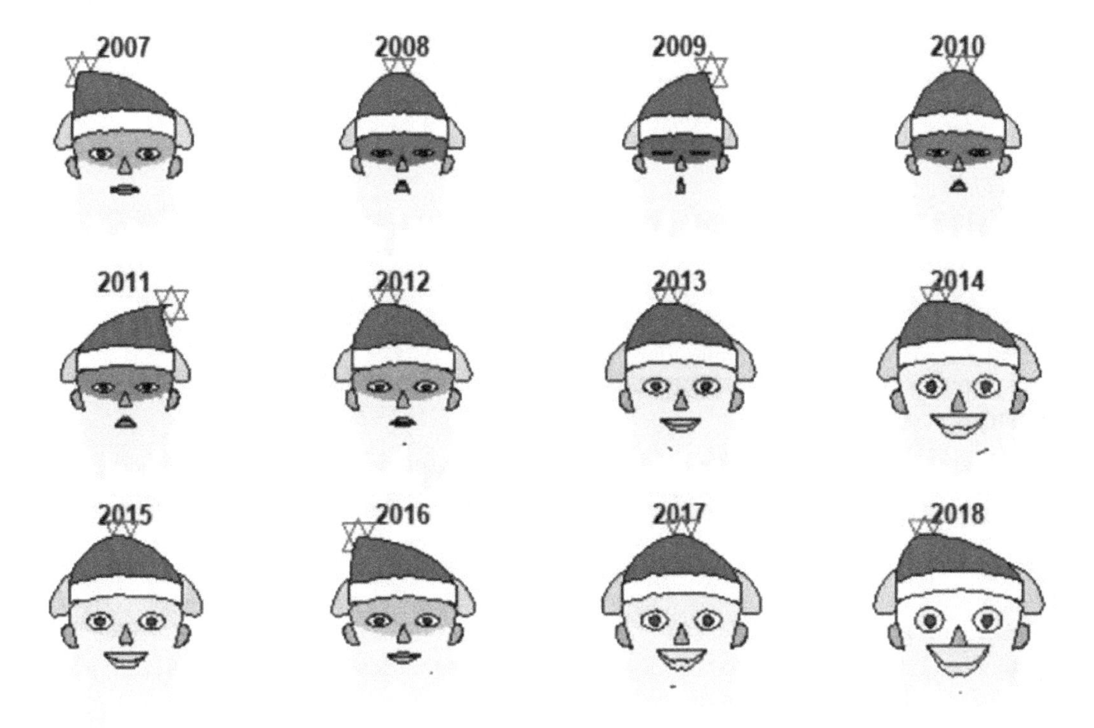

Legend:
Height and width of face: Low
Height and width of mouth: High
Smile and eyes: Close

Figure B.4 Representing Average AXP Stock Prices from 2009 to 2017

so.) The rcorr() function expects a matrix data structure, not a data frame. Therefore we cannot call it on StockPrices. Instead, we first use the ***as.matrix(DataFrame)*** function to create a new Hype matrix data structure, on which we can now run the rcorr() function. So,

```
rcorr(as.matrix(StockPrices[c(5,7,8)]))
```

produces the output below, which tells us that while closing price and trading volume are significantly correlated with volatility, closing price correlates insignificantly with volume.

```
           Close Volume Volatility
Close       1.00   0.18       0.65
Volume      0.18   1.00       0.55
Volatility  0.65   0.55       1.00

n= 11501


P
           Close Volume Volatility
Close             0      0
Volume      0            0
Volatility  0     0
```

We can visualize a correlation matrix by generating scatterplot matrix. A ***scatterplot matrix*** is multiple scatterplots displayed together. We use the ***pairs(DataFrame)*** function to generate the scatterplot matrix. For example,

```
pairs(StockPrices[c(5,7,8)])
```

produces the output in Figure B.5, depicting the correlation matrix from above graphically. The scatterplot matrix conveys more information than the correlation matrix does, though. It permits us to identify leverage points (i.e., data points or observations without which the observed relationship—graphical or numeric—between two variables would be weaker or stronger).

Running T-Tests

When we want to investigate how values of *one continuous dependent variable* differ across *one categorical independent variable with two possible values*, we use a t-test. If the data for the two values of our categorical variable are from independent samples, we would use an independent samples t-test. When data for the continuous variable for the two independent samples are in a single column, and the two groups for the categorical variable is in another column, we use a "~" in the ***t.test(Test)*** function to represent the comparison. To determine whether there is a significant difference in trading volume across days in which there was higher than average volatility (i.e., BadDay=TRUE) versus lower than average volatility (i.e., BadDay=FALSE), we can run `t.test(Volume~BadDay)`. This produces the following output.

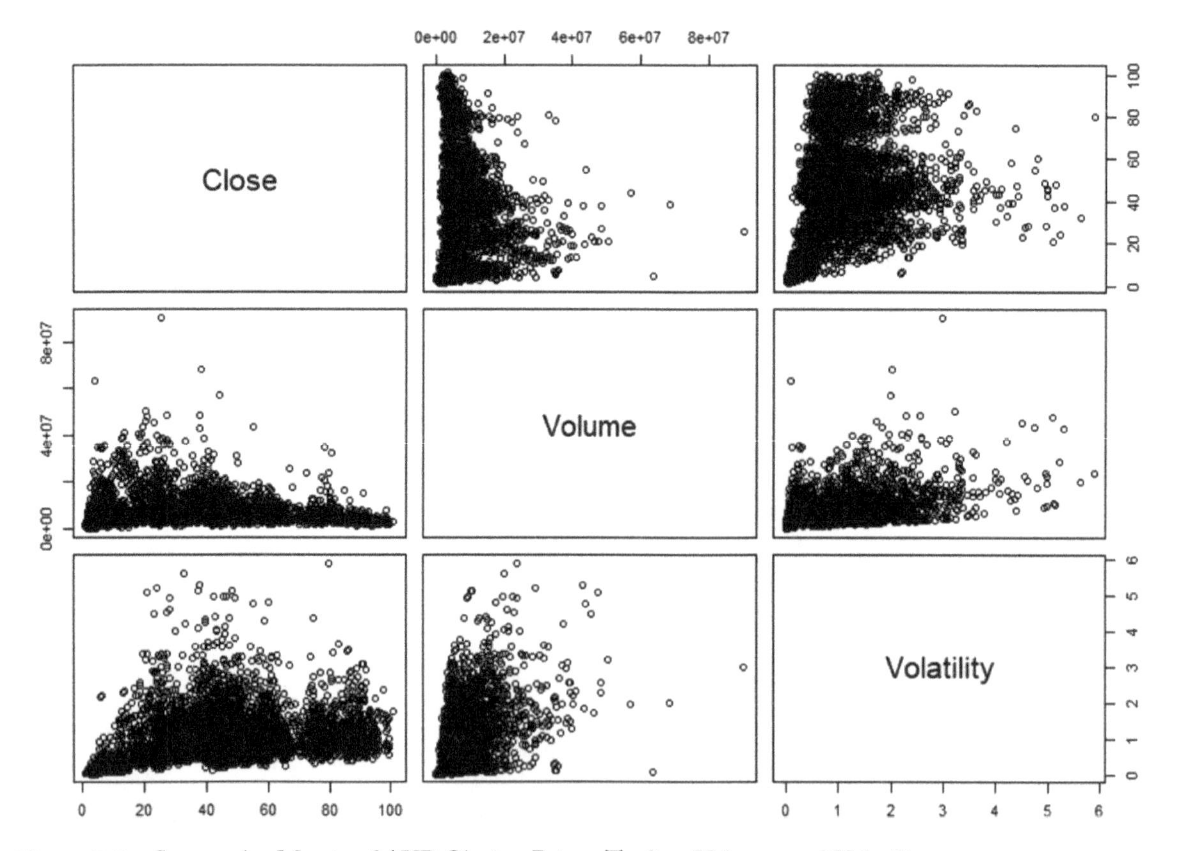

Figure B.5 Scatterplot Matrix of AXP Closing Prices, Trading Volume, and Volatility

```
        Welch Two Sample t-test

data:  Volume by BadDay
t = -39.513, df = 6049.8, p-value < 2.2e-16
alternative hypothesis: true difference in means is not equal to 0
95 percent confidence interval:
 -3884813 -3517556
sample estimates:
mean in group FALSE  mean in group TRUE
           3772627             7473812
```

The large t-statistic, together with the small p-value support the premise that trading volume is significantly higher on high volatility than low volatility days (BadDays). In R, if the data for the continuous dependent variable for the two independent samples appears in two separate columns, each representing a different categorical value of the independent variable, we would use ***t.test(COLUMN1, COLUMN2)*** (i.e., a comma instead of the tilde). When the data in the two columns are related, we add the "paired=T" argument. To determine whether there is a significant difference between the daily opening and closing prices of AXP stock, we can run **t.test**(Open, Close, paired=T). This produces the following output:

```
        Paired t-test

data:  Open and Close
t = -0.41946, df = 11500, p-value = 0.6749
alternative hypothesis: true difference in means is not equal to 0
95 percent confidence interval:
 -0.011445336  0.007410346
sample estimates:
mean of the differences
           -0.002017495
```

We see a modest t-statistic and a p-value close to 0.10, indicating a one in ten chance of seeing a t-statistic as large as the one observed purely by chance. The 95% confidence interval around the average difference between opening and closing prices contains zero, indicating that we are unable to rule out the possibility that there really is no true difference between the opening and closing prices.

Running Analysis of Variance and Ordinary Least Squares Regression

When we have more than two values of the categorical independent variable or more than one independent variable, we use an Analysis of Variance (ANOVA). When we are interested in how one or more continuous (or continuous and categorical) variables influence (or predict) a continuous or categorical dependent variable, we use regression analysis. Regression analysis is a vast topic, and we will focus only on ordinary least squares (OLS) regression.

We are able to use ANOVA and OLS regression when our data meet four criteria or ***assumptions***. First, the variables to be analyzed should be ***normally distributed***. When the dependent variable in our model is categorical or count, we have to use a logistic, poisson, negative binomial, or some other type of regression. Second, our independent variables should be unrelated to each other. Violation of this assumption is called ***multicollinearity***. Third, variances of the residuals (error in estimating the dependent variable) should be relatively stable across the range of values of the independent variable. To put this another way, the residuals should be uncorrelated with our independent variables. Violation of this assumption is called ***heteroscedasticity***. Fourth, the residuals should be uncorrelated with each other. Violation of this assumption is termed ***autocorrelation***. This problem typically occurs with time-series data (data in which observations are captured at different points in time) or data pertaining to individuals or other entities that are related to each other (e.g., social network data). So, before running OLS regression analysis, consider the likelihood that your data violate any of these criteria or OLS assumptions.

Earlier we created an Era variable, dividing our stock history into three eras—pre-dotcom, bubble, and dotcom. If we wish to determine whether volatility differed significantly across these three periods, we would run an ANOVA. We run ANOVAs in R using the ***aov(Test)*** function to conduct an ANOVA. To display the model results, we nest this model within a summary() function. To see whether volatility differed significantly across the three eras, we run **summary**(**aov**(Volatility ~ Era)). This produces the following output, which tells us that volatility does differ significantly across eras since the probability of obtaining an F-statistic of the size obtained purely by chance is miniscule. The warning issued tells us that our categorical variable, era, which previously was a text data type, was converted to a factor data type prior to running the analyses of variance.

```
                Df Sum Sq Mean Sq F value Pr(>F)
Era              2   2644  1322.1    6875 <2e-16 ***
Residuals    11498   2211     0.2
---
Signif. codes:
0 '***' 0.001 '**' 0.01 '*' 0.05 '.' 0.1 ' ' 1
```

Alternatively, we could have stored the aov() model using EraModel=**aov**(Volatility ~ Era) and then displayed the model with **summary**(EraModel). Since the output does not tell us which era has the highest volatility, we can run **aggregate**(Volatility, by=**list**(Era), FUN=mean), which tells us that volatility was highest in the bubble era:

```
    Group.1         x
1    Bubble 1.4153080
2    DotCom 1.0709241
3 PreDotCom 0.1661594
```

The ***coefficients(Model)*** will display the coefficient for the independent variable in case we wish to develop a predictive model. Thus **coefficients**(**aov**(Volatility ~ Era)) produces the following estimates, which we can combine to predict future volatility.

```
(Intercept)    EraDotCom EraPreDotCom
  1.4153080   -0.3443839   -1.2491486
```

For tomorrow, which is in the DotCom era, we would estimate volatility as 1.4153080 – 0.3443839*1 (for DotCom = TRUE or 1) – 1.2491486*0 (for PreDotCom = FALSE or 0). This equates to a volatility of 1.070924 in the DotCom era.

We can visualize our model using the ***boxplot(Model)***. This will display a box-and-whiskers plot depicting the average of our dependent variable for each level of our independent variable. For example, the statement below generates the output in Figure B.6.

```
boxplot(Volatility ~ Era, col='pink', xlab='Era', ylab='Volatility')
```

The ***plot(Model)*** option offers four postestimation diagnostics. Let's try **plot**(**aov**(Volatility ~ Era)). This produces the diagnostic plots depicted in Figure B.7. Note that you have to press the Enter key in the Console panel in order to view each of the available diagnostic plots. The top and bottom left charts in Figure B.6 depict the distribution of residuals (difference between predicted and observed values) and standardized residuals respectively for volatility across the three eras—Dotcom, preDotCom, and Bubble. To confirm homoscedasticity, we would like the distribution of these residuals or error terms to be approximately

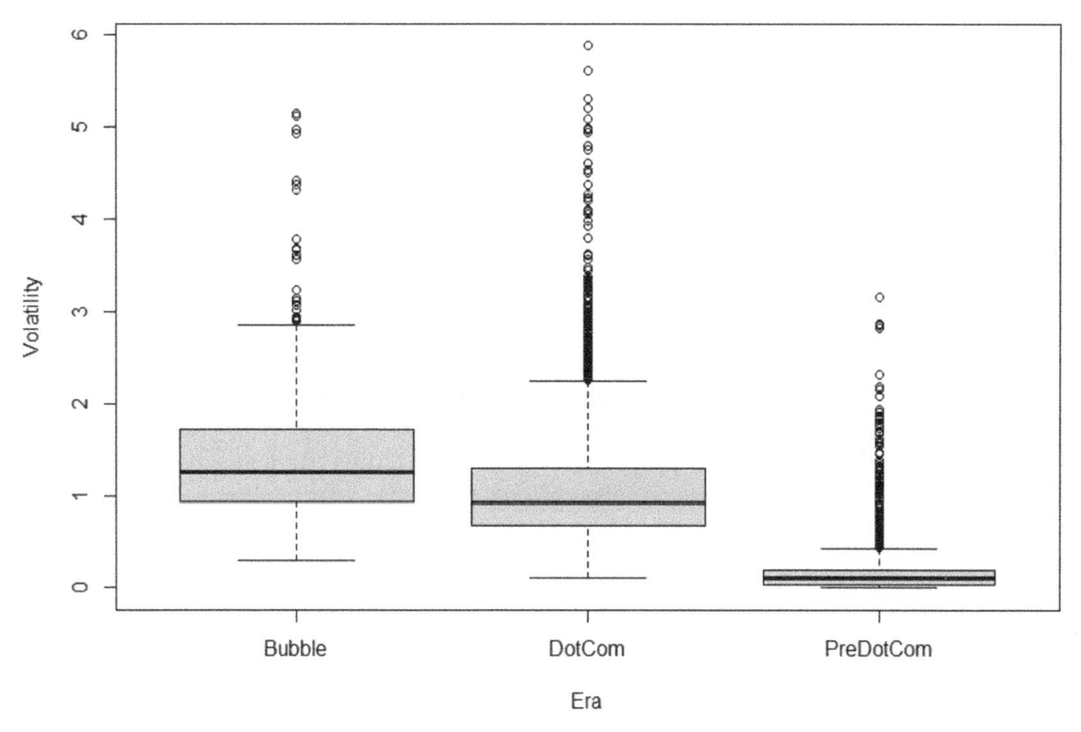

Figure B.6 Boxplot of AXP Price Volatility by Era

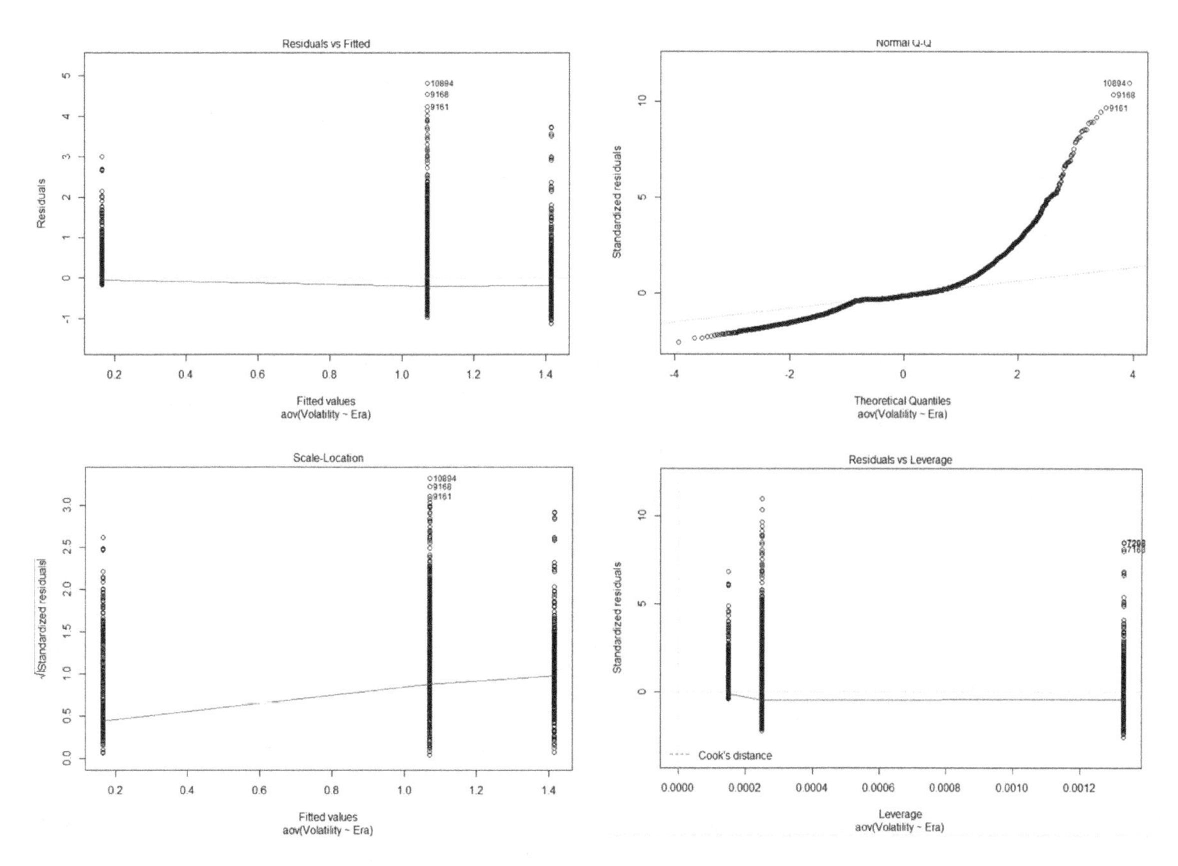

Figure B.7 Diagnostic Plots Following ANOVA of Volatility across Three Eras

the same. Here, we see that the distribution is greatest for the Bubble era and lowest for the perDotCom era, violating the homoscedasticity assumption. The top right chart is a Q-Q (quantile-quantile) chart, which helps us check for the normality assumption. This is a scatterplot of a theorized normal distribution against the observed distribution. If the observed distribution mimicked the theorized distribution, we should see a straight diagonal line. The curved line suggests that the observed distribution is skewed, violating the normality assumption. The bottom right chart identifies two "leverage" points—observation #7168 and #7208. These are points without which the predicted model would change.

One commonly used R function for regression analysis is the ***lm(Model)*** function. Once again, we can nest the lm() function within a summary() to request that R display the model results. To explore the extent to which volatility of AXP stock is a function of volume traded and year, we use

```
summary(lm(Volatility ~ Volume + as.numeric(format(as.Date(Date), '%Y'))))
```

This yields the following output:

```
Call:
lm(formula = Volatility ~ Volume + as.numeric(format(as.Date(Date),
    "%Y")))

Residuals:
    Min      1Q  Median      3Q     Max
-2.8280 -0.2619 -0.0695  0.1552  4.2156

Coefficients:
                                          Estimate Std. Error t value Pr(>|t|)
(Intercept)                             -5.373e+01  6.721e-01  -79.94   <2e-16 ***
Volume                                   4.508e-08  9.533e-10   47.28   <2e-16 ***
as.numeric(format(as.Date(Date), "%Y"))  2.710e-02  3.379e-04   80.20   <2e-16 ***
---
Signif. codes:  0 '***' 0.001 '**' 0.01 '*' 0.05 '.' 0.1 ' ' 1

Residual standard error: 0.4357 on 11498 degrees of freedom
Multiple R-squared:  0.5505,      Adjusted R-squared:  0.5505
F-statistic:  7042 on 2 and 11498 DF,  p-value: < 2.2e-16
```

The output indicates that both volume and year have a significant impact on volatility—that is, the probability of obtaining the observed t-value by chance is exceedingly remote (very close to zero). The R-squared statistic, adjusted for the number of variables in the model, is 0.5505. This tells us that ~55% of the variance in volatility is accounted for by trading volume and year. These parameter estimates permit us to estimate future volatility. For example, if four million shares were traded on January 21, 2019, we would estimate volatility as

$$-53.73+0.00000004508*4000000+0.0271*2019=1.1652$$

Using `plot(lm(Volatility ~ Volume + as.numeric(format(as.Date(Date), '%Y'))))` produces the diagnostic plots depicted in Figure B.8. Since we would like our residuals to be distributed similarly around our predicted (fitted) values to satisfy the homoscedasticity assumption, the two graphs on the left suggest the presence of some data anomalies. Once again, the Q-Q plot at the top right suggests a violation of the normality assumption, as the scatterplot does not form a straight diagonal line. The graph at the bottom right graph suggests specific data points—high "leverage" data points—we may want to consider removing from the analyses. Alternatively, this plot may suggest we consider another regression approach such as quantile or weighted least squares regression (which is beyond the scope of this book).

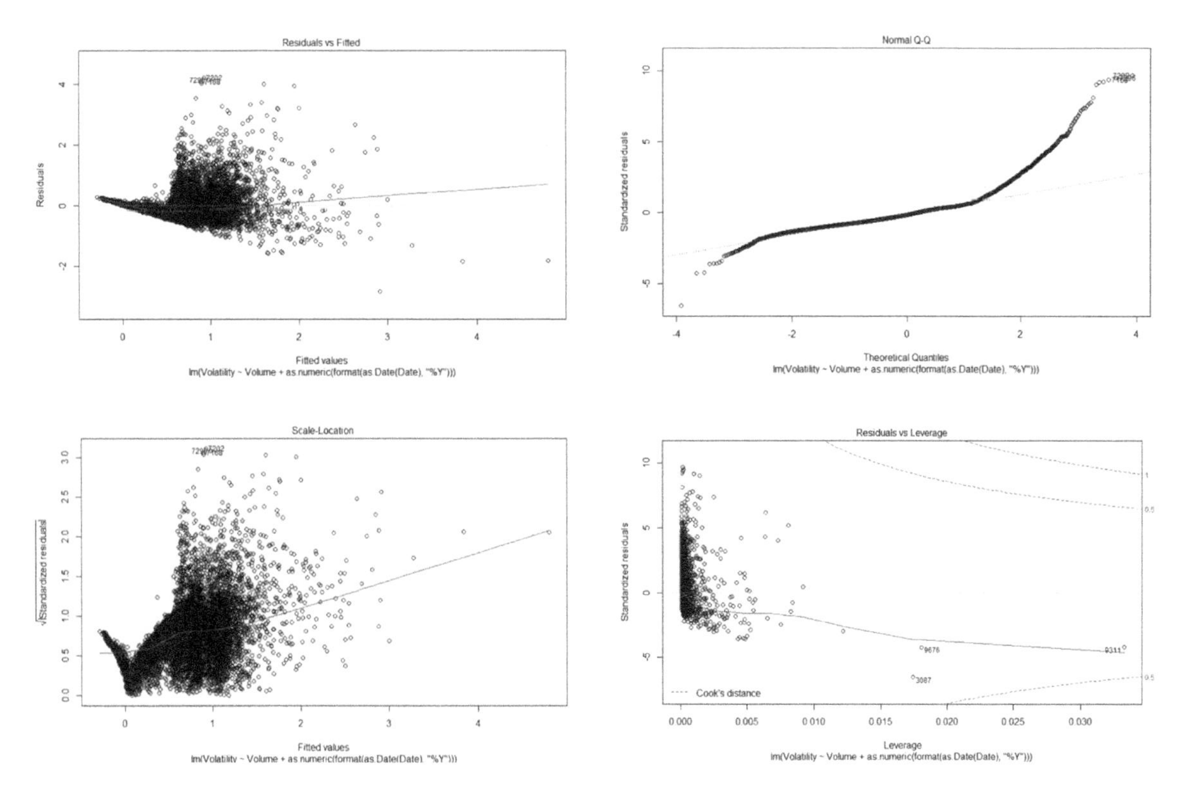

Figure B.8 Diagnostic Plots Following Regression of Volatility on Volume and Year

If we wanted to generate a data set of predicted big data values based on the *current* data set, we could simply use the ***fitted(Model)*** function. We can add a PredictedVolatility column to our StockPrices data frame using

```
StockPrices$PredictedVolatility=fitted(lm(Volatility ~ Volume + as.numeric(format
    (as.Date(Date), '%Y'))))
```

We now can investigate how closely our predicted values of volatility correspond with our actual values using

```
cor(StockPrices$Volatility, StockPrices$PredictedVolatility)
```

This produces a correlation coefficient of 0.7419802, which is modestly high, suggesting our current model does a reasonable job predicting volatility.

Tutorial B.1. Analyzing the Amount of Buzz about Two IT Innovations

In this tutorial, we will use the "IT Hype.csv" file. See the IT Hype Data insert for a brief description of the data. Also, feel free to inspect the file itself. The first thing we will need to do in order to access the file into set the working directory—or path to our file. To do so, we use

```
setwd('PathToRTutorialFiles')
```

We then read the file into a data frame named ITHype using

```
ITHype=read.csv('IT Hype.csv',header=T)
```

The ITHype data set has missing values for SocialMedia data for 2014. These missing values were set to the number 9999. We can recode them in R to NA using

```
ITHype$SocialMedia[ITHype$SocialMedia==9999]= NA
```

We can check whether this worked with

```
is.na(ITHype)
```

which checks whether any column in the ITHype data frame contains NA or

```
is.na(ITHype$SocialMedia)
```

which checks specifically for whether the SocialMedia column of the ITHype data frame contains NA.

We then have to decide how we wish to handle the missing values. We can omit the entire observations with

```
ITHype=na.omit(ITHype)
```

We would prefer to handle the missing values in our individual computations instead. So, let's reload the ITHype data frame (`ITHype=read.csv('IT Hype.csv',header=T)`) and rerun the `ITHype$SocialMedia[ITHype$SocialMedia==9999]=NA` statement.

To obtain the quarterly average number of social media press releases, we need to use the na.rm=TRUE argument as below:

```
mean(ITHype$SocialMedia,na.rm=TRUE)
```

This calculates the mean of the SocialMedia column as 25.1875.

If we request the correlations among the Year, SocialMedia, and BigData columns using

```
rcorr(as.matrix(ITHype[c(1,3,4)]))
```

we get the following output, which, in addition to providing us with the correlation coefficients, tells us that n = 36 for the Year and BigData columns and n = 32 for SocialMedia. Thus we used all available data for determining the correlations among these variables.

```
            Year SocialMedia BigData
Year        1.00        0.94    0.57
SocialMedia 0.94        1.00    0.74
BigData     0.57        0.74    1.00

n
            Year SocialMedia BigData
Year          36          32      36
SocialMedia   32          32      32
BigData       36          32      36

P
            Year  SocialMedia BigData
Year              0e+00       3e-04
SocialMedia 0e+00             0e+00
BigData     3e-04 0e+00
```

To replace the missing values with the column mean, we can use

```
ITHype$SocialMedia
   = ifelse(is.na(ITHype$SocialMedia),
     mean(ITHype$SocialMedia,
     na.rm=TRUE), ITHype$SocialMedia)
```

Next, we obtain the total buzz—about social media and big data—for each quarter using

```
ITHype$Buzz = ITHype$SocialMedia + ITHype$BigData
```

We create a categorical variable, called Period, which has the value "Early" until 2009 and "Late" after that, using

The IT Hype Data

Since we will be using the *IT Hype* data set in this appendix, some notes on the data are in order. The data set records the quarterly number of press releases issued by the 2012 Fortune 50 firms containing the words "Social Media" and "Big Data." These press releases provide a window on the diffusion of the two IT innovations over time. Looking at the data set, we see that "Social Media" did not begin to diffuse among these firms until the third quarter of 2006. "Big Data" began to diffuse in the first quarter of 2008, but with a significant gap in diffusion until 2010.

```
ITHype$Period = ifelse((ITHype$Year<=2009), 'Early', 'Late')
```

We also create a diffusion Stage variable with four categories—Innovator, EarlyAdopter, LateMajority, and Laggard—using a nested ifelse():

```
ITHype$Stage = ifelse(ITHype$Year<=2007, 'Innovator',
       ifelse(ITHype$Year<=2009, 'EarlyAdopter',
       ifelse(ITHype$Year<=2011, 'LateMajority', 'Laggard')))
```

Now that we have set up our data set, we would like to produce some descriptive statistics. First, we would like a frequency distribution of our SocialMedia and BigData columns. We get this using

```
table(ITHype$SocialMedia)
table(ITHype$BigData)
```

And we get the following frequency distributions of quarterly press releases about social media and big data, respectively:

```
      0       1       2       3       4      11      14
      3       2       2       2       1       2       1
     16      24      25 25.1875      30      31      32
      1       1       1       4       1       1       1
     34      38      40      41      42      43      44
      1       2       1       1       1       1       1
     45      54      56      58      63
      1       1       1       1       1
```

```
 0  1  2  3  4  5  8 10 13 16 25 29 36 43 46 51 63
15  3  2  2  2  1  1  1  1  1  1  1  1  1  1  1  1
```

To get a distribution of big data press releases by year, we use the following command to obtain the distribution below:

```
table(ITHype$Year, ITHype$BigData)
```

```
     0 1 2 3 4 5 8 10 13 16 25 29 36 43 46 51 63
2006 4 0 0 0 0 0 0  0  0  0  0  0  0  0  0  0  0
2007 4 0 0 0 0 0 0  0  0  0  0  0  0  0  0  0  0
2008 3 1 0 0 0 0 0  0  0  0  0  0  0  0  0  0  0
2009 4 0 0 0 0 0 0  0  0  0  0  0  0  0  0  0  0
2010 0 1 2 1 0 0 0  0  0  0  0  0  0  0  0  0  0
2011 0 0 0 0 0 1 1  1  0  1  0  0  0  0  0  0  0
2012 0 0 0 0 0 0 0  0  1  0  1  1  1  0  0  0  0
2013 0 0 0 0 0 0 0  0  0  0  0  0  0  1  1  1  1
2014 0 1 0 1 2 0 0  0  0  0  0  0  0  0  0  0  0
```

Next we want the means, medians, and standard deviations for the SocialMedia and BigData columns. So our output is easy to read, we want the column names to represent the descriptive statistics. We can do this using the following command to produce the output below:

```
cbind(Means=sapply(ITHype[3:4],mean), Medians=sapply(ITHype[3:4],median),
      SDs=sapply(ITHype[3:4],sd))
```

```
               Means Medians      SDs
SocialMedia 25.18750 25.1875 19.12879
BigData     10.16667  1.5000 17.11390
```

We also can store the descriptive statistics to a data frame and, if we had not already specified column names, specify the column names in a second line of code.

```
Descriptives=data.frame(cbind(sapply(ITHype[3:4],mean), sapply(ITHype[3:4],median),
     sapply(ITHype[3:4],sd)))
colnames(Descriptives)=c("Means", "Medians", "SDs")
```

This produces the data object depicted in Figure B.9 that we can inspect later in the *R* session and save to a file for later use.

Depending on how we need to use the descriptives in the future, we also can use rbind() and rownames() to transpose the data frame as follows:

```
Descriptives=data.frame(rbind(sapply(ITHype[3:4],mean), sapply(ITHype[3:4],median),
      sapply(ITHype[3:4],sd)))
rownames(Descriptives)=c("Means", "Medians", "SDs")
```

Next, we would like to sum the press releases by year into a new data frame called Summary.Hype. We do this with

```
Summary.Hype = aggregate(ITHype[3:4], by=list(ITHype$Year), FUN=sum)
```

	row.names	Means	Medians	SDs
1	SocialMedia	25.18750	25.1875	19.12879
2	BigData	10.16667	1.5000	17.11390

Figure B.9 Data Frame of Descriptive Statistics

Adding

```
colnames(Summary.Hype)=c('Year','SocialMedia','BigData')
```

enables us to specify the column names for the new data frame, generating the data frame depicted in Figure B.10.

Now, we want to generate some graphs. We begin with a histogram of social media buzz:

```
hist(ITHype$SocialMedia, col='green')
```

We can superimpose a BigData frequency distribution over the SocialMedia frequency distribution by running the hist() function again with the BigData data with the "add=TRUE" argument as depicted below to produce the graph in Figure B.11.

```
hist(ITHype$BigData, col='blue', add=TRUE)
```

Untitled14* × Summary.Hype ×

9 observations of 3 variables

	Year	SocialMedia	BigData
1	2006	2.00	0
2	2007	16.00	0
3	2008	20.00	1
4	2009	88.00	0
5	2010	126.00	8
6	2011	161.00	39
7	2012	183.00	103
8	2013	210.00	203
9	2014	100.75	12

Figure B.10 Data Frame Containing Total Press Releases by Year

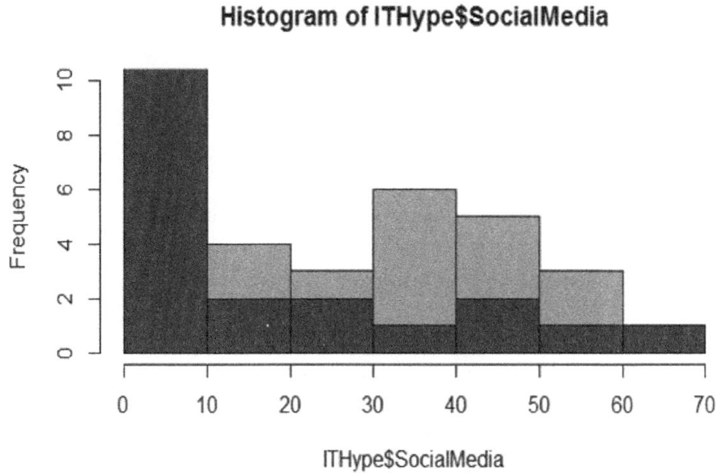

Figure B.11 Initial Histogram of Social Media and Big Data Buzz Frequency

Of course, it would be nice if we could see the frequency of zero social media buzz, which is hidden behind the zero big data buzz frequency bar. To do so, we have to make our bars transparent. We do this by using the ***rgb(RedSaturation, GreenSaturation, BlueSaturation, Transparency%)*** function in our "color" argument. The first three arguments of the rgb() function specify the desired saturation of red, green, and blue colors, respectively. The last argument declares the transparency level, where 0 would be entirely transparent, 1 would be entirely opaque, and .5 would be halfway in between.

We change our x- and y-axis labels to something more meaningful with the "xlab=" and "ylab=" arguments. Note that while we use the xlim function below, we preserve the current range of 0-70. Feel free to play with the range though so you can see how the graph changes. We wonder whether we are seeing all the social media frequency data on the zero buzz bar. So we change the y-axis range with the "ylim=" argument, again in conjunction with the c() function to convert the values to a vector. Finally, we would like to change the graph title to something more meaningful. We do so with the "main=" argument, being sure to set "main=NULL" when developing the second histogram.

```
hist(ITHype$SocialMedia, col=rgb(1,1,0,.5), xlab='Buzz', ylab='Frequency
   (Quarters) ', xlim=c(0,70), ylim=c(0,25), main='Social Media and Big Data
   Buzz')
hist(ITHype$BigData, col=rgb(0,1,1,.5), add=TRUE, xlim=c(0,70), ylim=c(0,25),
  main=NULL)
```

Alternatively, we could end with our title, being sure to suppress the default title on each histogram with a "main=NULL" argument. Below, we also use the "labels=TRUE" argument to display the data values associated with each bar:

```
hist(ITHype$SocialMedia, col=rgb(1,1,0,.5), xlab='Buzz', ylab='Frequency
   (Quarters) ', xlim=c(0,70), ylim=c(0,25), labels=T, main=' ')
   #equivalent to main=NULL
hist(ITHype$BigData, col=rgb(0,1,1,.5), add=T, xlim=c(0,70), ylim=c(0,25),
   labels=T, main=NULL)
title(main='Social Media and Big Data Buzz')
```

Tacking on a ***legend(WhereX, WhereY, Text)*** command rounds off our display. The first two arguments of the legend() function provide the XY coordinates of *where* the legend will be displayed; the third provides the text for the legend. The optional "lty=" argument defines the type of line and the "lwd=" argument the width of the line. The "col=" argument sets the color—copy this from your hist() command to ensure a visual match. Notice our use of the c() command once again.

```
legend(40, 25, c('Social Media', 'Big Data'), lty=c(1,1), lwd=c(5,5),
   col=c(rgb(1,1,0),rgb(0,1,1)))
```

Now, we have a nice visual, as depicted in Figure B.12. The following code will produce the chart in Figure B.13.

```
barplot(ITHype$SocialMedia, col=rgb(1,0,1,.75), xlab='Buzz', ylab='Frequency
       (Quarters)', ylim=c(0,72), main=NULL)
barplot(ITHype$BigData, col=rgb(1,1,0,.75), add=T)
title('Social Media and Big Data Buzz')
legend(0, 70, c('Social Media', 'Big Data'),
       lwd=c(5,5),col=c(rgb(1,0,1,.75),rgb(1,1,0,.75)))
```

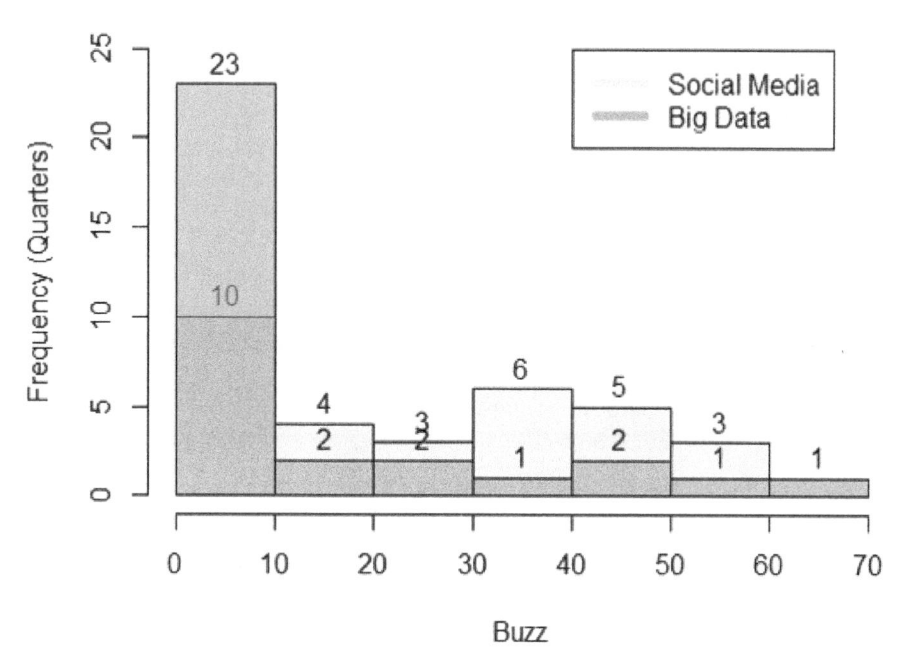

Figure B.12 Final Histogram of Buzz Levels

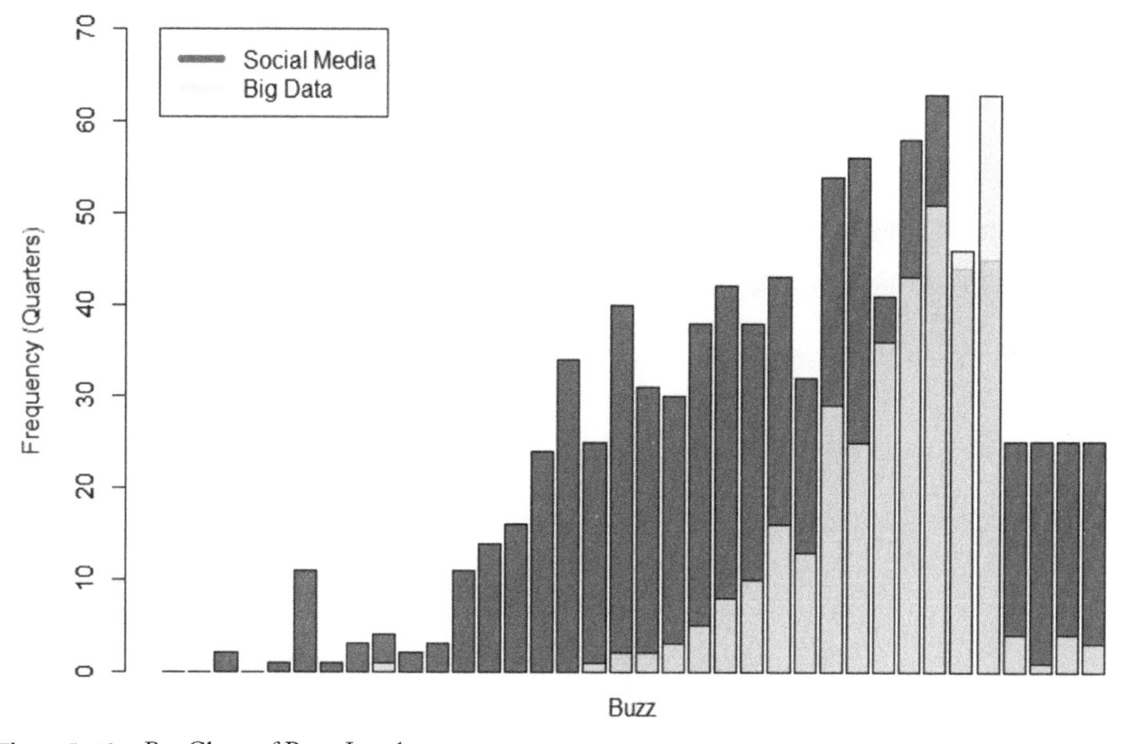

Figure B.13 Bar Chart of Buzz Levels

The code below allows us to visualize the relationship between year and big data buzz:

```
plot(ITHype$Year, ITHype$BigData, xlab='Year', ylab='Big Data Diffusion')
```

Adding a title statement

```
title(main='Diffusion of Big Data between 2006 and 2013')
```

provides us with the visual in Figure B.14.

Finally, we would like to display the data as Chernoff faces. We wish to display social media buzz in the height of the faces and big data buzz in the width of the faces. Because all other parameters are set to zero, no other attributes vary, minimizing viewers' distraction from the key attributes we wish to display.

```
faces(cbind(Summary.Hype[2], Summary.Hype[3], 0, 0, 0, 0, 0, 0, 0, 0, 0, 0, 0, 0, 0),
   face.type=0, labels=Summary.Hype$Year)
```

Adding

```
title(main='Social Media (face height) and Big Data (face width) Buzz \n')
```

produces the visual displayed in Figure B.15.

Lastly, we would like a scatterplot matrix of year, social media buzz, and big data buzz. Following this with a title() statement as depicted below produces the scatterplot matrix in Figure B.16, which is a visual equivalent of the correlation matrix above.

```
pairs(ITHype[c(1,3,4)])
title(main='Scatterplot Matrix \n  \n ')          # '\n' = new Line - spaces title
```

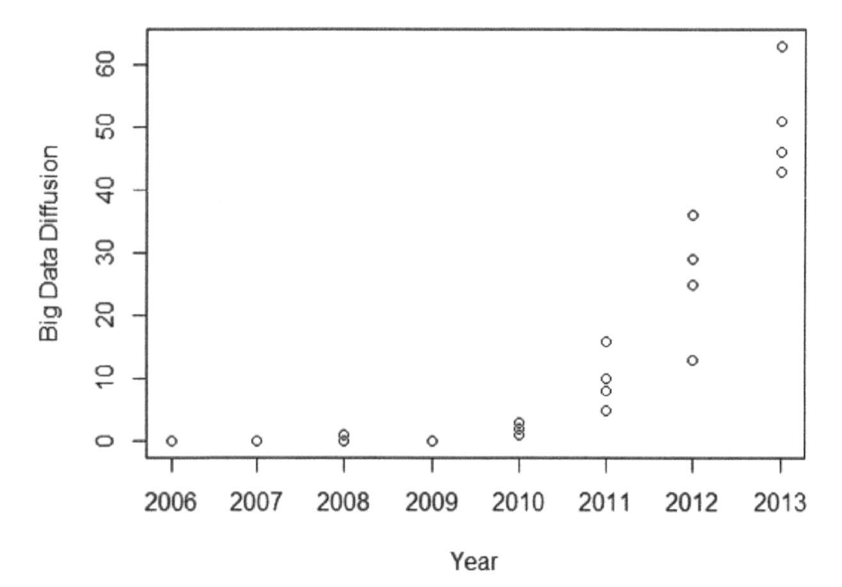

Figure B.14 Scatter Plot of Big Data Buzz and Time

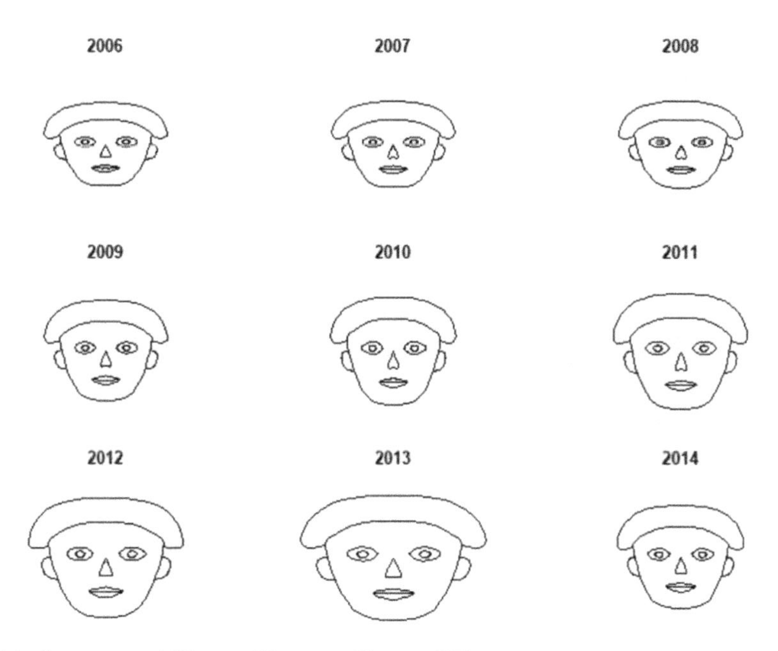

Figure B.15 Multidimensional View of Buzz as Chernoff Faces

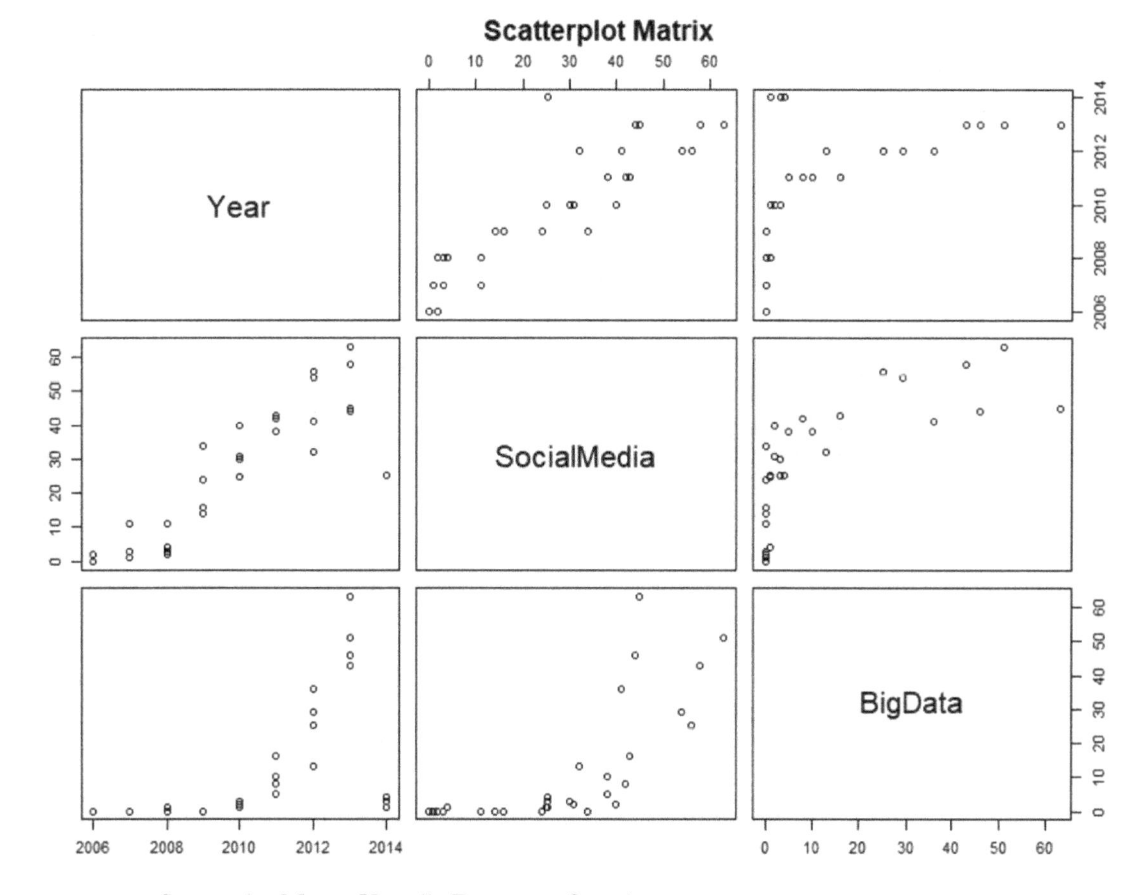

Figure B.16 Scatterplot Matrix Visually Depicting Correlations

Now, we would like to determine whether there is a significant difference in social media buzz in early versus late periods. We do so with the following statement

```
t.test(ITHype$SocialMedia ~ ITHype$Period)
```

which produces the following output:

```
        Welch Two Sample t-test

data:  ITHype$SocialMedia by ITHype$Period
t = -8.5594, df = 33.925, p-value = 5.442e-10
alternative hypothesis: true difference in means is not equal to 0
95 percent confidence interval:
 -38.56197 -23.76303
sample estimates:
mean in group Early  mean in group Late
             7.8750             39.0375
```

This tells us that, on average, there were ~8 (precisely 7.875) press releases per quarter between 2006 and 2009, and ~39 press releases per quarter thereafter. As one would expect after seeing these mean differences, the difference is very significant (worth our attention), with a p-value very close to zero.

Next, we want to determine whether levels of quarterly buzz differ for social media and big data. We do so with

```
t.test(ITHype$SocialMedia,ITHype$BigData, paired=TRUE)
```

which produces the following results. The mean of the differences tells us that, on average, there are approximately fifteen more press releases about social media than about big data in a quarter. The t- and p-values suggest that this difference is highly significant.

```
        Paired t-test

data:  ITHype$SocialMedia and ITHype$BigData
t = 6.7002, df = 35, p-value = 9.345e-08
alternative hypothesis: true difference in means is not equal to 0
95 percent confidence interval:
 10.46964 19.57203
sample estimates:
mean of the differences
               15.02083
```

To compare total buzz levels across the four-category Stage variable instead of the two-category Period variable, we run an ANOVA instead of the t-test. The ANOVA statement for investigating whether the amount of social media buzz differs across the four Stage levels is

```
summary(aov(ITHype$Buzz ~ ITHype$Stage))
```

which produces the following output:

```
              Df Sum Sq Mean Sq F value   Pr(>F)    
ITHype$Stage   3  25385    8462    18.8 3.25e-07 ***
Residuals     32  14399     450                     
---
Signif. codes:  0 '***' 0.001 '**' 0.01 '*' 0.05 '.' 0.1 ' ' 1
```

Alternatively, we could use **summary(aov(**Buzz ~ Stage, data=ITHype**))** for the same result.

We have a hunch that firms' interest in big data is increasing annually and is influenced by their interest in social media (because some researchers believe firms need big data tools to capitalize on their social media investments [3]). We can test this using the following statement, which produces the predictive model below:

```
lm(BigData ~ Year + SocialMedia, data=ITHype)
```

```
Call:
lm(formula = BigData ~ Year + SocialMedia, data = ITHype)

Coefficients:
(Intercept)         Year  SocialMedia  
  -38.96008      0.01628      0.65123  
```

If we wanted to use our current data to predict future big data buzz, this information would be useful. Specifically, if we knew how much social media buzz there was and in which year, we could predict big data buzz as follows:

*Big Data buzz = -38.96008 + 0.01628 * Year + 0.65123 * Social Media buzz*

We would like to store the predicted Big Data buzz values for our current data set for later analysis. First, we create a new data frame named Predict.Hype that includes all the data from our ITHype data frame. Then we add the predicted—or fitted—values from this model—column BDModel1—to that data frame as below:

```
Predict.Hype=ITHype
Predict.Hype$BDModel1=fitted(lm(BigData ~ Year + SocialMedia, data=ITHype))
```

If the amount of social media buzz in some quarter in 2019 is 350 press releases, we would anticipate ~222 press releases (precisely 221.83974, but fractional press releases are not meaningful, so we round) about big data from our Fortune 50 firms:

221.83974 = -38.96008 + 0.01628 * 2019—0.65123 * 350

However, this output does not tell us how good our model is. To obtain this information, we run the following statement to produce the more detailed output depicted below:

```
summary(lm(BigData ~ Year + SocialMedia, data=ITHype))
```

```
Call:
lm(formula = BigData ~ Year + SocialMedia, data = ITHype)

Residuals:
    Min      1Q  Median      3Q     Max
-17.813  -8.656  -1.265   5.634  39.882

Coefficients:
              Estimate Std. Error t value Pr(>|t|)
(Intercept) -38.96008 2519.23296  -0.015 0.987754
Year          0.01628    1.25504   0.013 0.989728
SocialMedia   0.65123    0.17181   3.790 0.000607 ***
---
Signif. codes:  0 '***' 0.001 '**' 0.01 '*' 0.05 '.' 0.1 ' ' 1

Residual standard error: 12.05 on 33 degrees of freedom
Multiple R-squared:  0.5327,     Adjusted R-squared:  0.5044
F-statistic: 18.81 on 2 and 33 DF,  p-value: 3.535e-06
```

First, we see that our model adjusted R^2 is 0.5044, which is reasonably high. Paying attention to the significance of the individual t-values though tells us that our hunch about firms' interest in social media being related to their interest in big data is correct, but our hunch about big data interest increasing annually is not. Given how very recently interest in big data has spiked, perhaps the influence of social media on firms' interest in big data increases over time. To test this hunch, we add an interaction (multiplicative) term to our model, resulting in the output depicted below:

```
summary(lm(BigData ~ Year + SocialMedia + Year*SocialMedia, data=ITHype))
```

```
Call:
lm(formula = BigData ~ Year + SocialMedia + Year * SocialMedia,
    data = ITHype)

Residuals:
     Min       1Q   Median       3Q      Max
-10.8025  -4.9122  -0.3013   2.9889  30.5436

Coefficients:
                   Estimate Std. Error t value Pr(>|t|)
(Intercept)      8282.83639 2138.87648   3.873 0.000500 ***
Year               -4.12667    1.06528  -3.874 0.000499 ***
SocialMedia      -524.19935   82.17569  -6.379 3.64e-07 ***
Year:SocialMedia    0.26103    0.04087   6.387 3.56e-07 ***
---
Signif. codes:  0 '***' 0.001 '**' 0.01 '*' 0.05 '.' 0.1 ' ' 1

Residual standard error: 8.112 on 32 degrees of freedom
Multiple R-squared:  0.7946,     Adjusted R-squared:  0.7753
F-statistic: 41.26 on 3 and 32 DF,  p-value: 4.173e-11
```

The increased adjusted R^2—from 0.5044 to 0.7753—suggests this indeed is a better model. We also see the previously insignificant t-value for Year now is significant and, surprisingly, Year and social media interest both have negative effects on big data interest. Thus, once we account for the contingent effect of social media interest over time on big data interest, the direct effects of social media interest and time on big data interest are negative. We add the predicted values based on this model to our Predict.Hype data frame using

```
Predict.Hype$BDModel2=fitted(lm(BigData ~ Year + SocialMedia + Year*SocialMedia,
   data=ITHype))
```

Finally, we would like to save our work for future analyses or to share with others. The statement below outputs our predicted big data values for the thirty-two quarters to a text file.

```
write.table(Predict.Hype,file='predicted.txt', quote=FALSE, sep=' ')
```

The statement below outputs our predicted data to a predicted.csv file.

```
write.csv(Predict.Hype,file='predicted.csv', quote=TRUE)
```

Finally, we can send our output to a PDF file with

```
pdf('HypeOutput.pdf')
    faces(cbind(Summary.Hype[2], Summary.Hype[3], 0, 0, 0, 0, 0, 0, 0, 0, 0, 0, 0, 0,
        0), face.type=0, labels=Summary.Hype$Year)
    summary(lm(BigData ~ Year + SocialMedia + Year*SocialMedia, data=ITHype))
dev.off()
```

This will send Figure B.15 and our final regression output to HypeOutput.pdf.

Exercise: How to Write a Successful Yelp Review

The purpose of this exercise is to understand what qualities of a Yelp review make it successful. The *YelpReviews.csv* file contains data on ten thousand reviews. The file contains the following Yelp information:

- UserID: source of the review.
- Business: ID of the business being reviewed.
- Date: date of the review.
- Text: review content.
- Votes.Useful: number of users who indicated the review was useful.
- Votes.Cool: number of users who indicated the review was cool.
- Votes.Funny: number of users who indicated the review was funny.
- Stars: number of stars the reviewer gave the business being reviewed.

In addition, review text was analyzed using LIWC and the following metrics of the text content are provided:

- WC: number of words in the review.
- WPS: number of words per sentence.
- prep: percentage of words that are prepositions. This tends to "signal that the speaker is providing more complex and, often, more concrete information about a topic" [4: p. 35].
- negate: percentage of words that are negations (e.g., no, not, never).
- adj: percentage of words that are adjectives.
- posemo: percentage of words depicting positive emotion.
- negemo: percentage of words depicting negative emotion.
- differ: percentage of words used to differentiate (e.g., but, else).
- drives: percentage of words referencing different drives or motives such as affiliation, achievement, power, reward, or risk.
- comma: percentage of words that are commas.

The purpose of this exercise is to understand what makes for a successful Yelp review—specifically, a review that results in higher numbers of useful, cool, and funny votes.

Individual Assignment

1. In order to understand the data, begin by describing at least ten variables graphically using at least three of the following:
   a. A histogram
   b. A bar chart
   c. A scatterplot matrix
   d. Chernoff faces
2. Create the following variables:
   a. PositiveTone, a continuous variable computed as posemo/(posemo+negemo)
   b. Tone, a categorical variable with three levels
      i. Negative: if negemo > posemo
      ii. Neutral: if negemo = posemo
      iii. Positive: if posemo > negemo
   c. One other categorical variable of your choice that converts one of the continuous variables into categories based on values of its mean or median
3. For at least two of the Yelp review success metrics, answer the question: To what extent does Tone affect review success?
4. For at least two of the Yelp review success metrics, find a model that best predicts success.
5. Save all code output to a Word file named with your first and last name (e.g., ShailaMiranda.docx). Annotate your output with a brief description of the analyses you ran and why, and your interpretation of results. Note data anomalies and assumptions that may have been violated.

Team Assignment

Put together your team's analyses into a PowerPoint that tells a story about what—according to Yelpers—makes a review useful. Your first slide should name all team members. Your story should reveal at least five insights that explain or predict and lead you to tangible recommendations.

Works Cited

1. Chernoff, H., "The Use of Faces to Represent Points in k-Dimensional Space Graphically." *Journal of the American Statistical Association*, 68(342; 1973): 361–68.
2. De Soete, G., and W. Do Corte, "On the Perceptual Salience of Features of Chernoff Faces for Representing Multivariate Data." *Applied Psychological Measurement*, 9(3; 1985): 275–80.
3. Kane, G.C., "What Is Social Media, Anyway? (And Why Managers Should Care)," in *Big Idea: Social Business*. Cambridge, MA: MIT, 2013.
4. Tausczik, Y.R., and J.W. Pennebaker, "The Psychological Meaning of Words: LIWC and Computerized Text Analysis Methods." *Journal of Language and Social Psychology*, 29(1; 2010): 24–54.

APPENDIX C

Scraping Twitter with R

This appendix introduces you to working with APIs. It then provides you with the information necessary to obtain Twitter authorization credentials, which you will need to access Twitter data via Twitter's APIs, and to use Twitter's search and streaming API to harvest tweets.

Learning Objectives

The purpose of this appendix is to introduce you to scraping Twitter data with R. The appendix covers the fundamentals required to:

1. work with APIs;
2. obtain your Twitter credentials;
3. harvest tweets using Twitter's search and streaming APIs.

Packages Relevant to Harvesting Tweets

We need two sets of packages for harvesting tweets. The first set are those essential to authentication: **ROAuth** and **RCurl**. The second set enables us to interact with Twitter feeds. We will use **twitteR** and **streamR**.

Working with APIs

In order to download data from Twitter, you first will need to authenticate your R connection to Twitter. This will require you to get your own Twitter credentials. The process for doing so is described below. This is something you will need to do only once. Thereafter, you can save those credentials and load them into future R sessions from which you wish to search and download data from Twitter. You can run these sessions from any computer that has access to the credentials file you store.

To download Twitter data, we have two API options (see the "What Is an API?" insert). The first is using a ***Search API*** (part of Twitter's Rest API). The Search API downloads historic data that matches a specified search criterion. The second option is to use a ***Streaming API***. This permits you to download tweets matching your search criteria in real time (i.e., as they are being posted).

Which API should you use? When you wish to track anticipated tweets around a specific event, the Streaming API tweet is useful. When you wish to obtain tweets from recent history (one or two weeks—accounts on this period differ), use the Search API. In other words, Search API is backward looking, while Streaming API is forward looking. Note that both Search API and Streaming API are rate-limited, but rate-limiting operates differently. Search API, as we have seen in NodeXL, limits the number of calls or tweets that can be downloaded in a fixed period of time (180 calls per 15 minutes). Streaming API delivers only about 1% of the complete Twitter stream, unless you pay for it [1]. If you plan on extended data capture tasks, it is worth acquainting yourself with Twitter's rate limit policies to avoid the possibility of being blacklisted [2].

Below we walk through the steps for obtaining your Twitter authentication credentials and then establishing a "handshake" between Twitter and R. We then examine packages and functions that permit each of the two APIs.

What Is an API?

API stands for "application program interface." It provides a set of tools and specifications for one program to interact with another. Sure, we can bypass APIs and write our own code to scrape websites and social media platforms. We would do this in a digital imitation of the steps we would manually take to scrape the necessary data. When the website changes its architecture or layout, though, our digitized data capture process breaks down. An API call therefore provides a more robust interface because it supplies the necessary parameters in an XML-type format rather than relying on our program's ability to glean the information off the site itself.

An API represents a contract or handshake between the requester program and the program providing the requested data. When R attempts to obtain data from platforms such as Twitter, it does so using the APIs supplied by those platforms. In other words, it enters into a contract with that program, cemented with a "handshake." Keep a lookout for this "handshake" in our R code.

Getting Your Twitter Authorization Credentials

The first thing we need to do in order to download data from Twitter is to obtain our own authentication codes. You will need a Twitter account to do so. Then, go to https://apps.twitter.com/. If necessary, sign in. You should see an interface similar to that in Figure C.1. Click the "Create New App" button.

Now, complete the application information requested. Your application Name can be something like YOURNAME-OnTwitter. The Description can be any text you wish. For the Website, use https://twitter.com/. Set the Callback URL to **oob**. This is important for the API to correctly return the required PIN for the streamR package.

Select "Create My Access Token" to finalize the process. When done, you should be able to select the Keys and Access Tokens tab. This should provide you with your Consumer Key, Consumer Secret, Access Token, and Access Token Secret as depicted in Figure C.3. Make a note of these—we will need them to authenticate our R connection to Twitter.

Using the Twitter Search API

The **twitteR** package provides us with functions necessary to take advantage of Twitter's Search API. Prior to querying Twitter, we need to authorize Twitter to send back information to R. To do so, we need to supply Twitter with our authentication credentials. We can do so by assigning each of the four credentials to a variable and then using those credentials in the ***setup_twitter_oauth(APIKEY, APISECRET, ACCESSTOKEN, ACCESSTOKENSECRET)*** function. This function establishes the "handshake" between the

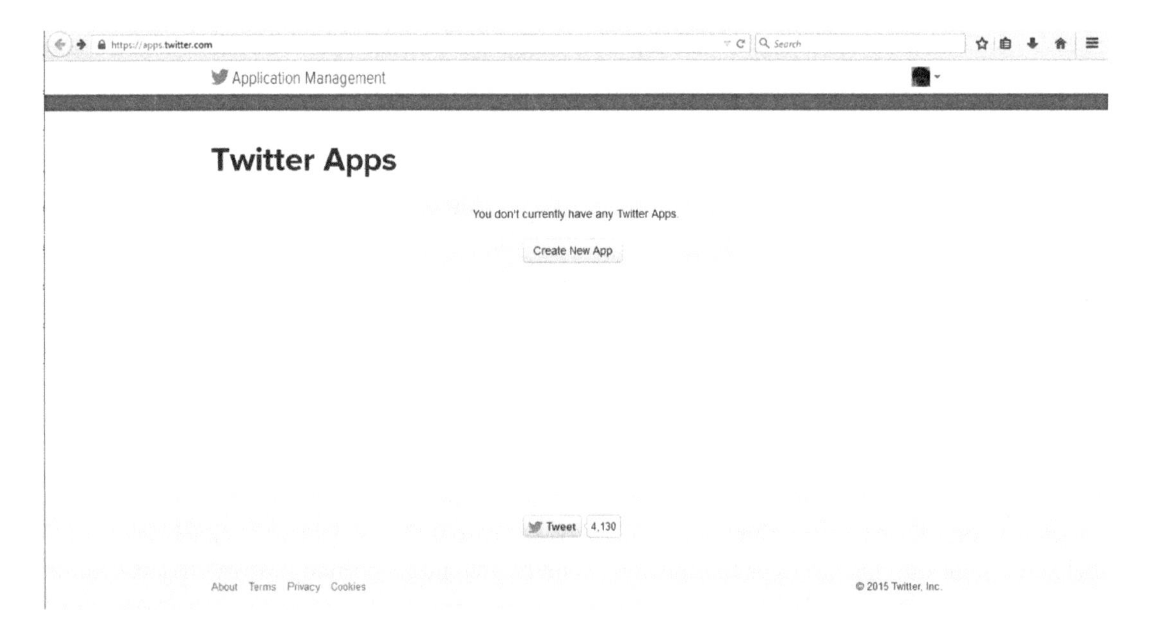

Figure C.1 Twitter Apps Interface

R session and Twitter. The following statements will establish the handshake. (Of course, we could skip the first four and enter our credential information directly into the setup_twitter_oauth() function.)

```
apiKey='YourConsumerKey'
apiSecret='YourConsumerSecret'
token='YourAccessToken'
tokenSecret='YourAccessTokenSecret'
setup_twitter_oauth(apiKey, apiSecret, token, tokenSecret)
```

This will produce the following prompt asking whether the authorization credentials should be locally cached. Select 1 for Yes.

```
[1] "Using direct authentication"
Use a local file ('.httr-oauth'), to cache OAuth access credentials between R
sessions?

1: Yes
2: No

Selection:
```

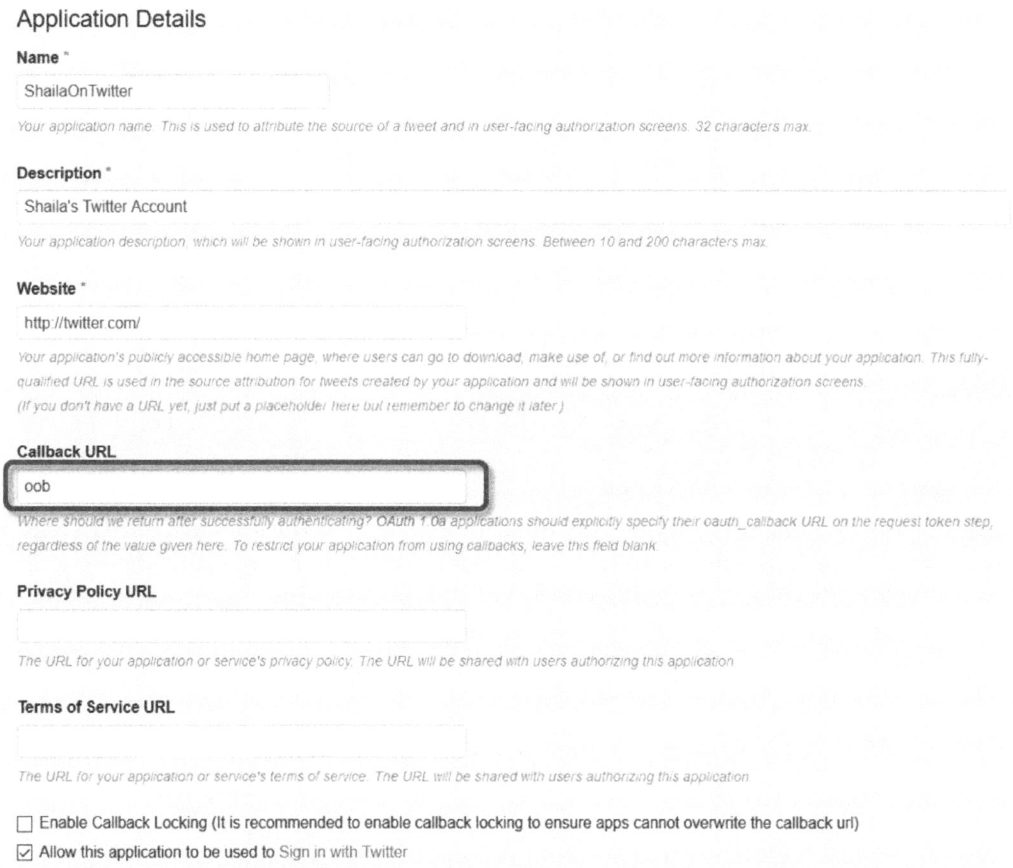

Application Details
Name *
ShailaOnTwitter
Your application name. This is used to attribute the source of a tweet and in user-facing authorization screens. 32 characters max.
Description *
Shaila's Twitter Account
Your application description, which will be shown in user-facing authorization screens. Between 10 and 200 characters max.
Website *
http://twitter.com/
Your application's publicly accessible home page, where users can go to download, make use of, or find out more information about your application. This fully-qualified URL is used in the source attribution for tweets created by your application and will be shown in user-facing authorization screens.
(If you don't have a URL yet, just put a placeholder here but remember to change it later.)
Callback URL
oob
Where should we return after successfully authenticating? OAuth 1.0a applications should explicitly specify their oauth_callback URL on the request token step, regardless of the value given here. To restrict your application from using callbacks, leave this field blank.
Privacy Policy URL
The URL for your application or service's privacy policy. The URL will be shared with users authorizing this application.
Terms of Service URL
The URL for your application or service's terms of service. The URL will be shared with users authorizing this application.
☐ Enable Callback Locking (It is recommended to enable callback locking to ensure apps cannot overwrite the callback url)
☑ Allow this application to be used to Sign in with Twitter

Figure C.2 Defining the Application Details

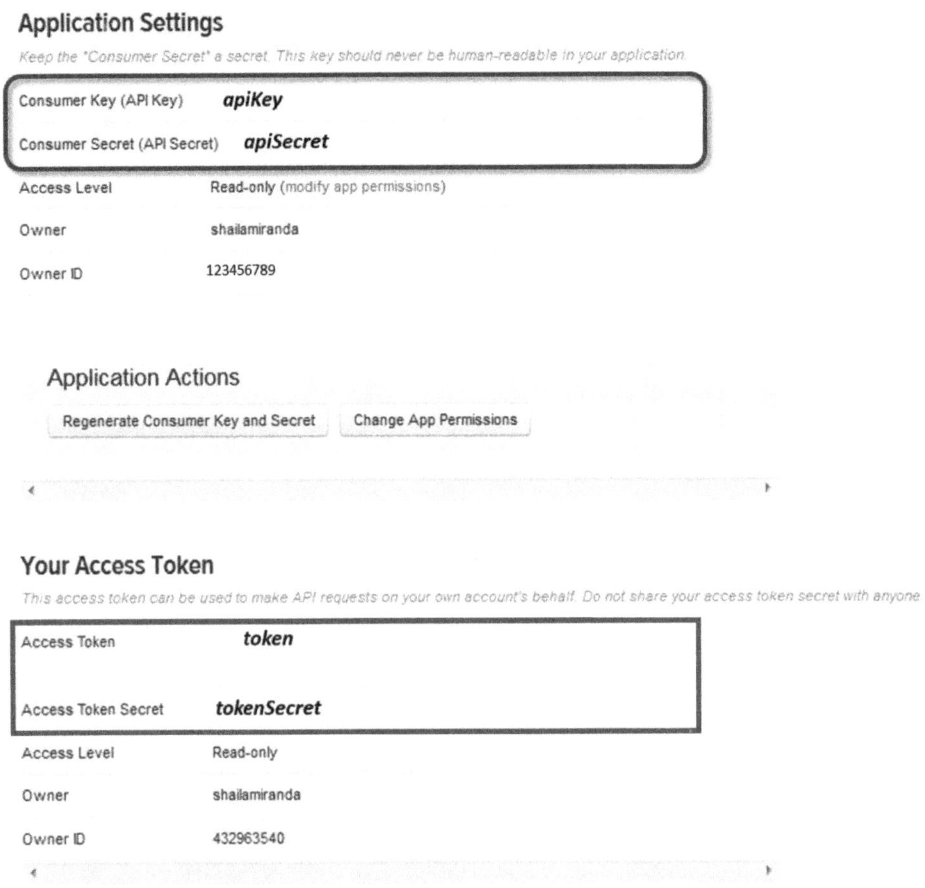

Application Settings

Keep the "Consumer Secret" a secret. This key should never be human-readable in your application.

Consumer Key (API Key)	***apiKey***
Consumer Secret (API Secret)	***apiSecret***
Access Level	Read-only (modify app permissions)
Owner	shailamiranda
Owner ID	123456789

Application Actions

Regenerate Consumer Key and Secret | Change App Permissions

Your Access Token

This access token can be used to make API requests on your own account's behalf. Do not share your access token secret with anyone.

Access Token	***token***
Access Token Secret	***tokenSecret***
Access Level	Read-only
Owner	shailamiranda
Owner ID	432963540

Figure C.3 Twitter Credentials

You should see the following prompt:

```
[1] "Using direct authentication"
```

To query Twitter, we use the ***searchTwitter(SEARCHSTRING)*** function. This function accepts the query arguments depicted in Table C.1.

For example, to retrieve 1,500 English language tweets mentioning "immigration," we can run `immigrationTweets=searchTwitter('immigration', n=1500, lang='en')`. To convert the list of tweets imported to an R data frame, we can use the ***twListToDF()*** function. For example, we can create an immigrationDF object using `immigrationDF= twListToDF(immigrationTweets)`. Now, we can apply our social network analysis or text analytics to immigrationDF data frame or save our tweets to a file for future analysis.

We also can obtain the profile information for users who have tweeted about a specific topic. We do this using the ***lookupUsers('SCREENNAME')*** function. To access the output, we must remember to convert the JSON format to a data frame using the TwListToDF() function. This will return the following profile attributes: description, statusesCount, followersCount, favoritesCount, friendsCount, url, name, created, protected, verified, screenName, location, lang, id, listedCount, followRequestSent, and profileImageUrl. To obtain this information for my own account, I can run `twListToDF(lookupUsers('shailamiranda'))`. If I want profile information for all users appearing in my immigrationDF data frame, I can capture this using `immigrationTweeters=twListToDF(lookupUsers(immigrationDF$screenName))`.

Table C.1 Twitter Query Options

Argument	Explanation	Values
First argument	Search string	Text
n=	Number of tweets to be returned	Number
lang=	The language of the tweets to be returned	en for English
since=	Start date for tweets	Date
until=	End date for tweets	Date
geocode=	Tweets within a specified radius of a specified geocode	Geographic coordinates
retryOnRateLimit=	How often to retry when Twitter's rate limit is reached	Number
cainfo=	Certification authority necessary for Windows environments	cacert.pem

Finally, we also can use the twitteR package to obtain a user's friends and followers. We obtain a friends list with the ***getUser('UserName')$getFriends()*** function and a followers list with the ***getUser('UserName')$getFollowers()*** function. For example, `MyFriends= getUser('shailamiranda')$getFriends()` will return a list of my friends, and `MyFollowers= getUser('shailamiranda')$getFollowers()` will return a list of my followers. Again, remember to convert these JSON lists to a data frame using the TwListToDF() function. For large friend or follower lists, we can add a retryOnRateLimit=NUMBEROFTIMES argument inside the getFriends() or getFollowers() function. For example, `OUPriceFriends= getUser('OUPriceCollege')$getFriends(retryOnRateLimit=180)` will retry the query 180 times upon encountering Twitter's rate limits.

Using the Twitter Streaming API

We use the **streamR** package to access Twitter's streaming API. The streamR package goes through a more explicit handshake process than the twitteR package. Thankfully this is something we will need to do only once. Thereafter, we can save these handshake credentials to a file and simply load that file at the start of a streaming R session.

Establishing the handshake also requires the **RCurl** and **ROAuth** packages. After installing and loading these packages, we need to do three things. First, we need to set up an SSL certificate, which we do as follows:

```
options(RCurlOptions = list(cainfo = system.file('CurlSSL', 'cacert.pem', package
                                ='RCurl')))
```

To harvest tweets in a Windows environment, we also need to download a file containing authentication certificates (cacert.pem):

```
download.file(url="http://curl.haxx.se/ca/cacert.pem", destfile="cacert.pem")
```

Note: Be sure you have set your working directory appropriately.

Second, we need to set up the API variables to connect to Twitter. This requires the following URLs for two token requests from Twitter and an authorization request.

```
requestURL = 'https://api.twitter.com/oauth/request_token'
accessURL = 'https://api.twitter.com/oauth/access_token'
authURL = 'https://api.twitter.com/oauth/authorize'
```

Third, we need to input our Twitter access codes. The streamR package requires only our Consumer Key and Consumer Secret credentials.

```
apiKey='YourConsumerKey'
apiSecret='YourConsumerSecret'
```

Now we can authorize our connection with

```
twitCred = OAuthFactory$new(consumerKey=apiKey, consumerSecret=apiSecret,
     requestURL=requestURL, accessURL=accessURL, authURL=authURL)
```

We now have our credentials stored in twitCred. We can establish the handshake between our R session and Twitter by supplying these credentials along with the ***twitCred$handshake()*** request. For a Windows environment, we can ensure it is able to establish the SSL certificate by supplying the parameters indicating the path for the SSL certificate using `twitCred$handshake(cainfo = system.file('CurlSSL', 'cacert.pem', package='RCurl'))`. You then will see the following in your console:

```
To enable the connection, please direct your web browser to:
http://api.twitter.com/oauth/authorize?oauth_token=QRYUdHgItmgPSlAwHog4FdP16aiIVC7P
When complete, record the PIN given to you and provide it here:
```

If the command did not automatically open up a browser window as depicted in Figure C.4, copy the URL provided into your browser, being sure to change the "http:" to "https:" (for an SSL connection). Then, go ahead and click "Authorize App." **Note: If you saw "SSL is required" instead, you forgot to change "http:" to "https:".**

You then will see an authorization PIN as depicted in Figure C.5. Copy the PIN to your *Console* panel in RStudio, and press <ENTER>.

To save these credentials for future use, we use `save(list='twitCred', file='Credentials')`. For all future R streamR sessions, we can bypass all authorization steps by using `load('Credentials')`.

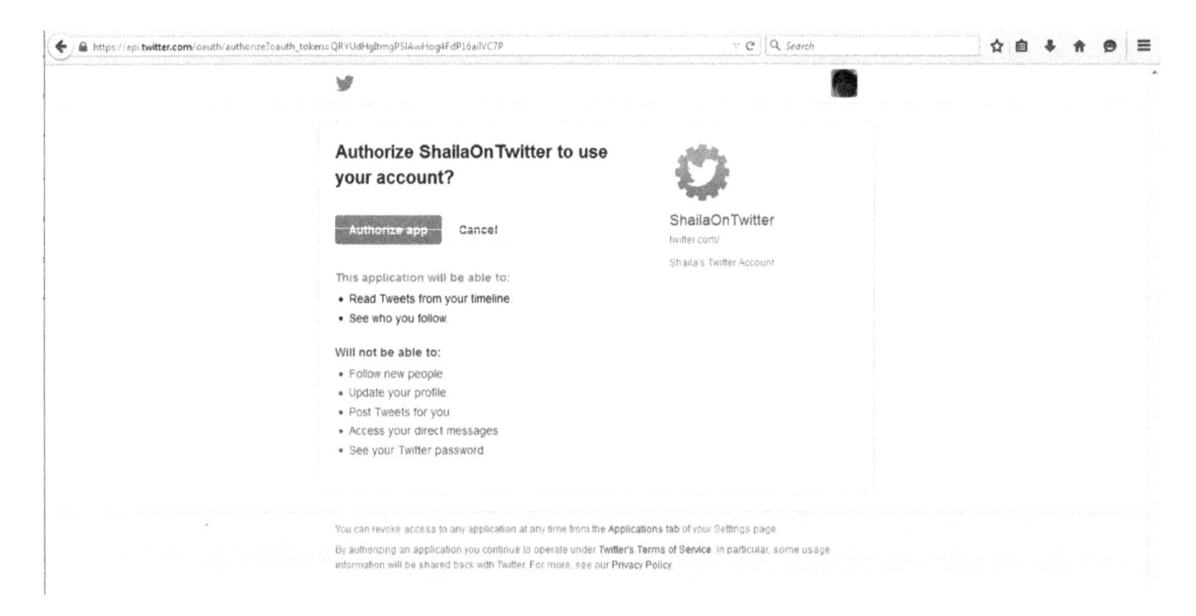

Figure C.4 Twitter Authorization Screen

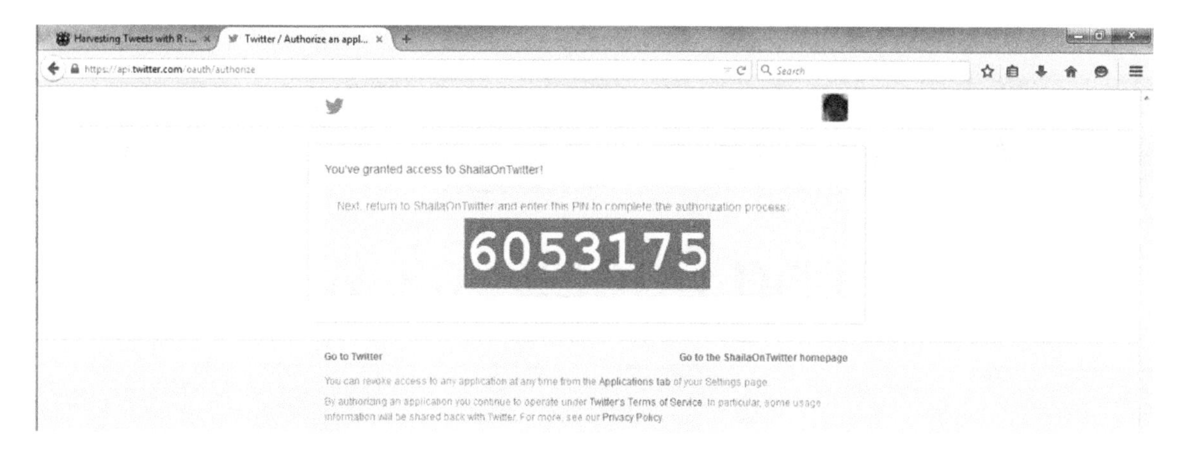

Figure C.5 Twitter Authorization PIN

We now are ready to download tweets through R. We can obtain a stream of tweets from the authenticated user account using the ***userStream(oauth=CREDENTIALS)*** function. Note that this will obtain *only* tweets from your own account. For example, `userStream(file.name='twitterData.json',with='followings',tweets=10,oauth=twitCred)` will stream ten tweets from my account and/or from accounts I follow.

To obtain streaming tweets that meet a specified search criterion, we can use the ***filterStream(file.name=FILENAME, track=SEARCHSTRING, oauth=CREDENTIALS)*** function. For example, `filterStream(file.name='president.json', track='donald trump', timeout=600, oauth=twitCred)` captures ten minutes of tweets about the president (and possibly others named Donald Trump), sending it to a file named president.json. By default, filterStream() appends to the specified file. So, if interrupted, we can continue to route further streams to the existing file. Beware of burgeoning file size, though. It may be preferable to stream the tweets to separate files for easier file management.

The "track=" argument, available also with the userStream() function, permits us to specify a search string for our streaming capture. This need not be a single hashtag or search term. For example, in a recent project on the conversation about immigration on Twitter, we used the search string `track=c('immigration', 'immigrant', 'refugee', 'illegals', 'amnesty', 'anchor baby', 'illegal alien', 'deport')`. Running a search with multiple terms rather than multiple searches with a single term—perhaps from several computers—is preferable because it limits duplicate tweets.

The "timeout=" argument, also available with userStream(), permits us to specify the duration of the stream. For example, we specified timeout=86400 to stream data for a 24-hour period. The default timeout of 0 leaves open the connection indefinitely.

We can extract our tweets to a data frame using ***parseTweets('FILENAME')***. For example, we can extract the president tweets to a data frame named PresidentTweets using `PresidentTweets =parseTweets('president.json')`. Of course, PresidentTweets now may be exported to a .csv or other type of file format.

APPENDIX D

Scraping Facebook with R

The Facebook API permits search only, not streaming. As with Twitter, Facebook periodically changes its API, changing the data that you can import into R. With some workarounds, though, we still can obtain substantial useful Facebook data. Below, we examine the packages and functions that permit us to harvest Facebook data. Of course, accessing Facebook data must begin with a credentialing process. We look at the steps necessary to obtain the credentials for accessing Facebook data.

Learning Objectives

The purpose of this appendix is to introduce you to scraping Facebook data with R. The appendix covers the fundamentals required to:

1. understand the different Facebook objects;
2. get a Facebook access token;
3. load the package necessary for scraping Facebook;
4. obtain Facebook profile information;
5. obtain Facebook page information;
6. obtain Facebook group information.

Packages Relevant to Harvesting Facebook Posts

The package for accessing Facebook data via R is the **Rfacebook** package. I have not found any alternatives to this package yet.

Facebook Objects

Before attempting to scrape Facebook data, it is useful to understand the different Facebook objects through which we communicate with each other. A Facebook presence begins with a ***personal profile***, which documents an individual person. This personal profile contains descriptions about the individual—their name, gender, birthdate, etc.—and the list of the individual's Facebook friends (which necessarily are mutual relationships). Profile updates or posts, unless public, may be viewed only by your friends [1].

Once we have created a personal profile, we can create fan pages and/or groups [2]. When creating a fan ***page***, Facebook prompts us to assign it to one of six categories: local businesses or places; companies, organizations, or institutions; brands or products; artists, bands, or public figures; entertainment; causes or communities [1]. An example of a local businesses or place is that of Candles Off Main, a store in Maryland that sells candles, perfumes, and home fragrances. Candles Off Main also permits visitors to its Facebook page to shop and be apprised of and obtain coupons and giveaways through its Facebook page. Examples of pages for companies, organizations, or institutions include Starbucks' corporate Facebook page, the page for activist organization MoveOn.org, and that for Price College of Business at the University of Oklahoma. An example of the brands or products category is the luscious Nutella page. Artists, bands, or public figures include President Donald Trump, Jeff Bezos, and celebrities such as Katy Perry and Vin Diesel.

Fan pages may be created by the individual or organization being featured (e.g., the Barack Obama page), or by the individual or organization's fans (e.g., the Obama Lovers page). A little blue checkmark against the account name on Facebook lets us know that we are viewing a "verified page," created by an individual or organization. While an individual may have only a single profile, they may have multiple fan pages. Further, multiple individuals may contribute to or manage a fan page [1]. And anyone can like a page, and page posts are visible to the public.

A ***group*** is a collection of people, typically who share an interest in a topic. There is a group for Facebook developers and a multitude of watchdog and protest groups targeting Facebook [3]. There are technology support groups such as Users of R Statistical Package; special interest groups such as Researchers of the Socio-Technical; patient support groups such as the Support Group for Parents with Kids with ADHD, ADD, Autism, and Other Issues; and activist groups such as The Political Resistance against Donald Trump. Unlike pages, which tend to be the public face of a public figure or organization, groups are more community-oriented. Groups may be open, permitting anyone can join, or closed, where new members must be admitted to the group owner or by an existing member. Group posts typically are visible to all group members.

Getting a Facebook Access Token

In order to download data from Facebook, we first need to authenticate our R connection to Facebook. We may do this by obtaining a short-lived (temporary) or long-lived Facebook access token. Short-lived tokens last about two hours; long-lived tokens last about two months. Since both must be renewed, we will look at using the relatively easy-to-generate short-lived—or temporary access—token.

Obtaining a Facebook token first requires we have a Facebook account. So go ahead and create one if you do not already have an account. We then need to register the account as a Facebook developer. We can do so by logging into our Facebook account and then going to https://developers.facebook.com/docs/apps/register. From there, we follow the flowchart depicted in Figure D.1.

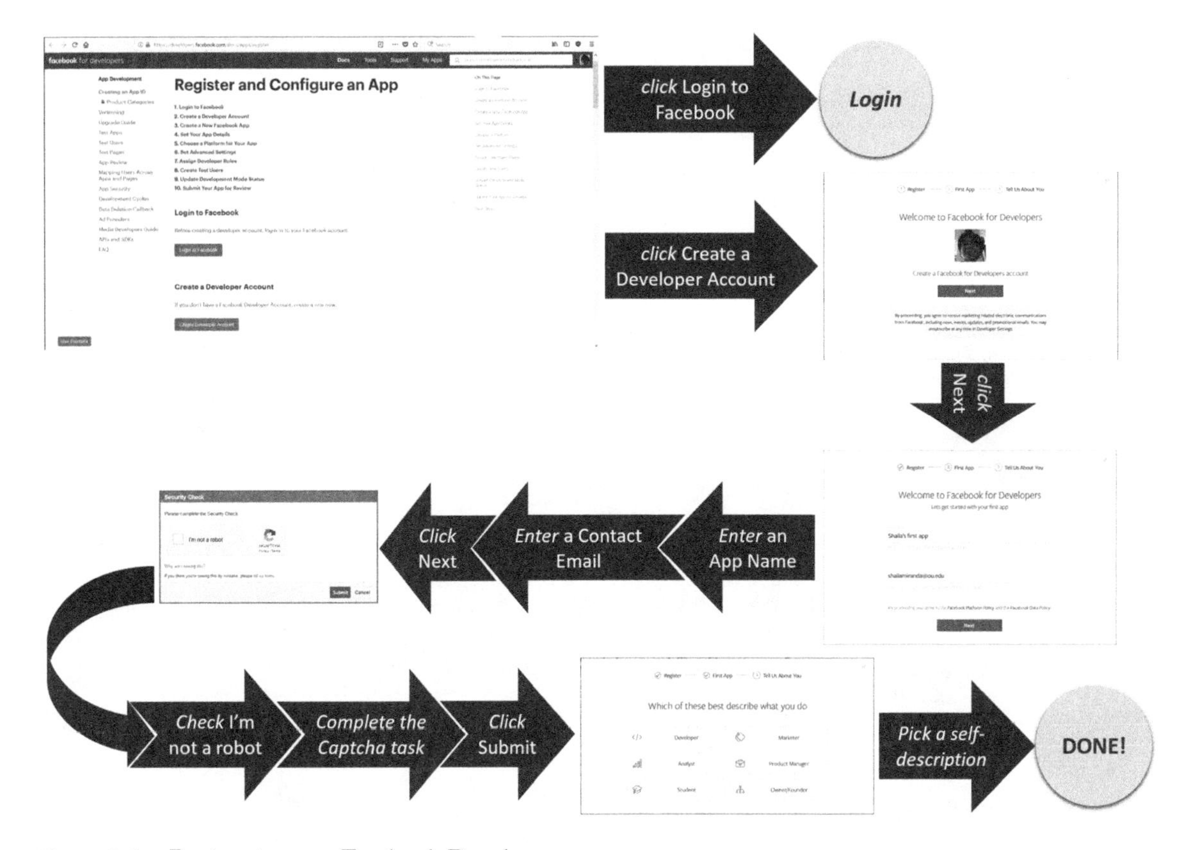

Figure D.1 Registering as a Facebook Developer

Now we can get a temporary access token at https://developers.facebook.com/tools/explorer/. From the site, click Get Token. This will bring up an interface as seen in Figure D.2, which permits us to set the permissions for sharing data. Let's ignore the permissions and simply click the Get Access Token button.

This will return an Access Token string as depicted in Figure D.3. We can copy this token string and paste it into an assignment statement in R. For example, `MyToken='TokenFromFacebookDevelopersSite'` assigns the pasted token string to the variable MyToken. We will reference MyToken in the various R functions through which we attempt to obtain data from Facebook.

Obtaining Facebook Profile Information

To obtain user profile information, we use the ***getUsers('UserID', token=FBToken)*** function. We can obtain our own public information with `mePublic = getUsers('me', token=MyToken)`. This yields ten

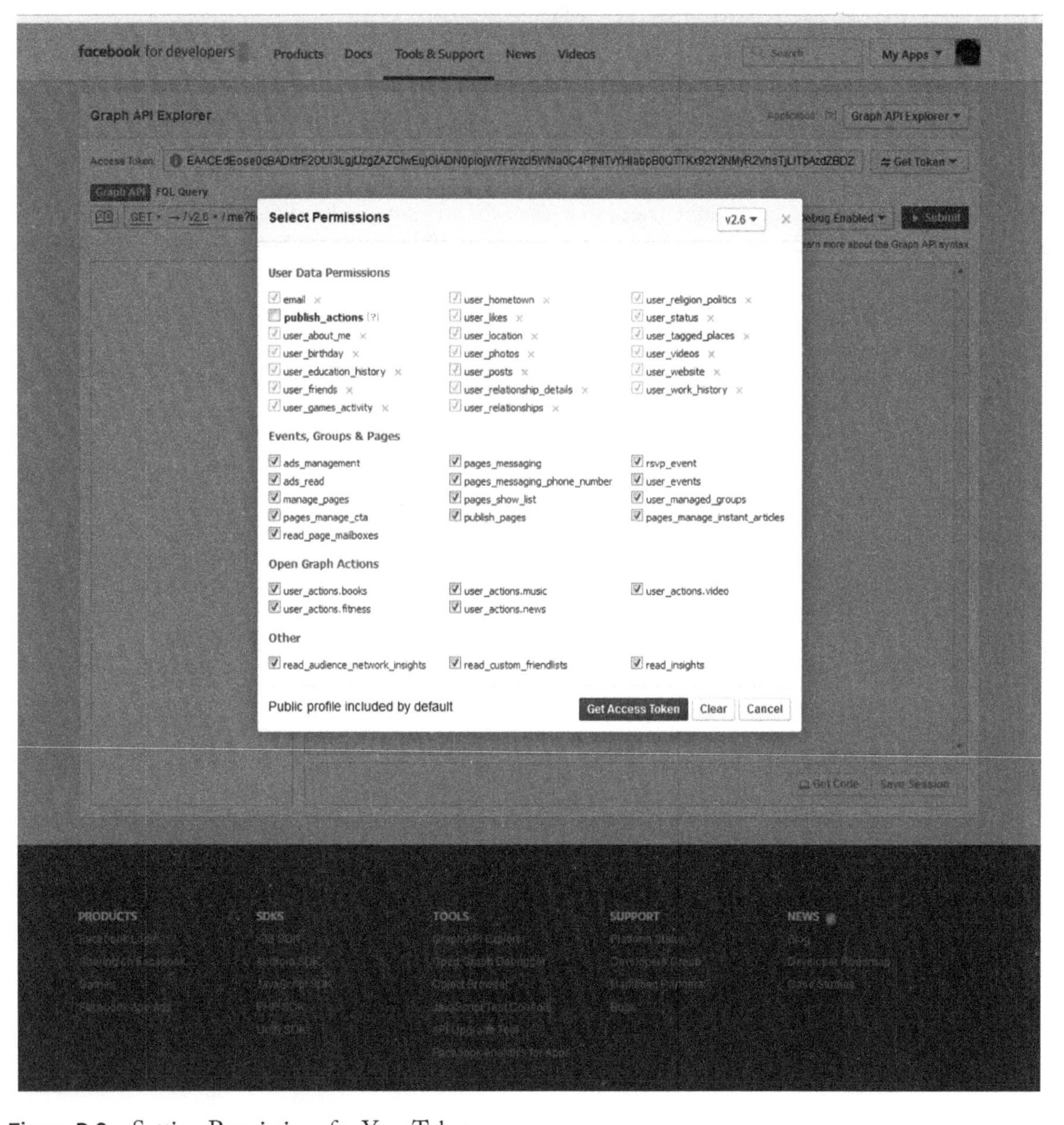

Figure D.2 Setting Permissions for Your Token

attributes about my profile. Adding the "private_info=T" argument to the getUsers() function (i.e., **mePrivate = getUsers('me', token=MyToken, private_info=T)**) provides access to private profile information. For me, this yields four additional profile attributes. In all, the getUsers() call provides the following fourteen pieces of information: id, name, username, first_name, middle_name, last_name, gender, locale, likes, picture, birthday, location, hometown, and relationship_status. Of course, which of these are public and which are private for your account will depend on your Facebook privacy settings.

Facebook will return information for profiles other than our own. However, it no longer permits this search by screen name. To obtain other users' profile information, we first must obtain the user's Facebook ID. Browse the Internet for hacks that show you how to do so. Once you have a user id, that will be the first argument in the getUsers() function (e.g., **getUsers(1276658182, MyToken)**) will return my profile information.

Obtaining Facebook Page Information

The *getPage(FACEBOOKUSER, FACEBOOKTOKEN)* function returns posts from a specified page. For example, **PresidentsPosts = getPage('donaldtrump', MyToken)** will return twenty-five posts (i.e., the default number of posts) from Donald J. Trump's Facebook page. We obtain the following eleven data elements: from_id, from_name, message, created_time, type (video, status, or photo), link, id, story, likes_count, comments_count, and shares_count. We can change the requested number of posts to be returned with the "n=" argument. Alternatively, we can specify a date range with the "since=" and/or "until=" arguments. Adding a "feed=T" argument will return posts not originating from the page owner. For example, **OUPrice= getPage('oupricecollege', MyToken, feed=T, n=5000)** will return up to 5000 posts from the OUPriceCollege page. As will be apparent from the partial data frame in Figure D.4, not all the posts emanate from the OUPriceCollege account.

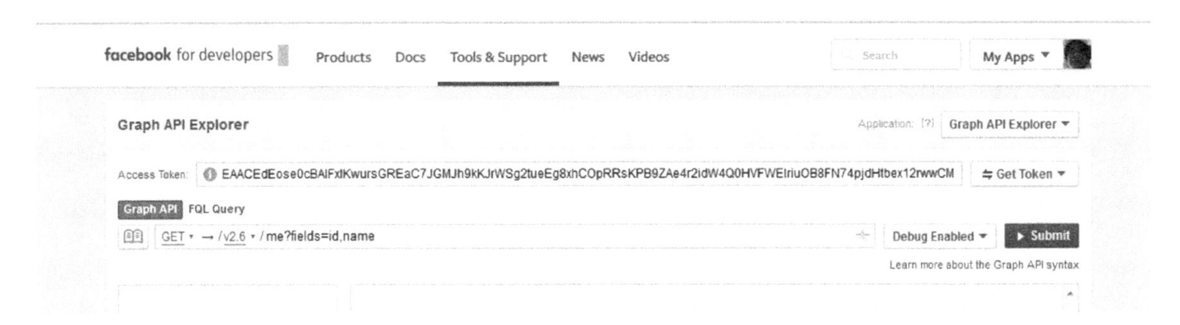

Figure D.3 User Access Token String

	from_id	from_name	message	created_time	type
586	204374265759	Price College of Business at the University of Oklahoma	Words of inspiration from Nelson Mandela: 'Education i...	2013-12-10T16:42:37+0000	status
587	204374265759	Price College of Business at the University of Oklahoma	NA	2013-12-08T02:03:52+0000	link
588	204374265759	Price College of Business at the University of Oklahoma	OU campus is closed today, Friday, Dec. 6. Be safe. Stay ...	2013-12-06T08:42:02+0000	status
589	204374265759	Price College of Business at the University of Oklahoma	Price Seniors.........Quick reminder to look for and compl...	2013-12-05T14:51:01+0000	status
590	204374265759	Price College of Business at the University of Oklahoma	Farewell to Dan Wren, our professor, friend and mentor ...	2013-12-02T22:00:00+0000	photo
591	204374265759	Price College of Business at the University of Oklahoma	Providing opportunities for our Price students. That is w...	2013-12-02T14:52:21+0000	link
592	204374265759	Price College of Business at the University of Oklahoma	Welcome back after a long weekend, all. We're glad you...	2013-12-02T14:10:24+0000	status
593	204374265759	Price College of Business at the University of Oklahoma	Price College welcomed over 130 guests for Sooner Satu...	2013-11-25T18:44:17+0000	photo
594	204374265759	Price College of Business at the University of Oklahoma	The Norman campus will open at 930 am Monday, Nov. 2...	2013-11-25T00:58:05+0000	status
595	204374265759	Price College of Business at the University of Oklahoma	Looking forward to Sooner Saturday tomorrow and mee...	2013-11-22T14:59:49+0000	status
596	204374265759	Price College of Business at the University of Oklahoma	Combined AMA and APICS meeting this Thursday at 6 p....	2013-11-18T19:41:36+0000	status
597	10206455328845079	Zach Lewallen	Selling a student ticket to OU/Iowa St. $32 OBO. Call or ...	2013-11-13T22:37:44+0000	status
598	204374265759	Price College of Business at the University of Oklahoma	Please join the JCPenney Leadership Center in supportin...	2013-11-13T17:25:08+0000	status
599	204374265759	Price College of Business at the University of Oklahoma	Donuts with the Deans tomorrow (11/13) at 10 a.m. in Cl...	2013-11-12T14:52:11+0000	status

Figure D.4 Posts to the OUPriceCollege Facebook Page

If we wish further information about a post, we can use the ***getPost(PostID, FacebookToken)*** function. This function returns two lists: a list containing information about specified posts themselves and a list of information about the comments in response to the post. For example, `OUPost=getPost(OUPrice$id[292], MyToken)` will request information about the 292nd post in the data frame in Figure D.4. Following this with `OUPost$comments` produces the following output:

```
           from_id           from_name                          message             created_time
1 10153044718372318      Julia Lynne Eck                 Hector Alanis <3 2016-05-02T19:48:44+0000
2 10204771167025295 Fatima Aranda-Shakra This is awesome! Get it, Hector! 2016-05-02T21:54:31+0000
3 10102446276753667        Lizzy Tahsuda      Robin Huston <3 Miss y'all! 2016-05-03T00:28:49+0000

  likes_count comments_count                                    id
1           1              0 10154837163535760_10154837610200760
2           1              0 10154837163535760_10154837960600760
3           1              0 10154837163535760_10154838242895760
```

Works Cited

1. Beese, J., "Facebook Fan Page vs. Profile: Know the Difference," *Sprout Blog: Facebook*, 2016, https://sproutsocial.com/insights/facebook-fan-page.
2. Hicks, M., "What's the Difference between a Facebook Page and Group?," Facebook Tips, 2010, https://www.facebook.com/notes/facebook/facebook-tips-whats-the-difference-between-a-facebook-page-and-group/324706977130/.
3. AdweekStaff., "The 25 Facebook Groups with Over 1 Million Members," Brand Marketing, 2009, http://www.adweek.com/digital/the-25-facebok-groups-with-over-1-million-members/.

APPENDIX E

Advanced Visualization in R

> **Learning Objectives**
>
> The purpose of this appendix is to develop your ability to produce snazzy visualizations of your social data. Specifically, we look at:
>
> 1. advanced graphing concepts underlying and how to implement them in R; and
> 2. mapping geocoded data in R.

Thoughtful and aesthetically-pleasing visuals enhance the impact of our analyses. This appendix introduces advanced visualization topics. It describes the procedures and provides the code for producing some of the more compelling visuals depicted in some of the chapters and offers pointers to further our analysis.

Visualization Packages

We begin by examining the graphing concepts underlying the versatile **ggplot2** package and examining its functionality. We also will use the **png** package to embed images in our graphics. We then examine the **maps** or the **ggmap** packages for geocoding.

Advanced Graphing

We don't have to use Tableau to produce the awesome graphs we see in news media such as *The Economist*. The ggplot2 package enables us to produce professional, aesthetically pleasing visuals. However, because the package employs a different "grammar" than that used by the R plot() function, using it to produce simple graphs can be cumbersome.

The ggplot2 grammar parallels that laid out by Wilkinson [1]. In his introduction to *The Grammar of Graphics*, Wilkinson notes that a grammar consists not only of words, but also of rules for their combination into statements. He notes that just as "Grammar makes language expressive," the "grammar of graphics takes us beyond a limited set of charts (words) to an almost unlimited world of graphical forms (statements). Wilkinson eschews the conventional typology of "charts," noting that thinking about pie versus bar versus other types of charts is overly limiting, as we may have hybrid or entirely new types. Instead, he recommends we think about a visual data representation as a graphic, which is created in three stages—specification, assembly, and display.

In the **specification stage**, we identify the data and any transformations on that data. The syntax for specifying the data is ***ggplot(DATASET, aes(x=XVar, y=YVar))***. Note that the "y=YVAR" argument is optional for graphs such as histograms. The ggplot() function alone will not depict a chart, though. For that, we minimally need the assembly stage.

In the **assembly stage**, we define the structure of the chart. Chart structure includes the geometric object to be projected and the coordinate system upon which it is to be projected. Some commonly-used geometric objects are ***geom_area()***, ***geom_boxplot()***, ***geom_histogram()***, ***geom_line()***, and ***geom_point()***. We add these geometric objects to our ggplot() function with a +. For example, to create the chart in Figure B.1 in Appendix B, we use `ggplot(StockPrices, aes(x=Volatility)) + geom_histogram()`. For a line graph relating volatility to opening price, we use `ggplot(StockPrices, aes(x=Open, y=Volatility)) + geom_line()`. Nine coordinate systems are available via ggplot. The default is the cartesian coordinate system that plots data along two perpendicular axes (i.e., ***coord_cartesian()***). Two frequently-used alternatives are

coord_flip(), which swaps x- and y-axes, and ***coord_polar()***, which provides a pie chart or its variant coxcomb chart.

In the **display stage**, we add guides such as titles and labels, change superficial aesthetic attributes—unrelated to the data elements, and apply faceting. We continue to layer these options onto our display with "+"s. The ***xlab('AxisTitle'), ylab('AxisTitle')***, and ***labs(title='ChartTitle', subtitle='ChartSubTitle')*** functions permit us to add axes titles and chart titles/subtitles. For example, `ggplot(StockPrices, aes(x=Volatility)) + geom_histogram() + xlab('Volatility') + ylab('Frequency') + labs(title='Stock Volatility')` will change the x- and y-axis labels and add a title to our graphic. To change the aesthetics on graphic elements such as background color, title colors, fonts, and size, we can access standard ggplot themes. The following functions provide the standard ggplot themes: ***theme_gray()*** (the default theme), ***theme_bw(), theme_linedraw(), theme_light(), theme_dark(), theme_classic()***, and ***theme_minimal()***. Alternatively, we can develop a custom display using the ***theme()*** function. This function permits granular control of various aspects of the graphic via a multitude of arguments. A few of the most useful arguments are summarized in Table E.1. Each argument references a specific type of graph element. These elements are invoked as a function, each with its own set of valid arguments.

Faceting implements the "small multiples" graphing approach advocated by Tufte [2]. It enables analysts to display more than two variables without overwhelming viewers with overly complex graphics. We implement faceting with the ***facet_wrap(FacetSpecification)*** function. The FACETSPECIFICATION should be either a formula such as ~VAR1 + VAR2 or a character vector such as c('VAR1', 'VAR2'). The result of faceting is a panel of graphs. The optional "ncol=" enables us to specify the number of columns in the panel.

The code below puts together the specification, assembly, and display elements to produce the visual depicted in Figure E.1. At the specification stage, we apply log transformations to normalize the otherwise skewed Open and Volatility data with the ***log()*** function. At the assembly stage, we request a line graph with geom_line(). At the display stage, we specify a graphic title with the labs() function, specify a custom theme with theme(), and facet months, extracted from the Date column of the StockPrices data, with the facet_wrap() function. This faceting permits us to compare the relationship between opening prices and stock visibility across months. Further, the "ncol=3" argument results in the graphs for each quarter appearing on separate rows. Notice also the use of '%m: %B' formatting in the faceting specification. This lets us order the facets correctly, while displaying the month as text; using only '%B' would order the facets alphabetically, positioning April and August first and October and September last.

Table E.1 Arguments for the theme() Function

Argument	Associated Element	Element Function Arguments	Possible Values
Text	element_text	color	Any valid color
plot.title		size	Integer
axis.title		family	'sans' (for Arial), 'serif' (for Times Roman), 'mono' (for Courier), 'symbol'
axis.text		face	1 or 'plain', 2 or 'bold', 3 or 'italic', 4 (for bold-italic)
Rect	element_rect	color	Any valid color
plot.background		fill	Any valid color
Line	element_line	color	Any valid color
axis.line		size	Integer
panel.grid		linetype	

```
ggplot(StockPrices, aes(x=log(Open), y= log(Volatility))) +
       geom_line() +
       labs(title='Opening Prices and Stock Volatility across Months') +
       theme(plot.title=element_text(color='white', family='serif', size=25, face=4),
             plot.background=element_rect(fill='midnightblue'),
             axis.title=element_text(color='white',face='bold'),
             axis.text=element_text(color='white'),
             panel.background=element_rect(fill='lightgray'),
             strip.background=element_rect(fill='powderblue')) +
       facet_wrap(~format(as.Date(Date,'%m/%d/%Y'),'%m: %B'), ncol=3)
```

Creating Figure 8.13 (Chapter 8)

In the example above, attributes of display elements such as size and color have been static. We also can vary display attributes based on values from our data. For example, the display in Figure 8.13 in Chapter 8 varies the color of the data points based on whether the syuzhet sentiment value is positive or negative and the size of the data point based on how positive or negative the value is. To vary the data point color, we use an ifelse() function, in conjunction with the ***scale_color_identity()*** function, which over-rides the default scale colors. We set the size of the dots proportional to the absolute value of the syuzhet sentiment score assigned to the tweet. We specify the labels for the x- and y-axes. For the x-axis, we specify the range as between 1 and 10, with 1-unit increments with the ***scale_x_continuous(breaks=BreaksArgument)*** function. With the theme() function, we set the text size, suppress the legend, and request boldfaced axes titles.

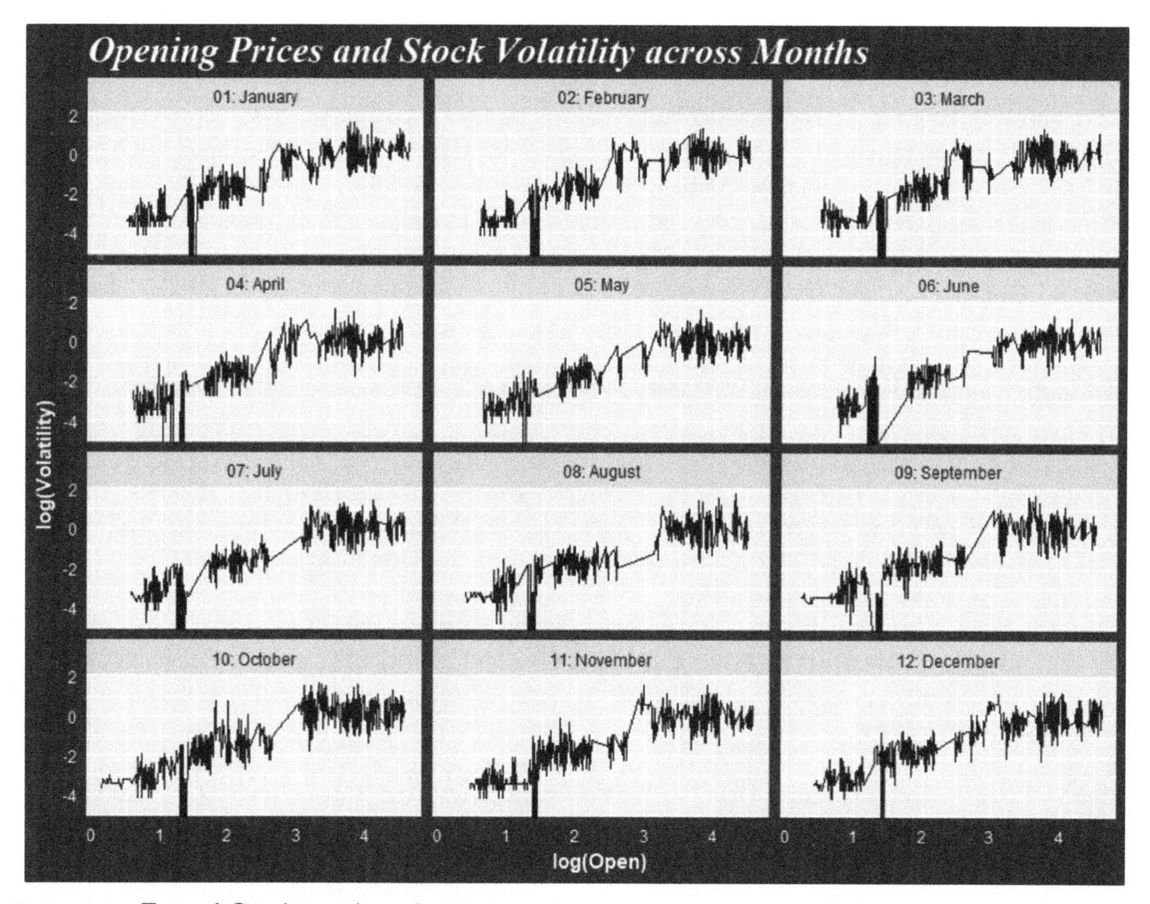

Figure E.1 Faceted Graphic with ggplot

```
ggplot(ReyPolarity, aes(x=week,y=syuzhet)) + geom_point(aes(color=ifelse(syuzhet>
   0,'forestgreen','firebrick3'), size=abs(syuzhet))) + scale_color_identity()
   + labs(x='Week', y='Syuzhet Score') + scale_x_continuous(breaks=seq(1,10,1))
   + theme(text=element_text(size=16), legend.position='none',
   axis.title=element_text(face='bold'))
```

Creating Figure 8.14 (Chapter 8)

To create this plot, we need two additional packages: reshape2 for its melt() function, which permits us to restructure a data frame, and the png package, which permits us to read .PNG files. We then read in the Plutchik.png image file, which is used as a legend in the figure.

```
mypng = readPNG('Plutchik.png')
```

Next, we restructure our data frame using the melt() function. We also reorder the emotion columns so they will appear in a sequence that matches the legend and exclude the last two columns—positive and negative polarity. Because we want our new data frame grouped by both week and tweet—the first two columns—we indicate that our id.var includes both columns. The newly created data frame will contain these two columns; a third column named "variable," in which the rows will be each of our eight emotions; and a fourth column named "value," which will contain the NRC score assigned to each emotion for each tweet. If we inspect the newly created data frame, we should see eight rows for each tweet and a total of 2,096 × 8 = 16,768 rows.

```
EmotionME=melt(ReyEmotion[c(1,2,3,5,8,9,6,10,7,4)],id.var=c('Week','Tweet'))
```

Now we're ready to begin constructing our plot. Because the code required to do so is so complex, I've broken it out into multiple statements, storing them to a named plot variable, EG (for Emotion Graph). This first statement specifies the data frame to be used in the plot. It specifies that the x-axis for our plot is the week in which the tweet was posted, the y-axis is the NRC value assigned to the tweets, and the color for the fill will depend on the variable, which is the emotion. Then, we specify that we want to display a stacked bar chart, summarizing the values as the average for the week. To convert our x-axis from the ggplot default continuous x-axis to a more meaningful set of integer values, we specify the breaks of 1 to 10 in increments of 1. We specify our x-axis and y-axis labels and the bar colors to correspond to those appearing in Plutchik's PNG, which will serve as our legend.

```
EG=ggplot(EmotionME, aes(x=Week,y=value,fill=variable)) + geom_bar(position='stack',
   stat = 'summary', fun.y = 'mean') + scale_x_continuous(breaks=seq(1,10,1))
   + labs(x='Week',y ='Average Emotion') + scale_fill_manual(values=c('red','magenta',
   'royalblue','lightskyblue','forestgreen','green','yellow','sandybrown'))
```

To this plot, we now add a theme. In this theme, we first suppress the default legend, since we will be supplying our own. We specify the size of the text appearing on the axes, along with the font and size for the axes' titles. We change the color of the background to black and the major grid lines to gray and minor grid lines to black.

```
EG=EG + theme(legend.position='none', text=element_text(size=16), axis.title= element_text
   (face='bold', size=16), panel.background=element_rect(fill='black',
   colour='black', size=0.5, linetype='solid'), panel.grid.major=element_line(size=
   0.5, linetype='solid', color='gray25'), panel.grid.minor=element_line(size=0.5,
   linetype='solid', color='black'))
```

Next, we layer on the PNG image with the ***annotation_raster(PNGFileName)*** function. The optional "xmin=", "ymin=", "xmax=", and "ymax=" arguments enable us to specify where the image is to be positioned and its size.

```
EG=EG + annotation_raster(mypng, xmin=5.3, xmax=11.3, ymin=1.65, ymax=5.15)
```

Finally, we layer on the text, which informs the reader that the image is the legend and which ring from the image is to serve as the legend. We specify where the text is to be positioned, how it is to be justified, its color and size.

```
EG=EG + annotate('text', label='LEGEND \n(second ring from inside)', x=5.75, y=4.75,
   hjust=0, colour='white', size=5)
```

Now we can view our graph with `EG`.

Mapping Geocoded Data

The maps or the ggmap packages permit us to visualize our data on geographical maps. This is especially useful for mapping tweets (or any other geocoded data). The ggmap package uses Google maps and, while somewhat more involved, provides a versatile set of visuals.

To depict a simple map over which we will superimpose our geocoded data, we use the ***map('Location')*** function from the maps package. Location options include world (for a world map), usa (for a map of the United States), state (to demarcate the states within the United States), and county (to demarcate counties within the United States). **Note that if your Plots pane is not sufficiently large to depict the map, R will return** `Error in plot.new() : plot region too large`**, so be sure to maximize the plot pane before attempting to render a map.**

Once we have the map, we use the ***points(x-coordinates, y-coordinates)*** function to mark the locations of the source of tweets. The x- and y-coordinates that we supply will be the longitude and latitude from our tweets. We optionally may specify a plotting character using the "pch=" argument and a plotting color using the "col=" argument. The "cex=" argument permits us to control the size of the dots to be depicted. For example, `map('world', col='antiquewhite', bg='aliceblue')`, followed by `points(Immigration$lon, Immigration$lat, pch=20, cex=2, col='red')`, produces the map in Figure E.2, depicting the source of tweets about immigration.

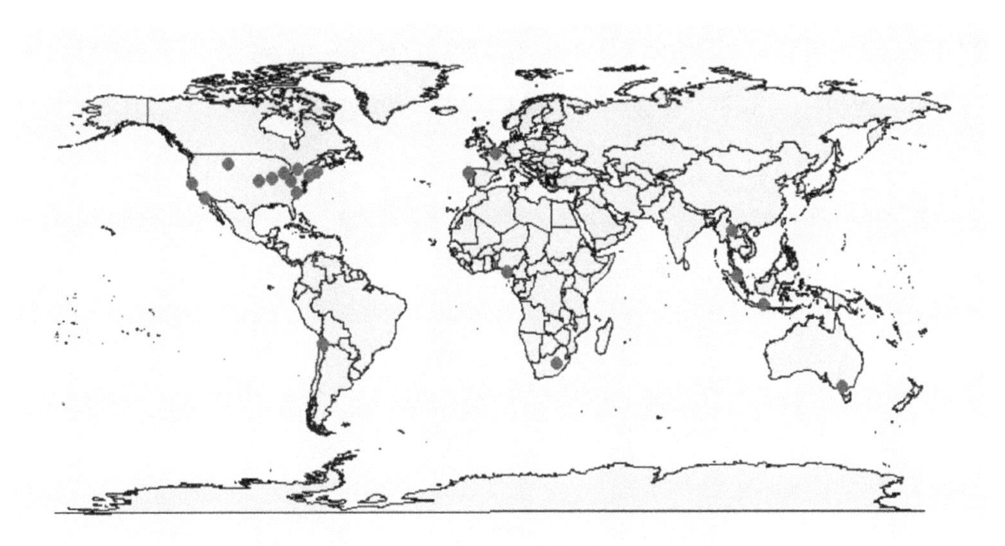

Figure E.2 Source of Immigration Tweets

Possible values of pch—the plotting character—are depicted in Table E.2. We can vary the plotting character to depict a specific data facet. For example, using the argument `pch= ifelse(Immigration$lan=='en', 19, 17)` will depict English tweets with a solid circle and non-English tweets with a solid triangle. Note that #16 and #19 render the same character.

To access Google maps from R, we use the ***get_map(Location, Zoom)*** function to query Google maps to obtain a map with the specified location and zoom. The location refers to the latitude and longitude for the center of the map. We can obtain the center of the map with `wlon=mean(Immigration$lon, na.rm=T)` and `wlat=mean(Immigration$lat, na.rm=T)`. We then use `world=get_map(location=c(wlon,wlat),zoom=2)`, followed by `map=ggmap(world) and map + geom_point(data=Immigration, aes(x=lon,y=lat), color='red', size=4, alpha=0.5) + xlab('Longitude') + ylab('Latitude')` to produce the annotated map in Figure E.3.

Table E.2 Plotting Character Options

1	2	3	4	5	6	7	8	9	10
11	12	13	14	15	16	17	18	19	20

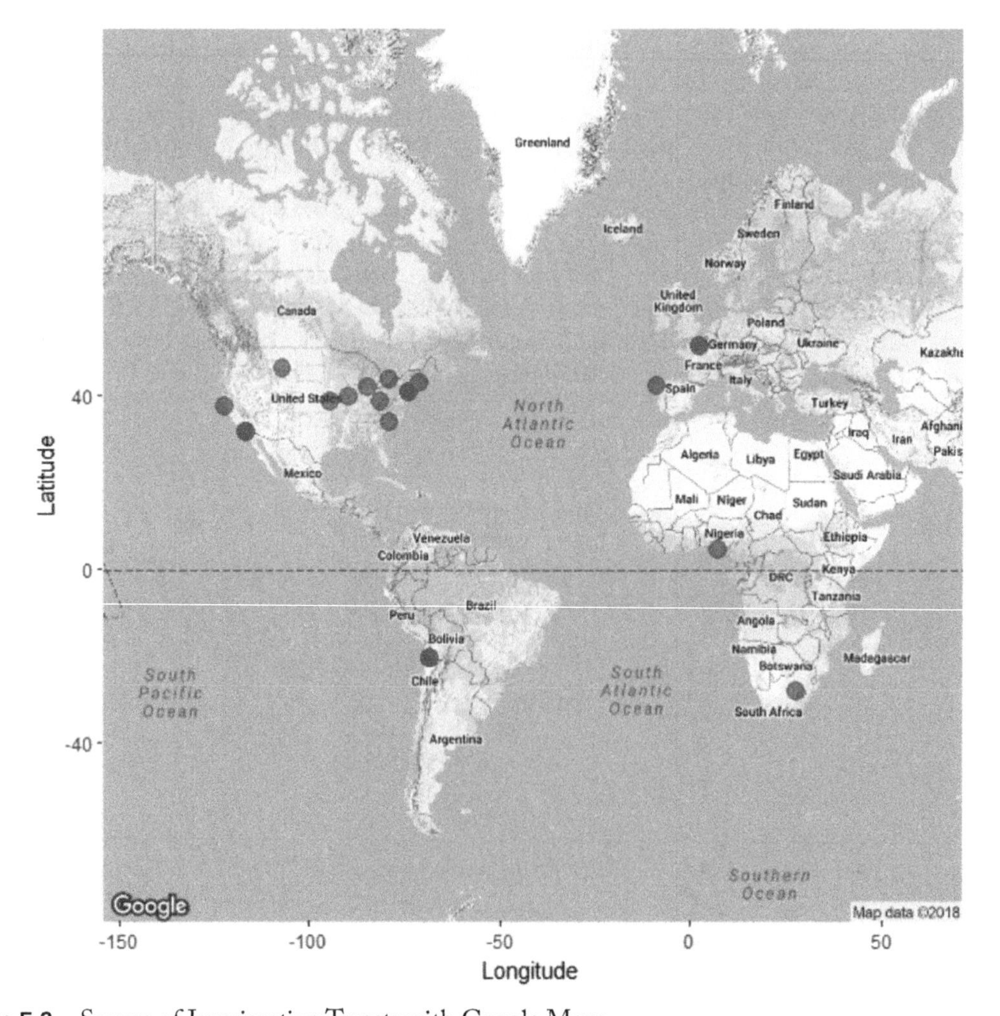

Figure E.3 Source of Immigration Tweets with Google Maps

Works Cited

1. Wilkinson, L., *The Grammar of Graphics: Statistics and Computing*, 2nd ed., edited by J.M. Chambers, D. Hand, and W. Hardle. New York: Springer Science & Business Media, 2006.
2. Tufte, E.R., *Envisioning Information*. Cheshire, CT: Graphics Press, 1990.

APPENDIX F

Additional R Resources

The following sites provide a great way to get up to speed with R.

1. The R Project for Statistical Computing: http://www.r-project.org/
2. R Tutorial: http://www.r-tutor.com/
3. RStudio Cheat Sheets: https://www.rstudio.com/resources/cheatsheets/
4. R-bloggers: http://www.r-bloggers.com
5. DataCamp: https://www.datacamp.com/
6. R for Beginners: https://cran.r-project.org/doc/contrib/Paradis-rdebuts_en.pdf
7. The R Inferno. http://www.burns-stat.com/pages/Tutor/R_inferno.pdf
8. R tips: http://pj.freefaculty.org/R/Rtips.pdf
9. Tutorials Point: https://www.tutorialspoint.com/r/index.htm
10. The Art of R Programming: http://heather.cs.ucdavis.edu/~matloff/132/NSPpart.pdf
11. LearnR: https://www.youtube.com/user/TheLearnR
12. How to R: https://www.youtube.com/channel/UCAeWj0GhZ94wuvOIYu1XVrg

These resources provide information on statistical analyses using R.

1. Statistics with R: http://zoonek2.free.fr/UNIX/48_R/all.html
2. A Little Book of R for Multivariate Analysis: https://media.readthedocs.org/pdf/little-book-of-r-for-multivariate-analysis/latest/little-book-of-r-for-multivariate-analysis.pdf
3. An Introduction to Statistical Learning: http://www-bcf.usc.edu/~gareth/ISL/
4. Elementary Statistics with R: https://www.youtube.com/channel/UC0MxOB6BCL976Dm2kPK-HgA

Index